NEXT YEAR COUNTRY

Stories of drought-stricken South Dakota in the 1930's

by

Louise Liffengren Hullinger

Editor: Carol Spelius
Lay-out Editor: Wayne Spelius

LAKE SHORE PUBLISHING
373 Ramsay Road,
Deerfield, IL 60015

Dedication

A few words of thanks:

I want to thank son Craig for teaching me the fundamentals of the computer and for nagging me to get the South Dakota book completed.

I want to thank my husband who carefully read everything I wrote, critiqued my facts, and at times smiled and pronounced the work "pretty good," which in the Midwest way is an extravagant accolade.

A FEW WORDS FROM THE AUTHOR:

I was born in Draper, South Dakota in 1924 before the doctor arrived. Grandmother, who at the last minute had to double as midwife, saw that I had not made the journey alone. She could only gasp, "Why Edna, here's another one!" (The crop that never fails.)

Louise Hullinger

Table of Contents

NEXT YEAR COUNTRY, 1933

South Dakota was always "next year country" but in 1933 when Franklin Roosevelt took office with his promise of a New Deal, we felt sure that "next year" had arrived.

Wheat prices had been getting steadily lower--grain sold for about 25¢ a bushel, grasshoppers had invaded in '31, and, for all the arsenic poisoning, with its banana oil scent, the hoppers were still alive and eating.

The country was so dry that wells had been poked all over to get enough water for the cattle. We knew, literally, what it meant to "prime the pump."

To rehabilitate the country, new agencies with long titles contrived work projects. Soon initials were being bandied about -- CCC, WPA, NRA, NYA. Men "on relief" built roads, dams, public buildings.

Many farmers, especially those whose parents had emigrated from foreign countries, refused proudly to have anything to do with WPA and couldn't understand those who felt so "poor" they had to "take help" from the government. Nor did they want the government telling them how to run their farms.

"Price controls" were an innovation, and there was disgusted talk about killing little pigs to eliminate the surplus. I remember my father listening to the little Atwater Kent radio, which he had installed on a little corner shelf beyond the reach of the children. He was baffled over such goings-on, yet hopeful those fools in Washington, those college educated men, the "Brain Trust," knew what they were doing. It was in 1933 that farm management by the government began in earnest.

Even so the economy was sluggish. College boys joined the National Guard for the dollar a week they offered. By 1942 rural school teachers who earned the county average in Jones County received $89 a month for nine months!

When the United States got involved in World War II teachers left the profession to earn three and four times as much at more glamorous jobs. Farm boys were deferred as essential, but many wanted to serve in the armed forces anyhow. There was a pervasive feeling that the U.S. was on the side of right, and that it was up to the U.S. armed forces to make sure that right won.

SIGRID'S PLACE

EXPLORING AT AUNT SIGRID'S

A horse silhouetted against the big sky was the first thing we noticed when we went to spend the summers in South Dakota with Aunt Sigrid. Her place was nestled in a valley with a big hill wrapped protectively around it. As soon as we arrived I'd shout to my sister, "Come on, Greta. Let's explore!" and off we'd go.

"Yes, let's explore," she said, echoing me as she always did, as she followed me up the hill. We had to pass the dam where Sigrid's white-faced, rust-red Hereford cows were munching grass. Their heads were bobbing up and down, up and down, as they wrenched the tough long grass from the prairie. Since they were on the other side of a barbed wire fence, we paid them scant attention.

It never occurred to us to question the wisdom of exploring land the rattlesnakes thought they owned. Our minds were focused on one thing: reaching Aunt Sigrid's horse.

We were within arm's reach when we heard, "G-i-r-l-s." It was Mother calling. She warned us to stay closer to the house so we were within hearing distance at all times.

We had to pass the same pasture when we headed down the hill. This time a skittish young heifer got glassy-eyed at the sight of us, let out a wild bellow, and set off the rest of the herd. All the cows cut loose, snorting, kicking dust and stampeding -- away from us! We froze at attention, Greta and I clinging together, hardly daring to breathe. Only when the animals were out of our sight could we bolster the courage to move on.

Mother and Aunt Sigrid were talking a mile a minute but stopped to tell us to calm down. Aunt Sigrid tried to reassure us by saying, "It's okay. The cows won't hurt you. They're more afraid of you than you are of them! You're the only little people they ever see so they have to put on a show for you."

Mother cautioned, "Slow down. Don't move so fast. They are not used to so much commotion around here."

When the door of the ice house loomed into sight, Greta stopped weeping and shouted, "Let's explore!"

The ice house was dug into the side of a hill half way between the barn and Sigrid's house. The wooden door on the side facing out had a shoulder-high knothole which invited us to look inside.

"Squint your eyes," I commanded Greta, with all the accumulated wisdom of someone at least one year older. After all, I knew things she didn't. "Then you can see into the darkness." I counseled.

Inside we saw straw, darkened by age and moisture. "Phew," I said, and Greta echoed me. We held our noses, closing our nostrils with thumbs and forefingers to keep out the rank odor from the dank straw.

4

It was important to check out the ice house early each summer. How else could we be sure the ice hadn't melted?

"Well, is there ice enough to last until the fourth of July then?" asked Aunt Sigrid. "Will there be enough to make ice cream in the wooden freezer for everyone?"

Then she got a far-away look in her eyes. She told us, "I remember when Papa built the ice house. Some of the neighbors laughed. But that didn't stop him. He said, "Laugh all you want, but next summer when it's hot who'll come begging for ice? Then who will be laughing?"

"Oh, Aunt Sig," Greta and I pleaded together, "We want to hear about Papa and Mama and what it was like when you were little. Tell us about when you first came to South Dakota, how there weren't any grocery stores, just places where horseback riders left the mail for families to pick up, and where you could buy sugar and coffee. And the prairie was your garden. Please. Pretty please. Tell us again."

"Sh," scolded Mother. "Don't be pestering Sigrid to tell you stories all the time."

"There will be time for stories later. I'll tell you all about what this country was like when I was a child, but now, I must show your mother the letters from Norway before she has to go. You run along, now."

Aunt Sigrid wasn't really our aunt at all. She was a long-time family friend who had emigrated from Norway when our grandparents did, and settled, as they had, in rural South Dakota. To us, Aunt Sigrid was ageless. She worked outside in the sunshine, like men do, but she could also do "inside" things -- and expected the same of us.

We were off next to explore the dry "creek" that ran below the farm buildings, ran, that is, only during the spring of the year, when the rains came a week at a time, or more, and caused flooding. This persistent rain cut away the banks along the creek.

Along the bottom of the cutbanks were what Aunt Sigrid called gulleys. They were narrow shallow gorges that filled with water. During the dusty "dirty thirties," when the creek was dry from lack of rain, we could sometimes find a little muddy water harbored in the deepest nooks along the cutbanks.

Half the fun of exploring was pretending that we had to skirt those little water holes by clinging desperately to the willow branches as we worked our way past them to the well.

When Aunt Sigrid heard us coming back, she called, "Go past the garden while you're out that way and dig up a few radishes for lunch. Bring in a little lettuce, too."

As soon as we had finished our lunch, Mother got up from the table and said, "I really must be on my way. Be good girls, and mind Aunt Sigrid. Your father and I will be back for you by the Fourth of July, if not sooner."

With a kiss and a wave goodbye, we scurried away. We explored every time we came to Aunt Sigrid's place and didn't stop exploring until we went home. Following the dusty path that the creek in its heyday had left, was high adventure.

Along the bank grew choke cherries, so named because the bitter taste will cause a cow to choke! Or any other animal that tries to eat them! Or so we were told.

We girls had no interest in picking choke cherries, but if Aunt Sigrid said we should, we did. It took a long time to pick a bucket full. If we forgot and bit into a choke cherry, we were left with an acrid, furry coating on the roof of our mouths. There was another part of choke cherry picking we never forgot either -- the chigger bites, proof we'd invaded enemy territory!

We didn't know then about fingernail polish -- that you can suffocate the buggers if you paint the itchy spot with nail polish. We had to make do by scrubbing with yellow laundry soap -- the kind Aunt Sigrid made by pouring lye over cracklings saved when she butchered a fat pig for her winter's meat supply.

We explored because it seemed tauntingly dangerous. Something was bound to happen if we wandered very far from Sigrid's buildings. One time it was turkey hens. They came at us with their sharp beaks and oversized flapping wings, squawking and making a great to-do, desperately trying to lead us away from their nests of huge speckled eggs. Greta and I covered our eyes with our arms as we fled to safety.

Later in the summer the turkey hens would emerge with three or four little turks tagging along behind, scratching in the grasses, little clones imitating their mothers.

Aunt Sigrid approved of turkeys because they ate grasshoppers. Turkeys were her secret weapon against hoppers. In those days in South Dakota, grasshoppers were a real problem. Sigrid had several turkey hens specifically to keep the hoppers in line.

Whenever we wandered far from the house, Aunt Sigrid had assignments for us. One "as long as you're out that way anyway," rule was to pump water. Greta and I struggled with the long pump handle, stretching with all our might, up and down, up and down, until finally a little water trickled down the spout and into the wooden trough placed there to catch water for the farm animals. Sigrid's strong arms could pump with ease, but for us it was hard work, and we soon scampered off to explore elsewhere.

We were always tired when evening came. After eating we cleaned up the dishes, clearing the table together. We took turns washing and drying the dishes. It was Sigrid's chore to put everything away.

Each evening we went to bed when the chickens did. Sigrid heard us say our prayers as the sun disappeared behind the hills and then began weaving her story. We fell asleep listening to her story in her lilting Scandinavian voice, silhouetted in the window against the stars and the moon in the upstairs bedroom of the house she had helped build.

SIGRID'S BEDTIME STORY

as told by Sigrid

Papa was a shoemaker in Norway. He traveled from place to place making shoes for each family. He stayed with each family until he had a year's supply of shoes made. Then he traveled to the next place. For his work he got room and board and a small amount of money. He saved the money until he had enough to come to America.

(*Sigrid pronounced esses (s's) like they were soft. I could always tell those who had parents who had been born in Norway by the soft way they pronounced their s's. Also, sometimes, when speaking of her parents she reverted to "chust" and "tink."*)

He and Mama left Norway in a small ship with many other Norwegians. When we set sail I was the youngest aboard, but while we were crossing the wide Atlantic Ocean another baby, a boy, was born. I was then no longer the baby. I have heard so many tales about seeing the Statue of Liberty, and Ellis Island that it almost seems as though I remember seeing them, but I must be truthful.

We first went to Minneapolis where we were met by relatives who helped us get to Iowa, where we settled. Iowa had many trees, and big, old white houses. And there were schools for children to attend. Then papa heard they were giving away land in South Dakota, and who could stop him?"

"Giving away land," were magical words to my father. No one had ever given away land. They were both proud, and would not accept hand outs. But land? Free land? Wild horses could not have stopped papa from getting in on free land!

My mother protested a little. "But will there be schools for little Sigrid? And aren't there wild Indians in South Dakota?"

But when Mama saw how determined Papa was, and had time to think it over she became as convinced as he was. Mama said, "We can teach Sigrid at home. And if we are kind to the Indians they will not want to hurt us. (I *can hear both of them saying, "Chust tink of it! Free land in Dakota chust for claiming and living on it for five years. Tink of it!"*

And so Papa pored over plats of the land, and Mama studied them as much as he did. Without seeing the land first, they chose a quarter section of land by a river. Word had gotten around that midwestern South Dakota was hot and dry so they felt sure that living by a river was right for them.

I remember Papa saying, "Ach, Mama, if we have water, we are sure to make a go of it. There is a long line on the north side of the property we want which says **river**. Surely it is a wise thing to claim land by a river."

9

Mama agreed. Neither she nor Papa thought to find out if the river had a name. The land had been surveyed so that was enough for them. They were in love with the idea of owning land, even if it was far away from their Iowa relatives, and had no schools."

I can remember Papa puzzling over the deed. He asked Mama, "What does it mean to build something hab-it-able? What would that be, Thelma?"

She peered closely at the piece of paper he held in his hand, and then looked the word up in her Norwegian-English dictionary. She sounded out each letter she said, "Aha, papa. I know it. It means that if they give us this land without charging us dollars we must build a house in which to live."

My father snorted, and said, "And do they tink because we do not speak goot English we don't know enough to come in out of the rain!"

My mother said, "Now, Papa, don't be silly. It is nothing about which to get upset."

Papa went on, "This also says we must cultivate the land. That would be plowing the land so we can grow wheat for bread, and digging a well so we have water. They did not haf to tell us what we already know."

There were acres that needed to be settled in America's heartland. And we were just the ones to do it! Here we could own our own land, and be our own boss. Girls, this land has been in our family ever since.

We traveled by train to Chamberlain, South Dakota, where we crossed the Missouri River. People were crowding in to get their free land. We traveled with Ole Anderson.

Oh, this land was beautiful! I remember the first sight of it. I was only six, but I remember. There were no fences any where. Just orange-red wild geraniums, blue bells and yellow johnny jump-ups all over. The entire prairie was my flower garden.

There was much work to be done. Papa sized up the cottonwood trees which grew by the creek. He didn't like to build with cottonwoods, but he said, "We must use what we haf."

Ole's wife and children stayed behind, so our cabin went up first, so we'd have a roof over our head. By the time Ole's wife came they had built a cabin for them, too. They knew how to notch the logs, and how to make wooden plugs to use instead of nails.

Mama told them. "We will fill the spaces with mortar made of mud. It will help keep out winter weather. And we will make do for now with one window, for glass windows cost too much."

While Papa was building the cabin, Mama and I planted seeds. The ground was hard; we couldn't dig it very deep with a hoe, but we transplanted lilac roots from Iowa for a hedge. Then we planted cuttings from rhubarb plants and potato eyes. Soon our own green things were growing.

Papa said we had to have a horse for plowing. I won't forget that first horse. His name was Prince, a bay gelding, calm and steady.

Prince is now in the place where good horses go when they die. But I like to tink he is waiting in heaven for us to join him.

The horse you saw now, is a pony, and ponies cannot pull heavy loads. It took real horse power to force the plow through the tough prairie grass. And Prince had real power!

11

I tagged along behind papa when he plowed, Papa held the reins and guided Prince as they cut straight narrow furrows. When Papa and his one-man plow overturned the virgin soil it smelled sweet. And if you looked closely at the newly plowed furrows in the sunlight they were **purple.**

The weeds and long grasses had long roots because they had never known the blade of a plow, and they resisted mightily. Papa milled the wheat into flour, and traded what we didn't need for sugar and coffee and other staples. Without Prince none of that would have been possible. It takes a lot of hard work to get ahead in this country, but it can be done.

As Papa and Mama got older they could no longer spend long hours doing heavy work, so the outside work more and more became my responsibility. When Papa and Mama died and went to heaven I knew how to run the place. I love it and wouldn't want to live any where else.

*   *   *

Sigrid's story seemed to always end in a place where she was telling us how nice it was that we had come to be with her.

THE LOG HOUSE

It seemed fitting that since we went "to bed with the chickens" each night, we should be awakened each morning by a cocky red rooster.He strutted around the barn door, daring anyone to sleep. He didn't need to worry about us not getting up. There was still plenty of exploring we wanted to do.

At the far side of Sigrid's property stood the old log house, the first home her papa had built for them in America. Every other settler in the county had torn down their first homes for one reason or another, but not Sigrid, who considered that a dreadful waste of resources. For her the precept, "waste not, want not," was **LAW.**

The old log house made a perfect storehouse -- a place to leave the quilting and fancy work Sigrid didn't want to put away each evening. Everything in the world that ever belonged to her could be found buried somewhere among the treasures in that cabin -- if not on the first floor, then up in the attic.

The attic was not easily accessible. It was an adventure to go to the attic! First, Greta and I had to find something high to stand on in order to reach the ceiling. Then we had to slide off the chunk of linoleum Sigrid had slid over the entry to the attic.

This piece, when pushed to one side, allowed us to bring down a ladder made of rope. After dropping it down a few feet we could position it so we could swing up into the attic. Looking back I think it would have been easier to use a step ladder!

It took real courage to climb the wobbling rungs on that rope ladder, but the delights to be found in the loft made it worth the effort. Stacked high in one corner was every issue of the Prairie Farmer that had ever been published. Next to it were piles of "The Household -- A Magazine for Farm Women." There were whole series of Sunday school leaflets from the days when Sigrid attended Lutheran Sunday school, and a Norwegian confirmation book that contained the ten commandments, and Martin Luther's, "What does this mean?," just as she had memorized it. Underneath each line she had carefully penciled in a few English word equivalents.

The trunks were not locked but we knew we had no business peeking into them, but we did, somewhat guiltily. Once Greta found a doll with a tin head, and a flat nose.

"Look at this," she squealed, holding the doll high and dancing around with it. "Padded body and arms, and shiny pink hands and feet."

We giggled at the narrow little wicker doll buggy and the old-fashioned wicker stroller for walking the doll. We laughed at the red, carved, wooden toy animals, which stood stiffly, had no joints, and only faintly resembled the way we imagined the animals of Noah's ark.

Sigrid must have saved every picture she had ever taken with her little Brownie camera. There were hundreds of photos in her attic, all neatly arranged in black albums and held in place with triangular, mucilage-backed corners of gold, red or blue. Above each picture Sigrid had written little notes in white or gold ink. These notes made us privy to information, surely sacred to Sigrid: "A good time was had by all," above a picture of a 1929 flivver with four people identified as cousins. We giggled hysterically at the notes and the pictures of young people who looked to us suspiciously like girlfriends with their boyfriends.

In one picture Sigrid was all dolled up in a 1920's hat with the brim half-folded back and a dress with a very short skirt. There was a ribbon far below where a waist line ought to be and a long string of round beads that reached almost to her knees. Standing next to her was a young man, not nearly as tall as she. The white ink printing under it said, "Sigrid and friend in front of Model T -- June, 1929."

"Do you think he was Sigrid's boy friend?" Greta asked. Being older and more worldly, I shook my head. Something stored somewhere in my memory made me think that either Sigrid's boyfriend died in the flu epidemic of World War I or that her old fashioned parents wouldn't let her go out with boys.

I told Greta, "No. I think after her father died, Sigrid stayed home to help her mother." Greta didn't ask anything else about it, but it set me wondering. Had Sigrid ever had a boy friend?

PEDALING THE GRINDSTONE

Out in front of the log house stood a grindstone, a concrete wheel fixed in place with a seat and pedals. Sigrid's father, a shoemaker in Norway, brought his trade with him to America. Because shoemakers need sharp knives, he had built himself a sturdy grindstone so he could keep the knives honed. Though he had been in his grave for years, the grindstone still worked. Etched on his headstone were a pair of leather soles.

Though Greta and I had never seen the grindstone used for the purpose for which it was intended, we used it for the purpose we intended! We used it as a team of racing horses, or a runaway car--steering, pedaling, pretend honking with pursed-up lips, and in our imagination, freely passing every other vehicle or animal on the road. Faster and faster our legs would go, until they were almost spinning, sometimes pretending to be grinding knives while driving a full team of prancing horses or a new Rolls Royce.

THE NEW HOUSE

Sigrid had, by herself, with very little outside help, built what she referred to as "the new house" circa 1930. Her windows were full of growing things--geraniums, violets, cactus that bloomed only at Christmas, and a huge, gnarled "rubber plant" that must have lived forever. Her plants not only filled every window, they also covered the tops of her piano and her Atwater Kent radio.

In the middle of her front room stood a small square table with carved legs. Each leg looked like a lion's paw holding a round glass ball. On the lower shelf of the table were Sigrid's most recent photos displayed for "company" to enjoy.

Letters from Norway for visitors to read were stuffed in a glass bowl on the table. Sigrid wrote to many people from her homeland and must have received letters, written in Norwegian, from all of them. She wrote to people she'd never seen -- friends of friends, friends of relatives -- and people she most likely would never meet. Neatly stored in their envelopes, their strange looking stamps still in place, the letters were savored and read and reread by those who could read Norwegian.

An old organ, out of which Sigrid could somehow coax music, occupied one corner of the room. Sigrid always said she preferred to hear others play. We took her at her word and banged on the organ until she must have rued the day she'd met the traveling organ salesman. She never complained, but before much time passed, she'd think of something else for us to do!

Churning sour cream into butter was one of the tasks she thought of. It was a job she believed dutiful children should do. Girls our age ought to be earning our keep. She'd dump the sour cream into the churn, set the wooden paddle in place, and direct us to turn the handle until we couldn't turn it any more.

Greta and I took turns, and just before the magic time when the cream separated into butter Sigrid reached into the churn, took out the thickened cream, and spread it on a thick crust of homemade bread for each of us. Then we'd watch her drain off the buttermilk, pat the butter into a ball, salt it and place it in little rose shaped butter molds.

Sigrid was preparing supper all the time we were churning and soon she'd call, "Come and get it. Time to eat."

Before we ate we had to ask the Lord's blessing, though she often enjoyed telling us, with an impish look, that if the meal wasn't worth more than fifteen cents we could forget giving thanks. It wasn't easy to figure the cost of the meal, but we felt sure it was more than that!

Fresh vegetables from her garden! New potatoes, or little green peas, but more often, corn on the cob. Canned chunks of the beef she herself butchered and put up, served with piccalilli made fresh each year, plus more of her home made bread, this time slathered with the butter we had just churned.

For dessert, a piece of dried-out cake -- because Sigrid insisted on using up the old cake before starting on a fresh one. She didn't indulge herself, and frowned upon those who did. Once I showed her a recipe for chocolate cake which called for two cups of sugar, twice what she usually used. Sigrid's lecture on thrift made an impression. Both Greta and I learned at Sigrid's knees that extravagance was not to be condoned!

The niceties of life were becoming commonplace in South Dakota by the late '30s with settlers well established, so it was deemed that outhouses (outdoor toilets) be set farther away from the houses. Thus, when Sigrid finished her "new" house, the outhouse was placed several yards down the hill. It was far enough so that when we were little we wouldn't go alone but waited for mamma to take us.

The privy had one high, and one low seat, and catalogues from both Sears Roebuck and Montgomery Ward, usually with all but the glossy pages torn out!

Rattlesnakes were always a worry when the weather was a certain temperature; we were always warned to watch out for rattlers on hot days. Sigrid told us of an incident that we never forgot. It stayed with us, hovering over us, for a long, long time.

A couple and their two year old daughter, Sunny, came to visit Sigrid one Sunday afternoon. The golden-haired child, the only child and the light of their lives, was never out of their sight for a moment.

The mother took the child with her to the "two-holer" where she was bitten by a rattlesnake, not just in one place, but in several. The father, who knew the treatment for snakebite, cut open the wounds where the child had been bitten and sucked out the venom before rushing her to the doctor, more than thirty miles away. But the distance was too great, and all of the bite wounds had not been found, and the youngster died.

It was rare to find rattle snakes around buildings where people lived, but Sigrid lived alone, and though she had lots of visitors, there was not usually much commotion around her place. After hearing what happened to Sunny we quit protesting about how big and careful we were. We were never able to get Sunny out of our minds.

SIGRID'S CHICKENS

Gathering eggs, which Sigrid called "picking eggs," was another chore she felt we could handle. On the hill, across from the barn, stood the chicken house, with its rows of perches for the chickens to roost on at night. Nests where the hens could lay their eggs were built on the inside walls of the chicken house. When Aunt Sigrid told us to gather eggs we searched first in the chicken house.

The cackling began when we arrived in the henhouse. The nimble hens scrambled out of our way while we gathered eggs. The setting hens, however, perched possessively on their nests, making low warning sounds, daring anyone to come near.

It took all the courage we could muster to grab a hen off her nest, toss her to the ground, and steal her eggs, but that's what we thought we were supposed to do. Those hens squawked, ruffled their feathers, and stalked indignantly around the chicken house, complaining loudly and endlessly. As fast as we could, we scooted out lest the hens start pecking at us.

Sometimes we would bring in "glass eggs," and how Aunt Sigrid would laugh. The glass eggs were fake eggs designed to suggest to lazy hens that they should lay more eggs, but Greta and I were the only ones fooled by the glass eggs!

We didn't limit our egg search to the hen house. We hunted everywhere, and nearly always found a few in the hayloft. Sigrid's hens made nests in mangers too, in the horses stalls!

Sometimes we'd find a whole nest of eggs that no one else had come across. If they sloshed they were rotten and we got to throw them away. The smell of rotten eggs is not easily forgotten; in fact it stays with you forever. We not only became experts at "pickin' eggs." We became experts at recognizing the sloshing sound of rotten ones!

Besides listening to the sloshing there was another way to find out if the eggs were good enough to save. Aunt Sigrid showed us how to candle the eggs by rolling a newspaper into a funnel. Then we held the egg up to the light and peered at it through the funnel. If it looked clear inside we saved the egg. If a hen had been setting on the eggs for a while the egg would be cloudy which meant a baby chick had been growing inside.

Aunt Sigrid expected her hens to hatch their own baby chicks, but since the hens were unpredictable, and couldn't be counted on to hatch as many as she wanted, she also ordered baby chicks from a hatchery.

When she ordered 100 or more baby chicks, the rural mail carrier drove down the steep winding road and delivered the baby chicks to her front door. The folks at the post office were anxious to get rid of those hungry, squawking babies and the mail carrier was anxious to see how many were still alive.

Fluffy baby chicks arrived one day in a big carton which had circular air holes so the babies could breathe. Sigrid lit the little lamp in her brooder for warmth for the newborns, and we were allowed to give them water in Mason jar lids.

Next we sprinkled oatmeal on the floor of the brooder. Sigrid picked each baby chick up and doused each little orange bill in the water to show them how to drink. In no time they were pecking away at the oatmeal, too. Those babies knew instinctively how to eat and drink, even with no mother to model behavior for them.

There were three little black chickens in one batch of baby chicks. All the other baby chicks were yellow, and because the black ones looked different the yellow ones all pecked at them. It was our first lesson in what happens to someone who is different.

Aunt Sigrid ordered the baby chicks so their arrival was at the same time that the eggs under her "setting hens" began to hatch. In that way her hens could be foster mothers to the new arrivals.

When the hens made clucking sounds, the chicks scrambled to follow them. Soon there were more babies tucked under a hen's wings than she could shelter! When their peeping began to hush, Aunt Sigrid said they were asleep for the night and that we should go to bed, too.

Aunt Sigrid always said, "Baby chicks grow like weeds." They were ready to be used as fryers by the 4th of July. Those that weren't eaten that summer stayed on and became full-fledged roosters.

We showered attention on them the first few days of their lives, but they promptly forgot all we had done for them. Once, almost a year later, after winter passed and spring rains ceased, Mother decided the roads ought to be dry enough so we should go see how Sigrid was doing.

She loaded us into the Model T Ford and we took off, wending our way through the gumbo, which is what Aunt

Sigrid called the mud near the "creek" where she lived. It rolled up on the wheels of the car like snow does when you are making a snowball. The tires on our car got so balled up with mud that the wheels could hardly turn!

When we arrived at Aunt Sigrid's one of the ungrateful roosters rushed at us, regarding us as intruders, and if we had allowed it, would have run us off the place. Greta and I thought that rooster had a lot of nerve--after all we had nourished him when he was a helpless baby. We talked a lot about ingratitude until Aunt Sigrid mentioned that we hadn't given gratitude a thought when we wanted fried chicken by the 4th!

4TH OF JULY

At last the big day arrived. Sigrid invited everyone, including neighbors and friends, to her grove. "We will have a picnic. We can have everything except fireworks, " she said. "It's too dry for fireworks."

Sigrid called it a grove. We girls called it a cattle pasture, with a dry creek running through, and with an abundance of chiggers. But there was a flat area, where we could join the men in playing baseball, of sorts, and horseshoes, which was Sigrid's private specialty, and joy of joys, we could freeze our own ice cream!

The first thing on the agenda was the ice cream. Greta and I tagged along behind the men when they broke into the icehouse. They used the same ice tongs they used when they put up the ice in January, which was the month when the dam water was at least two feet thick. Less than that and the ice wouldn't last the year.

Greta and I crept into the ice house, watched as the men dug under the discolored straw and fetched a chunk of ice. The ice was put into a gunny sack and the children were assigned the job of cracking it into pieces small enough to fit into the freezer. Wielding a hammer with all my might and main, I came down on it with what I imagined was great force. It didn't take long before I relinquished the maul to Greta. She lasted another minute or two. Eventually, with the help of the uncles and their friends, the ice was in smithereens small enough to be used to make ice cream.

It was also "kid's work" to poke the little pieces of ice alongside the metal canister that held the liquid ice cream mixture. I poked the ice until the spaces between the outside of the freezer and the metal container were filled and until I thought my hands had turned into icicles and would break off from sheer coldness.

We had to make sure to pour enough salt on the ice to make it melt and to turn the handle of the freezer until it could no longer be turned. Turning the handle on the old freezer until the mixture miraculously became ice cream took forever, but the hardest part was waiting for that first taste. The freezer had to be covered with heavy gunny sacks and left to set for a while to "ripen." As far as we were concerned it was as ripe as it needed to get.

Homemade lemonade was next on the list of things to do. We got to roll lemons until they lost their firmness and were soft and mushy inside. We found a smooth, hard piece of shale and rolled the lemons back and forth, beating them against the stone until the air was filled with a pungent lemony smell.

Then one of the mothers took a sharp knife and sliced the lemons into thin rings and carefully strained out the seeds. To make good lemonade the right amount of sugar and water had to be added, so that it would be tangy and not too sweet. Then, after the straw had been carefully washed off, a chunk of ice was added. Lemonade was a rare treat--but for us homemade ice cream, or any kind of ice cream, for that matter, was a bigger one!

It was cooler playing horseshoes than standing still, so a place was staked out for playing in the shade of the cottonwoods. Most of the older men gathered to play horseshoes, and some of the young folks joined them.

"Come on, Sigrid, show us how goot you are," called out a visitor one of the neighbors had casually invited to celebrate the 4th of July. His name was Jules Olson, and though he was a stranger to us, he seemed to know Aunt Sigrid.

We overheard the older woman say Jules' parents had homesteaded nearby, but had sold the place and moved east years before. Jules explained he was in the neighborhood and figured he "might yust as well come to the picnic, and yoin in a game of horseshoes."

Sigrid's face showed an amazing rosiness when she beat all of the men, including Jules, who exclaimed, "Yust like she did ven she vass young girl. Sigrid always could beat da golly bejezus outa all da boys."

When evening came the day was still warm so no one wanted to start for home. Jules had the idea that a swim in the stock tank was just the ticket for cooling off. He recalled the Trygve place before it became a part of Aunt Sigrids and claimed that he had cooled off in the water from the artesian well many times.

"The vater vass warm but at least it vass vet," Jules claimed.

Never mind that none of us had real swimming suits, we were willing to swim in anything if it meant we would be cooler. Greta and I begged mother to let us go swimming, and when she wouldn't agree we turned to Dad. "Ask your mother," he said. "She told us to ask you," we said. Back and forth we raced, pleading and cajoling and finally both of them agreed we could go if we promised to be careful, obey Sigrid, and not do anything foolish such as sticking our heads under the water too long.

It was dusk by the time everyone had gotten permission, and something to wear as a swimming suit. By the time we reached the tank and were ready to "swim" it was already dark, with stars shining overhead.

No one seemed to mind that there was barely room for us all in the stock tank at one time, nor that the water as it came from the artesian well was tepid; it relaxed our weary bodies. Under the peaceful skies, only the soft croaking of the frogs could be heard.

Then Jules, who had been conned into acting as "lifeguard" for the evening because it was his idea to swim, said off handedly, "Now is time for fire vorks."

In preparation he struck a match drawn from a little tin that he carried in his pocket. Even the slightest movement of air would cause the flame to go out so he cupped his hand against a slight thin evening breeze. Then he carefully held the match next to the pipe where the water surged up from the alluvial depths of the well.

Lo! there appeared a soft, greenish glow! A flame danced and flickered as it ran along the trickle of water that flowed from the pipe!

The phenomenon, a vestige from a former natural gas flow that had long since been abandoned as a source of gas, could still be produced if a match was struck the exact moment the gas emerged, before it dispersed into the surrounding air. Those fireworks were not as costly, nor as grand, as some I've seen many times since, but none has ever compared to the marvel of burning **water**!

AUNT SIGRID MARRIES

Jules Olson and Sigrid were married later that summer. "Ven you are our ages," Jules said, "Vy vait?"

They asked my mother and father to stand up for them as bridesmaid and best man. It is the only time I can ever remember being left home by my parents. For that one afternoon we were left behind in charge of the hired man who was like one of the family, like an older brother. We were exceedingly put out at our parents for going without us. We begged to go along and could see no logical reason why we shouldn't.

I heard my mother worrying that Jules was too old for Sigrid. My father countered that Sigrid was no spring chicken herself and she should take what she could darn well get.

That evening when they returned as man and wife the neighborhood was ready for them. Newly weds had to be shivareed and they were newly weds. They waited as quietly as was possible until Jules and Sigrid put out their lights, and then the young bloods from miles around began banging pots and pans, racing motors, loudly shouting, and firing guns into the air. Then they beat on the door until it seemed it would break, calling, "Come out, Come out. Time for a real ride."

Sigrid and Jules were good sports, as expected, and came out of their house cheerfully. They were told they were being taken for a ride in a coach designed for royalty like themselves. In reality it was a stone boat, a home made contraption with a barrel placed on two-by-fours and pulled by a horse. In its private life the barrel was regularly filled with water from the dam and dragged where ever water was needed.

For the shivaree the barrel would be filled with Sigrid and Jules and dragged around the creek bed, over washouts, and up steep side hills. The shouting and laughter did not die down until the horse was too tired to continue.

"Now" shouted Uncle Curt, "Time for treats. Jules, you get to treat the men to cigars. No hand-rolled cigarettes. Nothing but the best. "Prince Edward cigars, nothing else."

"Sigrid, you have to prove you know how to take care of a husband. It is up to you to fix scrambled eggs, bacon, sausage and hot coffee."

Jules and Sigrid laughed heartily, and led the way inside the house. By this time it was 4:00 o'clock in the morning. Nevertheless, the new bride and groom set about cracking open the eggs and fixing coffee.

It impressed me that Jules helped with the breakfast. He set the table, all the time the men were warning him, "Now Jules. Don't start things off on the wrong foot. If you start right in helping her, she'll expect it the rest of her life. We're warning you, Jules, don't let the little woman get the upper hand."

Greta and I fell asleep without having even a teeny taste of the scrambled eggs. Later we learned that when the party broke up and everybody headed home, Jules and Sigrid stood in the doorway and held hands and watched as the last star disappeared into the night.

It was already morning when we got home, but we missed seeing the sun come up. We missed hearing the rooster crow. But we hadn't missed having a wonderful time.

I have never forgotten that shivaree. Nor have I forgotten Aunt Sigrid's place. But it was sold, a few years ago, to a Texas cattle baron, who runs cattle over hundreds of acres in west central South Dakota. Now Sigrid's place, like the horse silhouetted against the sky, exists only in my memory and in my heart.

YOU CAN'T GO TO HER HOUSE WITHOUT EATING

My old aunt lives by the creek
all by herself (She's 86.)
In an old log cabin with well-worn chairs,
And rickety steps that lead upstairs,
to a secret nook,
Where I always hid to read my book.

There's a round carved table in the center of the room
Plants hang in her windows, and violets bloom.
When you go to her house she always serves cake
On an old family heirloom, A gold leaf plate.

You can't go to her house without eating!

There's an old stone sharp'ner, which I used to ride,
And plenty of places, to run and hide.
And an ice house dug into the hill,
And a garden plot which she likes to till.

She seeds and weeds, on bended knees.
With gnarled hands she picks fresh peas,
Serves corn on the cob, or dandelion greens
On a hand made mat, with woven scenes.

You can't go to her house without eating!

Still milks the cow, and aims a stream
into Cat's mouth. And then churns cream.
Still spreads fresh butter with a silver knife
On crusty bread, which she kneads at night.

When you go to her house she makes you wait
While she serves bread and butter on a gilt-edged plate.

You can't go to her house without feasting!

THE ROAD LESS TRAVELED

We were not used to much rain in central South Dakota during the 1930's and, in fact, we hardly knew what it was to have a washed-out road. There was a whole generation of youngsters who had never felt a sprinkle of rain on their heads until they were two or three years old. The children I taught in a one-room country school belonged to that era. Snowflakes they understood; raindrops were a mystery.

So when it began to rain in the spring of '42 no one imagined it would continue unceasingly until the creeks overran and the roads became impassable. South Dakota gumbo has to be experienced to be appreciated. The mud layers onto the wheels of a vehicle, like a snowball does when you build a snowman. It piles up so that the wheels can't turn. Today there are new inventions--huge tractor wheels, jeeps, four-wheel drives, but in those days, after a rain or a big thaw, drivers got "stuck" in the mud, and stayed that way.

That's what happened to me once after spending a weekend with my folks. It was important that I get back to school, even if the children could not, in order to be open for school the 180 days required by law. The roads were too muddy for cars; a few trucks might be able to plow through the gumbo, but only tractors could be relied upon to make it through. It's true that a horse could get through, but there was a limit to what could be carried on a horse.

We set out, my dad and I, on his big wheeled Farmall tractor to get to the rural school where I taught. We started out the evening before, thinking (or maybe it was hoping) that we could get to the school. After all the sun had been glaring down on the mud all day baking it into little squares with a hard crust on top with cracks along the edges. But we had no choice; I had to be at school the next morning.

We drove along easily for a while, exulting that we were probably going to make it, until we came to a washed-out place in the road near the bridge. We both jumped off the tractor to see if it was safe to cross. Exactly at that moment a shadowy figure emerged beside us in the dusk.

My father jerked back & spoke sharply, "Karl! What are you doing here? "You scared the living daylights out of me."

Karl stood mute, a huge robot of a man, his eyes blinking as one unaccustomed to daylight. He moistened his lips, sucking in his breath, but didn't say a word.

My dad continued, "Is the bridge out, Karl? Any chance of us getting across?" Still Karl made no attempt to answer, seemed oblivious to my father's questions. His hair was long and greasy, and his pallor made him appear other-worldly.

He stared first at my father and then at me, where his gaze seemed stuck as in a time warp. Yet whenever I turned to look at him, he looked away.

My father continued, "Has anyone tried crossing farther down? Is the section line bridge washed out, too?" My father was making an effort to keep the conversation going and at the same time trying to figure out what to do next. All the while Karl kept surreptitiously glancing at me, though he would not let his eyes meet mine.

Suddenly I began to shiver. Pulling my sweater tightly against my body I tried to stand in my father's shadow so I could hide from Karl's gaze. That's when I remembered.

My mother had told me about the strange family who lived "by the creek," who never ventured far from home. One boy, referred to as "Krazy Karl" by the local smart alecs, had once been sent for treatment at an asylum. I had never seen Karl, had never even heard that he was out of the asylum.

Karl was one of eighteen children reared by an odd couple, immigrants from "the old country," who hadn't really tried to adopt the ways or language of their new homeland. Though they lived in the shadow of the Lutheran Church, which served as a support center for all who were far from their motherland, and though my Grandmother had always made special visits to invite them to attend church, especially on Christ's birthday, they did not embrace the welcoming arms of the church. Something held them back.

The children were inordinately shy. Whenever someone drove by the children would disappear from sight, so that to an unobservant traveler it would seem that there were no children at all.

Eventually, a spunky county nurse convinced the parents that "the government" would be out to get them if they didn't send their children to school. It was, alas, too late for all but the youngest half dozen, for the oldest ones had already passed the age for required school attendance. Once in school the children learned to speak English quickly for they were bright. Yet their ways were backward, their clothes out of style. It was before the time when everyone had radios, and since they did not subscribe to local newspapers, they didn't know what was going on in the community. They seemed always to be out of step.

Of all the children it was said that Karl was strangest. None of them, however, had ever been given an opportunity to stretch their wings. Then a time came when my grandfather, an entrepreneur, of sorts, needed extra help at harvest time.

Pitching the bundles of grain sheaves into the hayracks, feeding or driving the horses, cleaning the barns were all things Karl ought to be able to do. And so my grandfather hired Karl. It was the first time Karl had ever been away from home.

To Karl's eyes, the daughters of the family must have seemed as devastatingly beautiful as fairy princesses. Karl could simply not concentrate on his work; it soon became apparent to my grandfather that if he were ever to get any work out of Karl the house would have to be off-limits.

And so Grandfather saw to it that Karl and the other hired men, came in only at meal times, and then just long enough to eat.

A corner of the haymow was fixed up for sleeping quarters; by the end of the day they were bone tired and probably fell asleep as soon as they hit the hay.

My mother had four sisters, but 18 year old Josie was the one that Karl fancied. It must have been love at first sight, total, consecrated, determined love. He watched her every move until she became frightened of him, and my grandfather had to dismiss him.

Still he kept coming around; he had found a path of escape from the mundane in which he had been captive all of his life.

He began to show up at odd times and in odd places. One night Grandfather caught him peering into the window, and sent him bounding home. Another night he was found in the haymow peering down at Josie as she milked the cows, her evening chores.

My grandfather, then, spoke sternly to Karl's father in his native tongue. At that the old man looked perplexed and made circle motions at his head to show that Karl was funny in the head.

My grandfather made it very clear that Karl was never again to set foot on the Bergland property. Despite the warnings there were times when the dog barked loudly, and later footprints were found under the windows. It became obvious that Karl was not to be easily put off.

My grandfather who knew his way around was not a man to put up with nonsense. He was a hard worker, a schemer, an operator. He hadn't been in America very long until he had built his own home. He soon owned lots of property and had men working for him. He knew how to manage. He knew how to make men work for him. But he did not know how to make Karl forget about Josie.

Others who were more hardhearted, or less forgiving, or who may have actually believed Karl could be helped must have arranged for Karl to be sent to what was then referred to as the Asylum. After he was gone there was no longer fear in the faces of the womenfolk when strange noises were heard, and Karl was forgotten.

The Bergland girls, all five of them, including my mother, were eventually married to fine young men, who were good providers and who loved and respected them.

All these things my mother had told me came rushing back in those few seconds and my father, noting Karl's preoccupation, and my fear, said sharply, in a voice that carried with it grim authority, "Karl. This is my daughter and you have never laid eyes on her before. And we have no time to waste. Now, can you show us where the stream can be crossed?"

Obediently Karl turned on his heel, leading us down stream below the washed-out bridge. My father followed Karl stepping carefully so as not to break an ankle, or fall into a gully formed by the rains and melting snows.

The long grasses along the cutbanks were still soaking wet, and I tried desperately to dig in my toes to avoid slipping. Karl bounded along as though he were weightless, running easily down the bank of the road, coming back now and then to see if we were still with him, and then loping along ahead of us. We soon realized that though it might be passable for Karl, it would be impassable for the tractor. However, from that vantage point, we could see the crossing a couple miles down stream.

We turned, then, to thank Karl but he was nowhere to be seen, had completely disappeared from sight. We proceeded on the old Plank Trail Road, a route which took a lot longer, but where there were fewer washouts. Along the way we passed other vehicles whose owners had abandoned them until the Dakota sun had time to turn its drying rays on the water-logged earth.

I boarded with a family who lived about a mile from school, and left for school early the next morning in order to stoke the fire in time to take off the morning chill, but I needn't have bothered. Someone before me had started a blazing fire; the room was warm and cozy. And, scenting the room delicately, was a tiny white pasque, stuck into my pencil sharpener. The only place nearby where pasques grew, though they were the state flower, was by the crossing.

The uneasiness I had felt at Karl's constant staring had disappeared when I saw how the command in my father's voice sent Karl bounding. It was obvious that the slightest hint of annoyance in my voice would send him on his way -- and it was sweet of him to bring the flowers.

For the rest of that school year there were either pasques, wild blue bells or yellow johnny-jump-ups in the pencil sharpener on my desk every morning, their faint scent a reminder of the less-traveled road.

My plans were to continue my education at Teacher's College during the summer, which meant I had to leave right after the last-day-of school picnic, which was in the middle of May.

It was in June that the neighbors found Karl where he had fallen. Clutched in his arms were a bunch of nicotinia, the sweet scented moonflowers that perfume the night. In his frayed, cowhide wallet was a picture of Josie when she was about the same age I was when I began teaching school. Everyone who saw the picture said that I was her spitting image.

BEND WITH THE WIND

"Dad, why don't you move into town?" "What'll you do if something happens to you?" "We worry about you way out here in the country miles from the closest neighbors." "It's time to pack it in, dad. Turn it over to someone younger and spryer."

Lined and weather-beaten as his prairie homestead, Ole Pedersen stubbornly resisted the railings of the South Dakota weather. He could withstand the railings of his children as well.

Pedersen was bonded to his farm. He had come to South Dakota as a young man, a homesteader, when there was nothing but land as far as the eye could see; no buildings to block a man's view and only a few willows along the creek. Ole liked it that way.

He cleared rocks from the fields, disked out the weeds, and planted grain on land that had never before had a plow blade put to it. In the bad years he coped with grasshoppers, and learned how to get by using water hauled in a stoneboat from a dam built in a low spot between two hills. He had an intrinsic, forever relationship with his land. He took the hardships as a matter of course; he didn't intend to let any long cold siege get him down.

The house was drafty as old houses always are in winter. There was much that needed to be done to keep a house in repair and now that no one reminded him these jobs slipped by undone. The floors were cold, and the heat that came from his oil burning heater wasn't enough.

The wind whipped around the buildings, rattling eaves and shaking shingles, trying to sneak in wherever it could. Pedersen, hearing the commotion, peered out his front door.

Overheard the stars, aloof and brilliant, shone clearly. The wind was tossing the cottonwoods and willows about. They were the only trees that could long survive in this drought-stricken, wind-scourged country.

Tonight the cottonwoods were taking a real beating--limbs that were brittle cracked and fell to the ground. The willows, more resilient, swayed, bending with the wind. Two feet of solid crusted snow covered the ground. Anchored at the corner of each building were deeper banks of snow, testifying to the cross purposes of the wind.

By squinting his eyes the old man could tell the barn door was safely closed. Sometimes the wind clawed at the door until it swung open. Tonight even Prince, his faithful old horse, had come seeking shelter -- it was too cold outside for man or beast.

A cat, eyes glittering, pushed the door open and slipped in, at home inside the house. In years past, Mother had never allowed animals in the house; she had seen to it that the door could not be easily pushed open. Now with Mother gone, and the kids all married, it was comforting to have something around which was alive.

Satisfied that all was well, Ole ducked back into the house and hooked the door, a concession to the wind, his advancing years, and to living alone. Doors here had no locks -- anyone who came to this isolated area was a friend, or needed one.

He missed Mattie tonight. On such evenings they used to sit reading and the radio would play softly, bringing the outside world closer. She would sew, or braid rugs until he'd challenge her to a game of rummy. She wasn't much of a card player, but played because he enjoyed it. They always ended with a fresh pot of tea and Mattie's homemade cookies.

When Mattie became ill she didn't linger long, nor suffer much, but it was a hard death anyhow. An unbearable loneliness closed in on him, afterwards, until he had to get in the car and go for a drive, or visit with neighbors and friends, until he was worn and tired, and his loneliness eased, and he could bear it again.

He'd always been able to make that old heater pour out extra warmth making the house cozy and friendly, but tonight he just went to bed, piling on an extra quilt.

By morning the wind had declared a temporary truce. Rabbit tracks zig-zagged across the freshly drifted snow. A few dried sunflower stalks, bent but still standing protruded through the snow, providing seeds for the sparrows and snowbirds as they twittered and pecked. A rooster, undaunted by the cold, crowed. A calf bawled, wanting to be let in with his mother.

Ole dressed warmly, after he had eaten, and pushed his way through the snow to the barn. The horse, stomping his feet, nickered a soft welcome, and nuzzled Ole's shoulder as he walked by the stall. A hen in the manger nestled closer to the hay and clucked a warning that she wouldn't take kindly to being moved.

The old tabby purred a greeting, rubbing her head against the old man, insisting that it was time she be fed. New born kittens, eyes still not open, huddled together in the hay for warmth.

The old man climbed slowly and carefully up to the haymow, using as steps the two-by-fours nailed to the barn wall for that purpose. The plump, gray pigeons in the cupola fluttered at his approach. He was glad there was plenty of hay, though it was sticky and dusty after the long winter storage. He pushed hay down for his horse, and then, for a treat, brought him a half gallon pail of oats.

Milking the cow was a chore Ole enjoyed, otherwise he'd have stopped it long ago; he didn't use much milk any more. He enjoyed spraying milk into the waiting tabby's mouth -- the cat would sit up on her haunches and meow until Ole aimed the warm milk toward her. It always surprised Ole how much milk that cat could drink, but he knew she had babies to feed.

Ole hung up the stool when he was done milking. Then he turned the cow out of the stanchion and into the pen where cow and calf lovingly caressed necks. It took Ole longer to do chores these days. By the time he was done it was time for the mail carrier from town.

The mail box was over the hill, quite a hike through deep snow. But he expected letters from his daughters and, of course, there was the weekly newspaper. It seemed to have become colder while he was doing the chores; the sky had turned bleak and gray. Ole maintained that changeable weather made life interesting, that it would be monotonous if the weather always stayed the same. It did occur to him that the time was about ripe for a northwester.

The sound of a motor humming caught Ole's attention and he supposed it would be the jeep carrying the mail. Few cars came this way and when one did, Ole about always knew who it was. He could barely see the jeep coming down the road, then, and ahead of it, leading the way, was a bulldozer clearing the way. Ole figured to hurry so he'd have a chance to talk to another human being.

He plodded up the hill, the wind, and the depth of the snow slowing him. The snow hadn't crusted as much as he thought it would, and it lay deeper on the hillsides. Before he got to the top of the hill the mail carrier had come and gone.

Letters did come from the children, and he hurried through them to see if everything was all right with them. After he got back to the house he would reread them, relishing the bits about the grandchildren, worrying over their minor defeats, enjoying their triumphs.

His daughter was once more urging him to move into town. It bothered her that he was alone during the winter months with no telephone, no communication, when the snow made the roads impassable. "I don't like you to be out there alone during the winter," his daughter had written. "Think about moving to town. I'll come and help you pick out a place to stay. You could still go out to the farm every spring, and live out there all summer.

"I know how you hate to leave the place you and Mom built up. You built dams, graded roads, rotated crops to get better yields, kept only the best of the cattle until you have one of the best herds in the country. But you aren't getting any younger, Dad."

His daughter was giving him advice, hesitantly as obedient children ought to be, but still as forcefully as she could. Ole knew his daughter was right, but it was hard -- hard to give up the land you'd wrested from the prairie, the weeds, the grasshoppers.

It wasn't easy to give up a home where you'd raised your family. And you'd have no say so if you moved off and let someone else live there. Many of the widowers, less self-sufficient than he, had moved into town when their wives had died. Some adjusted happily and easily to a life of bench-warming, and card-playing; probably he could too, but he didn't want to, not yet.

The wind was at his back as he went down the hill; even so it seemed to penetrate his bones, and with all the snow there was no place to rest.

The fenceposts were not visible and he could not discern exactly where the road was -- he tried to figure out where the path was by digging down with his boots so the walking would be easier, and somehow or other he stepped into a hole, twisted his ankle, and found himself sitting on the snow. When he tried to get up, there was a glancing pain in his right foot.

He sat a while, trying to think what to do, trying to crystallize his thoughts, until the cold seemed to penetrate the marrow of his bones, and he was chilled through. He'd lived in the country all his life and had never in all his seventy years had a broken bone. He hoped that maybe it was only a sprain. The thought that it might be broken irked him exceedingly -- breaking a bone was not a sensible thing to do. He tried to get up again, but he couldn't put any weight on his right foot.

"It can't be," he thought, feeling panicky, his thoughts tumbling, jumbled together. "It can't be. I'm still a ways from the house. It's getting colder by the minute. There probably won't be anybody by here until tomorrow when the mail carrier comes again. "Oh, God," he breathed, "don't let me freeze to death out here all alone."

He realized then that he'd have to crawl. There was no other way. If he didn't crawl, he'd freeze to death. His knees were stiff these days and his back hadn't been very strong the last few years, so crawling was tedious and painfully slow.

The snow pushed up between his gloves and coat sleeves, numbing his wrists, but he plodded on, understanding his predicament, knowing he must not give up, determined that he would make it to the house, he would make it to warmth. "Dear Lord, give me strength."

Over the grade of the dam he'd built, past the willows that with their crystal beading had looked enchanted when he'd been inside looking out, and up the last few feet of the hill he inched, dragging his foot behind him. While Ole sunk deep into the snow, floundering as he crept along, the cat to whom he'd given shelter, joined him, walking gracefully atop the snow, rubbing her back against his shoulder, generous with the warmth of her fur-clad body. Purring encouragement, her eyes showed concern whenever he'd rest to conserve his strength.

Somehow, the persistent circling and mewing of the cat goaded him so that he kept going. His mind told him that he must not stop and he ordered the Lord to keep him moving. "You're not going to let me die in front of my house, Lord. Let me keep going a little longer and I'll be there." Talking aloud seemed to revive him.

By now the brightness of the morning was completely hidden by an overcast sky. Large snowflakes were floating easily down, seeking to whiten the country anew.

By the time Ole reached the house the trail he had left was already partially covered by the falling snow. He blessed the door that the cat had been able to push open so easily, so near to total exhaustion was he that he could not have pushed anything heavier.

Stray thoughts flickered through his numbed mind -- how often he'd planned to set the house on a foundation, but had never gotten around to doing it. He thought now that he could never have crawled up anything higher in his weakened state; and of what infinitely small details God uses.

The heat from the house overcame him; he collapsed on the kitchen floor, his frost-bitten, swollen foot barely inside the door.

Ole awakened later, from the pain, but even that did not keep him awake for long. He tried to wiggle the toes of his injured foot, but he was too weary to persist. Drowsiness enveloped him and he slept again, but not so much like a dead man this time.

He was awakened when he heard a stamping of snow boots at his door. He half rose on his elbow, cocked his head to hear, and shaking the sleep from his eyes and head, he called, "Yeah? Yeah?" And then he recognized the fuel delivery man's voice.

"What's goin' on here? You haven't been gallivantin' around in this weather, have you?"

At first the fuel man could not see for snow blindness, and when he discovered Ole stretched out on the floor he exclaimed, "What the thunderation -- " and knelt to look at the twisted foot.

"Where were you when it happened? How far did you drag this foot through the snow?" His words came thick and fast, and he shook his head in disbelief.

Tears came into the old man's eyes, tears he hadn't shed at Mattie's death, nor with the strain of her illness, nor even with the sorrow he had felt at being left alone. Somehow the combination of pain, exhaustion, and the sudden relief of knowing that help had arrived was too much, and the tears began to roll down his cheeks.

Feeling foolish, he wiped his eyes with his hand and said gruffly, "You sure caught me in a good one. Twisted my ankle some fool way coming down from the mail box. Reading letters from my children. Couldn't wait. Shoulda known better at my age. I'm too old for such kid tricks."

"La-dy Luck, La-dy Luck," whistled the fuel man, shaking his head, "Lucky I thought of your fuel today. There's a blizzard forecast, figured I'd ought to check on everyone's fuel supply since the bulldozer cleared the way. This winter has been so long a lot of you folks must be about out of fuel oil."

"You could use a little oil on those joints of yours, too, 'pears like." The fuel man chuckled appreciatively at his own humor. "Tell me where your things are. I'll gather them up, and we'll take you in to see Doc. Might have to set this so it will heal right."

Ole was well aware that they'd have to go immediately, that he'd have to stay wherever they went, too. "Get a little house in town, dad," his daughter had written. He could hear the words now as though she was telling him, pleading with her soft voice. It was still hard to leave, but the time had come, and he knew it.

"Maybe you know someone who wants to rent or buy a darn good farm? I've been intending to move into town. They say there's a big demand for expert rummy players down in the pool hall. Give me a hand here, so's I can get up, and let's beat that blizzard into town."

LISTENING AT NIGHT

In the hallway of my parent's home
hung a blue picture of a howling coyote
baying at the moon.

In bed at night
I'd try to listen....listen
Straining to hear ....

I could see the moon
Leaning against the cupola
And the giant dipper ladling stars
into the navy night
And, sometimes,
if I listened far enough back
I could faintly, almost hear the howl...

I still listen in bed at night..
To outsized trucks with eighteen tires
To sirens shrieking,
Cars zig-zagging
And, sometimes,
                    if I listen far enough back
I can faintly . . . almost . . . hear.

BEST LAID PLANS

"Phil, you better practice that throwing arm. We got us a game with Fort Pierre."

"We got us a game with the champions? Nah? How'd you manage that?"

"Well you guys been thinking you're pretty good, and were wanting competition. I just up and asked them did they dare take us on, and they said they dared. Now it's up to us to show 'em."

The pick-up team had a hard time believing that Fort Pierre was willing to bother with them, the boys from a little stop in the road generally known as Vera. Hayseeds was the way the boys referred to themselves.

But they all figured **they** were ready. They had been playing ball in an old cow pasture, every Sunday as long as they could remember, and this year, with the grasshoppers devouring everything in sight, even the lace curtains, field work had about come to a halt.

So they didn't have to wait until Sunday. Come a Saturday afternoon and they'd chose up sides, divide up so the teams were about equal, and go for it. Phil, his hired man, his uncle Al, and Bro, his younger brother, on one side. Everybody else on the other. Bystanders were expected to fill in where needed.

If there were an uneven number, Tag, a first rate catcher, caught for both sides. Phil was the best pitcher, so whichever side he played for was generally the winning side. They didn't have to worry about their batting, either. Any one of them could connect with the ball and skyrocket it into the wild blue yonder and beyond. What the team lacked in numbers they made up for in spirit.

The thought of competition honed their eagerness to practice. "Play ball," said Hoot, tossing the baseball to Tag who ran into the outfield to catch it. "Play Ball" Tag echoed as he allowed the soaring ball to ease into his glove before he fired it to Phil who was already in place on an imaginary pitcher's mound.

Running under the brooding summer sun soon made them wringing wet. Big circles of perspiration under their arms was part of what the Dakota sun bequeathed its residents. Globules of sweat gathered on their foreheads, and dribbled down their chins every day during harvest. "Sweating is good for you," they told themselves."It cools you off." Wiping it away became second-nature.

"Better soak that thermos good," ordered Al. "So it cools off." Wrapped in a gunny sack, the home-made thermos stayed reasonably cool provided it was well soaked in water before the game started. Evaporation was what kept the water cool.

The Hayseeds knew baseball. Even Bro, the water boy, played. He couldn't run worth a darn because he had polio as a kid. Someone else ran bases for him. But he could bat as good as the best of them.

It was the last time Al had been in Fort Pierre, thirty miles away, that he negotiated for the game. He asked if they knew anybody needed beating bad for their Fourth of July Day celebration which was just around the corner. For the City slickers there was no resisting a threat like that. They promised to give the Hayseeds a trumping they'd never forget.

For the big game the Hayseeds invested in red caps from the Seed Store. It was all the uniform they had; it was a way to tell one team from another. And the new caps made the Hayseeds look and feel jaunty.

The Red Caps against the Blues. The Hayseeds against the City slickers!

The big city team (population 700) figured to win. Odds were for them. They had it on the cow pasture team for youth, skill, and not being farmers, they spent more time of an evening practicing, throwing out a few balls, catching a few, running bases, talking strategy. But they didn't have it on anybody for number of years rehearsing the game.

Al, self-appointed captain, made the plans. "Phil, you'll pitch," he said. "Tag Donegan will catch. We'll put our best batter up after bases are filled, and aim to bring everyone in when our man hits a home run. We're not going to settle for anything less than a home run outa Bro!"

The big day came. The plan was underway. Joe Swanson hit a single. The ball caught the outfielder off guard. Joe was speedy, or he wouldn't have made it to second base.

Hoot batted next. The opposition did their best to walk him on balls, throwing them either too high or too low. Then the opposition went into a huddle, came out with their own plan. They switched pitchers. Their immediate aim was to strike out the next three men at bat.

It looked for a few minutes as though the Blue Caps had them, when first one and then two of the Red Caps struck out. Then the opposition got careless. They got distracted, too, when Bro, the crippled water boy, came up to bat, probably because they knew someone else had to do his running. The kid hit the ball so far that it careened over the wooden fence and danced a jig on the vacant lot behind the ball diamond, all the while Tag was filling in as runner. The home run came at the right moment; all three made it home, cheering and yelling like crazy.

The score was three to zero at the end of the first inning. The city slickers took note and settled down to business. At the end of the evening, it was a tie game.

That night some of the bravado left the opposition. They had a hard time believing that a ragtag team of country bumpkins could give them so much competition. Their tone was no longer admiring. It was becoming downright obnoxious.

The Hay Seeds proved to themselves they could tie the City Slickers, yet were half afraid it might have been a fluke. "Let's challenge them to play where we're the home team," said Al.

"They'll never come down to Vera to play in a cow pasture," moaned the team in unison.

"If they won't we'll hafta play them on their field again. I'm gonna challenge 'em," said Al. "Watch me."

He walked over to the captain of the opposing team and said, "My men are ready to show you the finer points of playing ball as soon as you recover. I don't spoze you'd consider coming to us, meeting us on our own turf, or anything?"

The captain of the Blue Caps chortled, shaking his head. Al persisted, "OK, if a cow pasture isn't to your liking, how about we come here again on Labor Day? You could practice all summer getting ready for us." The date was set. Labor Day. It was two months away.

That called for a celebration. Since there was no money to spend, the Red Caps descended on Uncle Al's place, brought out the brewed-at-home near beer and replayed the game -- how Bro saved the day, how Tag ran like a whirl wind, how he had to slow down so he wouldn't beat Hoot home, how they'd given the City Slickers a rude awakening, how they better get an extra man or two for their next game in case someone coudn't play because of work or injury.

For the rest of the summer, whenever there were a few idle moments, before lunch, after supper, wherever they were, they kept in mind who they were facing off with come Labor Day. And they didn't let anything else get in the way of a Sunday afternoon. That was the time they practiced as a team, pitching high balls and low balls, catching the wayward ones, and dodging cow pies.

During the next two months they did their best to build up the size of their team so they'd have subs in case something happened to one of them. On weekends they batted the socks off other local teams. The entire county started claiming ownership of the Hayseeds, could hardly contain their pride. One of them came up with the idea of throwing a party for the team.

"Tell you what, boys, if you beat the City Slickers next time, I'll spot you for a sit-down fried-chicken dinner at the Railroad Cafe," he said.

"No way. We might get served fried cat," said Hoot. The boys chortled, and started embellishing the old fried-cat story for the benefit of the younger guys.

Hoot began. "You've heard about Jens, the old duffer who ran the cafe in town a few years back. Some out-of-town guy, a stranger, stopped by and ordered squirrel. Jens laughed at him, said they didn't have squirrel in these parts, but he'd sure enough have rabbit on his menu next time the salesman came through."

The story got wilder and wilder as the guys all joined in adding their own versions. Hoot continued, "Well, when the tourist came back a week later, he stopped by and said, "I'm here for my rabbit."

"Jens, a man who always intended to keep his word, told the tourist, 'Give me an hour or so, and I'll fix you rabbit that will beat any squirrel you ever had all to heck." Then he added. "Go right ahead and pick out the tunes you like best on the jukebox, while you wait.'

Then Jens got hold of his dishwasher, Nick, who would rather hunt than eat. He told him, "Bring me in a rabbit. Skinned and ready to fry and 50 cents is yours. I got me a tourist whose mouth is watering for fried rabbit. But it's got to be damn quick.'

"Nick was under pressure to get a rabbit but he couldn't scare one out for love nor money -- and he wanted that 50 cents bad. So he done the next best thing. You remember hearing about that old cat that scrounged everything in sight? Roamed up and down Main Street, snatching at left overs, walking all over the counter at the pool hall, no matter how many times he was swatted away. The old guy who ran the pool hall, let the cat stay because he was a good mouser. Well that ole tom walked by at the wrong time in the wrong place and Nick shot him. One shot did it."

"Nick cut off the head and the feet, skinned it, cleaned it up, and you couldn't tell it from a rabbit. Then he handed it to Jens. "I got one," Nick told him. "'It wasn't easy. It's a bad time of day for finding rabbits."

"And that's all he said. Jens never knew the difference. Fried it up and served it. The tourist licked his chops and said, 'That was mighty good. Not as good as squirrel, though. Come down to Louisville and I'll serve you squirrel. We know how to fix squirrel in Kentucky.'"

"You don't know for sure it was cat, do you?" questioned Phil.

"Don't know for sure. But ole tom cat ain't been bothering anybody around here for some time, has he?"

Jack Bensen, current manager of the pool hall, had been quiet long enough. He began, "I can lead you to something that's better than chicken or squirrel. And they are there for the taking."

"Yeah? What's that, Jack? Is there anything tastes better than chicken or squirrel?"

"Young tom turkey, that's what." said Jack. "You haven't et until you've had young turkey the way my wife fixes it."

"Yeah," says Al, "Where you gonna get young tom turkeys around here? This isn't 1910 you know. There's no wild turkeys left in these parts."

"Who said "wild" turkeys? I can show you where you can get all you can eat--if you can keep quiet long enough to sneak 'em out. All you have to do is hold their beaks under your armpits. If you beat Fort Pierre on Labor Day you deserve something special."

"Remember the wise guy who said Fort Pierre would never invite you guys to play? Said they wouldn't bother with such small fry. Wise Guy has a flock of young turkeys, waiting to be plucked. All we hafta do is wait around until he gets company. He'll be so busy telling everybody how important he is that he won't hear anything else.

"I'll drive the getaway car," Jack continued. "Remember. If the Redcaps win, it's my place when it's over."

"**If** we win? Let there be no doubt about who will win," echoed each of the ball players, one after another.

Oh, the boys were high when they beat the City Slickers. The team gloated, "Those guys never knew what hit 'em."

All but Phil and Bro, who took a pass, met at the pool hall after the game. Jack had his pickup at the ready in his driveway. Al climbed in the front with Jack, and the others scrambled into the back. Jack warned them to keep the noise down.

As they came over the hill near Wise Guy's place the boys got so quiet they could hear the frogs croaking in the pond behind the shed, the crickets in the grass, and each other's breathing. They didn't utter a sound and neither did the young tom turkeys, who didn't know what hit 'em. The Hayseeds were two or three miles down the road before they cut loose with a sound. "Whew" they said, in unison.

"See you tomorrow," said Jack, after they'd plucked and cleaned the next day's dinner. "My wife will have stuffin, cranberries and all the trimmings to go with the turkey. Come around noon."

Sunday afternoon found the gang gathering out in the country at Jack's house to enjoy the fruits of their stealth. They sat down at a long table, groaning with platters of roast young tom turkey, and were poised with knife and fork, ready to carve, when a car drove in.

"Now who might that be, this time of day, and on a Sunday to boot?" said Jack innocently. "Well, I'll be darned," he said, "It's the sheriff. Wonder how he heard about this."

That's when the Red Caps started gulping, hard. Out of the corner of their eyes they glanced nervously at one another, and at the sheriff. The next thing they knew was that Jack was inviting the sheriff to come on in.

"Sit down, sheriff," he said. "We're celebrating the winning streak our boys had, putting Vera on the map for us. May be you'd like to join us?"

"Don't mind if I do," said the sheriff, taking a place at the table. Then he added, "Ummm...tastes like young tom turkey. Where did you find wild turkeys around here? After a slight pause Jack said, "Oh, turkeys aren't hard to find, if you look a little. My wife offered to cook them if the boys would bring the turkey. I don't know, guys. Where did you get these particular birds?"

There was an extra long silence. The silence was thicker than it had been the night before when they were sneaking up on the creatures. The boys looked every where but at one another, gulping and pretending they were too busy chewing to answer. The sheriff went on as though he hadn't really wanted to know where they got them.

He didn't stick around for long. When he left he said, "Well, thanks a lot for the turkey feed, boys. You earned it."

As soon as the sheriff was out the door Jack began the needling. "You were the sickest looking lot I ever saw when the sheriff asked where you got them turkeys. Shouldn't have been that hard to answer."

TRAIL DRIVE

The reedy old voice cut through Big Mac's thoughts. "A sudden blizzard," Old Timer declared, "And you'd lose ever'thing. Ain't no sensible man driven cattle that far since steel fence posts was invented. Any man in his right mind would truck 'em. It's faster. It's safer."

There was truth in what the old man said, and Mac knew it, but he and Myrtle had talked it over, and came to the same conclusion. They would have to drive their cattle to market.

Everything depended on the weather. All they needed was a few clear days.

Mac, like most of his neighbors, ran cattle, and farmed, planting wheat for flour, and sorghum or sudan grass to feed the cattle. He ran over 300 head of cattle to balance the work and the income. When one crop failed the other was supposed to pull him through but it didn't always work that way. After a long siege of crop failures--droughts, dust storms, grasshoppers, and Mormon crickets, the less hardy South Dakotans had pulled up stakes and left.

Mac had asked Myrt, "What do you think? Should we head for the city?" Myrt's reply was short and sweet, "We can't afford to," she said.

And then she added, "Who wants to live where trees and buildings get in the way every time you try to look out? No, we couldn't do that to JR. Every kid wants to live on a ranch. And neither of us could stand living all hemmed in either. Are you forgetting this is "next year country."

"You're right, Myrt. Maybe next year prices will spiral up. Maybe next year the government will do something half-way intelligent. Maybe next year we'll strike oil!"

Mac wanted to believe it. But times had been so continually bad since '33 that they had to figure out a way to bring in a few dollars to live on. Selling off the cattle would be one way to go.

But shipping cattle cost so much they couldn't afford it, so Mac set to scheming. He told Myrt, "If I could get a couple more men to help ride herd, I think Crane and I could drive the cattle to market. And JR is 14 now. He's old enough to help. If we do it during Christmas vacation, he won't even have to miss school. It would be something he'd always look back on."

Myrt liked the idea. She said, "I'll bring out hot meals for the first coupla days. And bring JR home to sleep the first night out." The plan looked feasible.

Mac's answer to Old Timer said it all. "Driving cattle can be just as safe as hauling them and the price is right! It's a heck of a lot cheaper -- like the difference between going in the hole and realizing a little profit. Sure, it'll take more time, but in the winter, time is what we got." He paused a bit before adding, "Bullsitting, I call it. That's all we do most of the winter."

Myrt, never one to mince words, spoke up. "Ain't that the truth. Remember, it was you said it first!"

They studied the Farmer's Almanac from cover to cover, talked it over, and decided the time was right. When Mac showed the Almanac to his hired hand, Crane, he said, "See if you read into it what I do. If you can believe this Almanac we're in for a good spell, so now ought to be the time to start the trail drive."

Crane barely glanced at the Almanac. "If you say so," he said, disbelieving, and added, "I'll believe good weather when I see it."

"Everything else we could get hold of predicts the same thing -- a good spell right about now," said Mac. "But I know as well as you do that South Dakota weather is never predictable. It has a mind of its own--like the ornery critters who live here!"

Mac continued, "I guess that's one of the reasons I stick with it." He smiled and his eyes met Myrt's as he thumped her shapely hip. He said, "South Dakota weather is the only thing as tantalizing and unpredictable as a woman."

"Crane, tell Bascom to pick up Croix and be ready to go tomorrow morning, weather permitting. I'm gonna listen to the report now."

Mac yawned and stretched his rugged, six-foot frame toward the kitchen ceiling in the low homesteader's shack they called home. Every night, before he went to bed, he listened to the weather report on the little Atwater Kent.

"Pay no attention to those who say it can't be done," he thought. "It's the only way --." His thoughts were interrupted by the sputtering of the radio. He fumbled with the dial, trying to clear the static so he could hear. When the forecaster announced there'd be good weather, Mac's mind was made up; they'd start the trail drive as planned. He fell asleep with a smile playing at the corners of his mouth -- he dreamed that a giant, horned, long-eared animal he'd heard described to a stranger as a jackelope, was watching a herd of rusty colored cattle making their way down a slight rise of land toward a river.

Mac was up early the next morning; long before anyone else was awake he'd checked out the weather. Just as he came back into the house, Crane, ace hired hand, and just as big and husky as Mac, came down the stairs, shaking the sleep out of his head.

"Morning," Crane mumbled, heading for the wash basin which sat on a chintz-draped peach crate in the corner of the kitchen. Crane cupped his hands with cold water which he splashed on his face and dried himself briskly with a khaki colored towel which hung on a nail. Then, glancing into the mirror as he used a comb, he noticed how red and leathery his fair skin had become from the cold weather. When he sat down, he was ready for the steaming coffee and hot flap jacks that Myrt set before him on the oilcloth-covered table.

Not until Crane had buttered and poured syrup over his cakes and took his first bite, did he pause to ask, "How's it look outside?"

"Clear as a bell, sunny. And no snow left, except along the creeks. Not much ice left, either."

"Guess you know who to talk to about weather." Crane said. "Wish you knew half as much about when's a good time to sell."

And, then, chuckling, "You didn't have to call Sprout twice this morning. He's up there rushing around so fast he's putting everything on backwards and upside down!"

Mac, Jr. or JR, as his parents called him, looking like a younger clone of his father, came bouncing down the uneven steps that some makeshift carpenter had built to reach the attic. Without taking time to wash his hands, the kid sat down and started gulping down pancakes.

"Morning, Sprout. Ya'll set to drive that lead rack? Whatcha gonna do if some yokel sheep herder comes by with a passel of sheep? You gonna sit here looking fat and sassy, and let all 300 of our white-faces high-tail it? Ever try to stop a stampede?"

There was nothing JR liked better than making fast comebacks but his voice, which these days couldn't decide whether to be soprano or bass, hampered his delivery some, and before he could say anything his dad asked, "Almost ready, JR? Time's a wasting."

Crane added, "Reckon you got enough pancakes under your belt to keep a scrawny little guy like you from starving -- least 'til noon!"

The roar of a gunning motor caught and held their attention. "Probably Bascom bringing Croix. I let Bascom think we'd be pulling out before dawn. Figured it was the only way to get him here before noon. He'll be coming in, looking foolish, thinking he overslept, and apologizing for holding us back."

Mac and Crane donned fur-lined jackets over heavy, woolen sweaters, and pulled on old winter caps to protect their ears. They knew better than to wear their wide-brimmed Stetsons on a day like this when they were going to be outside all day. In unison they pulled on thick, heavy gloves. They had no need for conversation.

The two of them walked easily, boots solid against the frozen ground. Ducking their heads against the bite of the morning they headed for the corral. The sound of bawling yearlings echoed through the still, glorious morning. A few dried corn stalks, bent and gray in the morning cold, glittered with ice. A rooster, strutting around inside the chicken coop, crowed. Inside the corral the Herefords milled about restlessly.

JR snatched one last bite of pancake and then hurried to catch up. By the time Bascom and Croix turned into the driveway the others were ready to go.

Mac called to the latecomers as they hopped out of the pick-up, looking embarrassed, "We're going to start the herd down past the creek for a good long drink before we leave."

"Sprout," Crane motioned, "Keep an eye on these guys; don't let 'em fall asleep. It's awful early in the morning for anybody who needs sleep like these boys do."

Croix, half-French, half Sioux-Indian, remained expressionless, but good-natured Bascom countered with, "Some guys just ain't got a clear enough conscience to sleep."

Crane handed Bascom an axe and motioned for him to start chopping ice. Then, for JR's benefit, said, "Watch Sprout work circles around you both."

JR flushed and headed towards the dam, which lay in the crotch of two hills. The pasture hills were interlaced with draws, which caught and held melting snows. The dam, which had been steeply graded so as to hold water enough to last the season, had a foot thick coating of ice which had to be chopped through. The trail drive was underway by the time all the cattle were watered.

There had been talk about pulling the lead hay rack with the tractor, but they decided against it. Instead, the kid led the way, driving a matched buckskin team, Prince and Kate. The hay bales, stacked neatly in the rack, were supposed to lure the cattle along. In the evening the crew planned to spread

66

the hay around both for the cattle to bed down on and for them to eat.

It made a pretty picture, the white faced Herefords with their rusty backsides etched sharply against the blue of the sky. The herd strung out for a full quarter mile as the winter wind nudged them gently on, and they proceeded quietly, snatching mouthfuls of tufted grass to munch on as they moved along.

Croix, tall and lean, and Bascom, short and husky, sat astride sorrel ponies which they stationed at either side of the herd. Big Mac rode behind, sitting easily in the saddle, hazing the stragglers along. The right flank of his saddle pony was scarred by a Lazy M brand, the same brand carried on the cattle. Crane, mounted on a roan, brought up the rear.

The noon sun hung low in the south when Myrt came out bringing them a hot lunch she'd fixed at the house. "Hey, she called. "You're making better time than you thought you'd make. By my watch you are averaging about a mile and a half an hour."

"That's about what we figured." said Mac. "We made better time by following the section lines; didn't worry about trespassing. Think how good cowboys had it before fences!"

Bascom, who looked as though he'd never missed a meal call in his life, was the first in line for chow and he ate hearty. Crane allowed "From now on better let Bascom chow down **after** the rest of us have."

"Ah, shucks," Bascom responded, "I don't eat half as much you do. I just chaw each bite well so it takes me longer, that's all. I make the most of what I chaw."

The crew took turns sitting in the pickup to eat their lunches; at least it was warmer inside the pickup than it was riding. When it was JR's turn for chow, Myrt called to him, "I'll take over the team while you eat; you better get warmed through before it turns really cold tonight."

JR climbed down clumsily; the thickness of his winter clothing made it impossible to move quickly. His back had been to the wind all morning, and the cold had penetrated through to the bone. He took off his gloves in order to rub his nose, which was cold and red. Then he cupped his hands and blew into them the way he'd seen Crane do.

The heat from his warm breath eased the cold a little. He even gulped down hot coffee, something he'd never done before, until he noticed that his mother had brought a thermos of cocoa for him. To JR cocoa tasted way better than any kind of coffee.

By the time her son had finished eating Myrt was cold through and through, despite her fur-lined woolen coat, woolen slacks, and heavy overshoes. She was glad to climb back into the pickup though the heater did not throw out much heat in this weather. She was sure glad that JR would be able to sleep at home the first night out.

It was late afternoon when they reached the Little Ben River. They aimed to cross it before bedding the cattle down for the night, which meant working late. They had to spread sand over the ice so the cattle wouldn't slip; they couldn't risk any broken legs. The ice was frozen solid; that was important.

The Little Ben was shallow, even at its peak; nevertheless they couldn't chance waiting until morning to cross. Bascom and Crane rode on ahead and began to spread the gravel around. The cattle slowed, were beginning to bawl loudly; the sound carried along the hollows of the river bottom.

The cattle approached the ice cautiously, unsure of their footing, and then crowded across in a jerky, unsteady gait. When they reached the other side the animals broke into a little run to get the momentum needed to proceed up the slight rise of the river bank.

After they crossed, JR turned his hayrack toward the flat bottom land by the river's edge, where the canyon walls provided a little shelter. With his dad's help, JR threw bales of hay off the rack; the cattle began tearing and chewing the bales of hay, and as they did their heads bobbed up and down, until they had their fill.

Croix chopped holes in the ice, again, because the animals had to have water. After long draughts of ice water the Herefords turned back for more hay. Some bedded down on the hay bales for the night, or stood quietly chewing their cuds, now and then flicking a tail, or opening an eye, teary from the cold.

Bascom, who had been gathering kindling, built a brush fire. If you stood close enough, the flames, licking high into the air, provided a welcome warmth. Some of the crew found tree stumps to lounge on; the rest had to squat down. By the time Myrt brought them supper they were half-starved and bone-weary.

Only Mac and Crane figured to stay the night; somebody had to be there, in case the cattle got spooked. With sleeping bags for warmth they'd dig down, horn-toad style, into the hayrack. Mac knew JR would put up a fight about being sent home to sleep, and he did, but he went anyhow.

JR was so near asleep when they reached home that Myrt had trouble getting him into the house. She helped him tug off his heavy overshoes and plaid jacket and let him sleep fully clothed on the front room couch. He slept like a dead man!

Before dawn the next morning Bascom and Croix came for JR. Bascom, who was always looking for an easier way for himself, said. "It's too gol-dern cold for me. This boy's gonna ride herd in his Ford 4 V8 today." And then, turning to JR, said, "Your dad probably won't think much of it." JR knew what his dad would think: no vehicle is as reliable with cattle as a good horse is.

All Mac said to Bascom was, "What are you going to do with Beauty? She's your responsibility."

Their second day out passed uneventfully, the air continuing bright and clear, the sun still diffused little warmth. By noon Bascom asked, "Isn't this Indian territory?" Mac nodded, and said, "It's all right; Chief's a friend of mine. He allowed as it was all right for us to pass through. And Croix grew up on the Reservation." They stopped the second night at the old County Fair Grounds and Stockyard, once located there because of the water supply. "Here's where the stockyards stood. Some of the old posts are still here, dad," shouted JR, excitedly. "You can see the size of it. My teacher said they used to ship thousands of cattle out of here every year in the old days. When she heard I was going on a trail drive she made me read about the early cowboys and the cattle rustlers in these parts, and how they hated the settlers' guts."

"Yeah," said Bascom, "there was once range wars right here. And Indian wars, too. Hey, Croix, did you hear that?" But Croix was nowhere to be seen.

While JR and Bascom were loafing, Mac and Crane set about getting settled in. Mac said, "This lean-to was once used for a hot dog stand; it'll come in handy tonight. This old laundry stove is where the auctioneers warmed their hands on cold days. We'll soon have it so red hot you'll be backing away from it."

Myrt brought lunch and supper out again on the second day, and melted snow from the creek in an old pan so there was hot water to wash up with. As they sat savoring the evening meal Crane thanked Myrt. "This sure beats camping out and eating chow around the campfire," he observed, "Though I spoze Sprout feels cheated."

The coffee pot sat on the laundry stove all night, despite grumbling by Bascom, who, though he shied away from even a taste of alcohol, said, for JR's benefit, "Coffee? Is that all the liquid refreshments we're getting? We might just as well be them WCTUers. My pappy tole me a little whiskey in the summer keeps you safe from sunstroke, and a little more in the winter will keep you from freezing to death."

Dead tired from their restless night before, Mac and Crane fell asleep almost as soon as they'd eaten and when the warmth from the stove hit them; their plans were to wake up to take the midnight shift. JR fell asleep almost as soon, but the other two lit a kerosene lantern and got out a deck of cards.

"I'll teach you how to play Pitch," Bascom said, shuffling the red bicycle cards. Croix appeared to be a willing student, so they sat smack in front of the laundry stove where their bodies absorbed the heat before it got very far.

There were no windows inside the shack. Hinged shutters once swung down to make tables, but now the hooks that held the shutters in place were rusty, and so were the hinges.

Only a fool would try to open a window on a night like this, but it would have been nice to have one so they could peek out. As it was they had to poke their heads out the door now and then to check on the herd.

It was close to midnight when Mac awakened. Despite banking it, the little laundry stove had almost gone out, and the shack was getting cold. Bascom and Croix were both snoring loudly, mouths open, huddled under heavy wool blankets where they sat in front of the stove, arms limp at their sides. Mac stomped around, gathering the logs they'd laid in, trying to get the fire going again. Suddenly, Croix slumped over, coming to with a start. Bascom never did waken; instead he flopped over onto the floor, grunted a little, and snored louder.

Croix followed Mac out to look the herd over. They needn't have bothered; the herd was quiet. The sky seemed darker and the myriad stars more aloof than ever. In the distance a coyote howled, and a startled deer appeared momentarily at the river's edge and then slipped quickly away into the shadows, leaving only the telltale cleft hoof tracks.

The temperature was decidedly colder -- their second night out and an icy blast of frigid air had enveloped them. They hurried back in to the welcome warmth of the laundry stove. Mac beat the palms of his hands together, cracking his knuckles to get the circulation going again, and moved his shoulder blades up and down to get rid of some of the stiffness.

He wished he had a radio so he could hear the weather reports. His pocket watch said one a.m. He figured to take the rest of the night watch, and let the others sleep a little longer.

It was about four in the morning when the men started to stir. The little laundry stove hadn't gone out but it just couldn't throw out enough heat to warm the shack with the cold as bitter as it had gotten. The water in the basin had a thin layer of ice on it.

Bascom scurried around, apologetic for having fallen asleep when he was supposed to stand watch, and outdid himself preparing grub. Tossing flapjacks into the air, he caught them expertly with the pan they'd brought from home, and served them, hot and inviting, on tin plates. "As a night watchman, Bascom," drawled Crane, smacking his lips over the cakes. "You'd shore make somebody a good wife."

When they left the blue bluffs along the river and came out from the valley they felt the cold even more. Maybe it was a matter of getting cold to the marrow and not really warming up at night, but Mac felt himself bracing against the piercing wind.

The weeds which stuck through the snow along the fences had saucily weathered the winter, but were arching against the onslaught of winter. Snow birds, insulated by fluffed feathers, pecked furiously at whatever seeds they found. Along the ridge, a land mark lone tree stood chilled and forlorn, as though still vulnerable to the weather, despite years of exposure.

The herd moved right along, no problem there. Even a pasture filled with sheep didn't alarm them. "Never see anything like it," said Bascom. "These cows must be so blamed cold their imaginations are froze. Either that or they are so damn numb they can't tell a sheep from a fence post."

When it began to get dark, JR motioned to his dad to come closer to the hayrack and asked, "You sure you know where we're going, Dad? Maybe we got turned around somewhere."

"Trust me," said Mac. "These December days are the shortest days of the year; it gets dark by five o'clock. It won't be long until we reach the old school buildings where we're going to put up for the night."

"I hope those school buildings are still there." said JR. "Since they're not used any more somebody could have torn them down."

Mac responded, "Old school houses are still being used for township elections, and now and then, for a revival meeting or two. And they always keep coal on hand in case some hunter or trapper loses his way. Can't let 'em freeze to death. Don't worry, son. The buildings are still standing."

It was late when they finally arrived at their school. The ground was frozen hard and icy underfoot. The herd was weary. Usually they licked at the blocks of salt before they drank of the water, but they didn't bother this time. The cattle crowded against the sheltered side of the school building to be away from the wind. They huddled close together, seeking warmth from each other, or laid down, beat from the travel. The horses, glad for shelter, brushed against one another for warmth.

Mac's crew went into the schoolhouse to case the facilities. The first thing Bascom spotted was the teacher's desk. He stepped in place behind it, saying, "Ah. At last I know how it feels to be on the other side of the desk. I've always waited for the moment when I'd have a bunch of teachers in front of me so I could give the orders."

Then, in a high falsetto voice, "Come to order now kiddies, and let us not throw any more spit balls at the stove. Teacher doesn't approve of the vulgar way they sizzle."

Croix, too, found his niche. He went directly to the blackboard and began drawing with chalk--landscapes, horses, dogs--pictures of the land that he loved. He revealed with the chalk what he could never reveal with words. Mac had seen him thus before, absorbed for hours, painting in the village cafe, on cardboard with cans of enamel paint from the dime store. He sold the pictures for whatever he could get for them.

The school house was well equipped with a kerosene stove for cooking, heater, lantern, and even a cot, which the last schoolmom who taught in that school had used when roads became impassible.

When Bascom saw the kerosene range, he offered to make the evening meal. "First one to complain," he said, "does the dishes."

"I saw the couch first. It's mine." said JR, but Crane made a flying leap at the same time and captured it broadside. "It's mine fair and square, " Crane said, "First come, first served." He picked JR up and stuck him under his arm as though he were a kicking, wriggling sack of flour.

"Be good? Promise? No more shenanigans?" When Crane extracted a promise and let JR loose, the kid turned back squealing and tried to latch on to the cot again. That time Crane sat on him and pretended to be absorbed in reading an old schoolbook. JR struggled and kicked but Crane wouldn't let him go until he was too tuckered out to persist.

"This time," Crane said, "I'm not moving until morning." He didn't either, though nobody would bring him anything to eat, and when he stretched out towards the improvised table to snatch a bite to eat he had to make sure he had one foot firmly anchored on the couch.

The exercise did them all good, and they felt warm and relaxed. They even played cat and mouse on the blackboard, and hang-the-man like they'd done as kids.

Croix had gone outside while they were rough housing and hadn't returned. After a while Crane said, "I wonder where Croix could have gone? He went out into the night without saying a word to anybody." Mac looked thoughtfully, hand on chin "Croix grew up near here. You don't suppose he is out looking up relatives?

"Probably out looking for a woman," yawned Bascom. "Don't wait up for him. He'll be back. I promise you." Bascom spread his bed roll next to the heater, stretched and scratched, and got ready to bury his head under the covers for the night.

Concerned about Croix, Mac peered out into the school yard then, and noticed that large snowflakes had begun to float down. They were drifting lazily, intermittently, but the sky had turned black, and there were no stars visible.

Mac looked at Crane and without speaking each knew the others thoughts. Any change in the weather could be a change for the worse this time of year. What if the wind switched? They had only one long day left before they would reach the railroad shipping yard. Surely the storm would hold off that long.

Croix appeared then as silently as he had gone; his weather beaten face grim. "Soon will a storm be upon us. My brothers say that before the dawn the north wind will bring sleet and ice."

They were back in the saddles and ready to go within the half hour. The cattle bunched closer together, not stringing out as they'd done before and they were easier to drive. They seemed to sense the urgency the snow had brought; the pending storm stirred both man and beast and their tiredness was replaced with energy.

They were only a mile from the shipping yards when the blizzard began in earnest. The wind had switched again and was whipping down from the northwest. It was blowing gusts of snow across the road, whirling and tantalizing in its onslaught. The crew turned up their collars and hunched their necks deep down into their coats, and still they were cold.

The herd pushed forward, tired and hungry, filled with fear. Snow thickened their lashes so they had to peer through heavy lids; their tails became ice-matted, their nostrils encrusted with sleet.

The team balked, then, in the face of the sleet, and the Kid couldn't manage alone. Mac turned his horse loose, sure that his horse could find his own way, got into the rack, and worked for control with the team. Croix was not stoical in the excitement of the storm; he urged the herd onward, lashing at them with his lariat to keep them moving.

Snowflakes fringed the bleary eyes and leathery hides of man and beast, and ice clung to the corners of their mouths where the saliva had frozen, and to their ears and nostrils. The horses, heads down, were nearly exhausted.

When they turned into the stockyards in Redbud, the fence posts along the trail were barely visible. When Hathaway's crew saw them they came running out to help, shouting at them, marveling at their stamina. They corralled the herd, unsaddled the horses, cussed the weather.

Everyone talked at the same time, asking different questions. "Where were you when the storm hit? How did you manage to make it through? How far did you come? You mean this kid stayed with you all the way?"

Mac's crew, shielding their faces against the piercing sleet, ran towards the Hathaway house. They wiped numb hands across ruddy half-frozen faces, stomped snow from their boots, and shook their Mackinaws when they got inside.

The house inside was warm and steamy; a teakettle bubbled merrily on the kitchen range. Around the kitchen Mrs. Hathaway moved, setting the table, preparing something hot for them to eat.

"We made it, thank the Almighty," Mac droned wearily. He mumbled something else, before he nodded off. It sounded like " . . . enough money to tide us over for another year. Next year has gotta be better than this one."

SOUTH DAKOTA SAGA

Fort Pierre and Van Metre were sister cities
Who remembered Bad River and all his escapades
which made good telling
    As they sat rocking in their chairs at dusk,
        Watching the sun go down.

Who could guess that Bad River would overflow
      His banks each spring, sweep
Aside settlers who stood in his way? Snatch
    Four-legged animals, feathered ones
Who didn't fly fast enough. And buildings,
      Leaving only debris
    After he'd had his way with them.

Fort Pierre and Van Metre, sister cities,
      Nestled snugly against Bad River
Trusting. They needed his water,
    Admired his brightness, Counted on his fish.
  How could they know he was fickle?

Fort Pierre and Van Metre could tell
    About walking to school in the morning
    Among yellow johnny-jump-ups.
  Being rescued and rowed home at night.

Now only a rusted railroad bridge remains
    Lashed fast by sawgrass stubble.
Battered tobacco tins reflect sunbroiled cactus spines.
    Antelope cruise by, noses alert, heads high,
      Panning the scene.

THE HOMESTEAD

"We want to see where you and Grandpa lived in the olden days. Ple-a-se, grandma," the children pleaded. Sophie smiled in spite of herself at the thought that the children assumed that she and Methuselah were probably about the same age.

"Oh, no, children, it wouldn't be the same," Sophie said, "That was a long time ago. Let's go to the zoo or park, instead."

"No, Grandma. We've seen the zoo already. We want to see the house where our mother grew up, and the pastures, and the barns, and everything." Six-year old Jennie hooked her arm through her grandmother's. "Can't we, Grandma? Can't We? Pretty please."

A dozen years had passed since Matt's death; it hardly seemed possible. It wasn't easy to go back to see the home they had shared for fifty years, but the grandchildren were persistent.

There was a curve in the road just before they got to the homestead and Sophie caught a glimpse of the row of hardy cottonwoods that lined the creek below the house. Just beyond and up the road she could see the farm buildings nestled against the hillside. From the road the house looked much as it always had.

In her mind's eye Sophie could see the old yellow tabby cat basking in the sun on the outside ledge of her kitchen window. She could see the hens clucking about, scratching grass seeds from between the crumbling bricks of the walkway.

But the grass, now, was long and overran the walks, and next to the front door a pile of horse manure desecrated her yard where a horse had found shelter.

"Wouldn't you think someone would take care of this place," she muttered huskily, trying to stop the tears from dimming her eyes.

The grandchildren, in their eagerness, did not notice, but bounded out of the car and all three of them began at once to explore, calling, "Come on, Grandma." Then, running ahead of her, they added, "We want to see everything."

Inside the house, the rays of the late afternoon sun streamed through the uncurtained windows. Darker rectangles on the wallpaper revealed where her pictures had once hung.

The doors on a nearly bare cupboard hung open, and a half-used sack of navy beans was undisturbed. She remembered leaving the beans as well as cans of spices--provisions she wouldn't use any more when cooking only for herself. Her reasoning was that they might come in handy for someone stumbling about in a storm.

Clods of dried mud, where someone tramped through with wet boots, adorned the kitchen floor, but otherwise, her gay linoleum was just as she remembered it -- defiant with its saucy red and green designs. In the bedroom were a few empty hangers, waiting forlornly, and in the closet, hanging on a nail, an apron.

The big bay window, once filled with red geraniums, looked desolate. Sophie was proud that the house was still weather-proof; the rains hadn't found a way to sneak in. Matthew and Sophie had always been good stewards of their property.

Her three curious grandchildren traipsed eagerly through the house, up and down the crooked stairs. "Grandma, the pictures, the beds. Why did you leave them here?" Without waiting for answers they chattered on.

"The bear rug--the one dad told us he used to scare Aunt Ginny with--it's still here, Grandma," exulted Steven, her eight-year old grandson. He struggled to pick up the rug, hoping to play the same tricks on his sisters.

"Books, report cards." The girls called, delighted with the discoveries. "Hey, here is a perfect attendance award that Aunt Ginny earned when she was little. Why did you leave this house, Grandma?"

Sophie was glad, in a way, that the grandchildren did cavort about, with their lilting, happy questions. If she seemed a little dazed and answered slowly at times, it was because memories were crowding back. She bit her lip to try to put her emotions on hold. It bruised her that no one lived on the farm any more. Mass production had squeezed small farmers out of business; much of the land now belonged to "city farmers."

There was no longer a need for rural schools; children who didn't live in town, were bused in. Piano, swimming and dancing lessons, Little League, basketball--all were deemed more important than developing character through the responsibility of farm chores. It was considered too lonely for farm children to be raised without playmates. Sophie muttered to herself, "What was good enough for us, isn't good enough for them."

"Come on, Grandma, we're going to look outside." The grandchildren ran, sweeping up to the outhouse, an unimposing silvery gray building, with its door ajar. Inside, an old Sears Roebuck catalogue, with only shiny pages left, lay open on the floor.

The children peered down the toilet holes, grimaced and chortled cheerfully, then poked their fingers through the knot holes in the walls. They ran outside to peek in on each other, and tried to climb the anchoring wire, the better to hang over the roof and spy on the unfortunate soul who was inside.

Farther up the hill stood the old chicken house. Though it had stood empty for many years flies still buzzed about, and feathers still flew at the commotion made by the children's feet.

"Phew," they grimaced, holding their noses to keep out barnyard smells. They searched for eggs in the improvised nests -- peach crates nailed to inside walls and filled with straw.

"Maybe we'll find a glass egg, Grandma," Steven said, remembering stories Sophie had told them.

Next they spied the sandbox, made from a tractor tire cut in half. The sandbox, barely visible through the wheat grass, was still half-filled with sand. Sophie's youngest child had often sat there playing by herself, sifting sand, sunlight pouring down on her golden hair, unspoiled by quarreling -- there had been no sand throwing, no crying that someone had wrecked the sand castles.

Over the hill by the grade of the dam was the old tree house, built in the cottonwood, years ago, by the children's father when he was a young boy. Sophie recalled sitting on the bank of the dam holding her youngest child, so they could be in on the good times, too.

While the children scrambled into the treehouse Sophie eased her stiff, bulky body onto the plank landing where she and Matt often sat of an evening, to fish and watch the sun go down.

She needed once more to drink in the loveliness of the view--the tall, golden sunflowers, the black-eyed susans, the snow-on-the-mountain, the purple milk weed. She smelled the wild onions, how she'd hated it when the milk tasted of onions.

"You put onions in everything all year, why do you mind when the cows do it for you?" She could almost hear Matt's gently joshing voice. Oh, how she missed him.

Behind the grade of the dam tin cans glistened, reflecting the setting sun. There had been no call to haul things away to garbage dumps in bygone days.

Deep hoofprints left by cattle when they came for water seemed inscribed in the mud; wild mallards floated placidly over the water, now and then dipping their heads into the water, then bobbing back up. Blue dragonflies, slim and shining as an embroiderer's needle, darted about in the twilight.

At dusk the fish splashed, jumping into the air, performing. Delighted, the children, ran to watch. In front of them a garden snake slithered by.

"Watch for rattlers," Sophie cried, suddenly alarmed. "Rattlesnakes are poisonous. They are very dangerous."

"Even if nobody else will live here, the snakes will," she said, half to herself. And then, realizing how bitter she felt, she sighed, "I wonder if I'll ever be able to see the old place in its proper perspective. "

"Don't feel so sad, Grandma." Her youngest grandchild looked beseechingly into her eyes and patted her lovingly on the cheek.

The skipping feet of her oldest granddaughter, Gayle, slowed, and came close. "Do you feel sad because you can't live here any more, Grandma?" she asked. When you feel sad, Grandma, it makes us sad."

"I shouldn't feel so bad," she said, "I left here of my own free will. And life is always like that; there is no turning back. Only a going forward."

Steven, climbing down from the treehouse, called, "We can go now, we don't have to stay any longer. It's getting dark anyhow." He leaned over to help Sophie to her feet."

Suddenly Sophie could see again, clearly. All was right with her world. She saw the tenderness in the eyes of her grandchildren--they were perceptive, loving, capable.

"You are young, and the young should be carefree," she said, wiping away a tear. "It is only when we grow old that we look back. We look back at an unreality and think everything was once better. For a little while I had completely forgotten that there were snakes then, too."

The setting Dakota sun diffused a golden glow over the world. A sweet poignancy seemed to settle in when the frogs began to croak, the crickets to chirp. Sophie thought, "Only one who has lived through it can truly fathom the beauty at the end of a day."

GETTING OUT OF LYMAN COUNTY

"Can you believe it, Carrie?" Charley said to his wife. "It's 1934 and Jake Barrett says he has never been out of Lyman county! He's never been in another time zone. All he'd have to do is drive through Murdo and he'd be in mountain time!"

"So?" retorted Carrie. "I've never been farther west than the White Clay Buttes. And if it hadn't been for the Iowa cousins I would never have made it that far. If you hadn't taken it personally when they said the people out here "sure stayed put" we wouldn't have ever driven all the way to White Clay Buttes either."

Charley chuckled. He remembered all right. Those Iowa folks weren't daring enough to move west but they would venture a visit now and then so as to be sure they'd made the right decision. Then they'd turn up their noses at drinking water from the dams like everyone else did, talked about how "barren" it was, how they "missed Iowa's trees."

Charley decided he'd show them "barren." He figured to take them for a joy ride in his truck to White Clay Buttes, a place so treeless it made Lyman county seem like the forest primeval.

Only a few of the highways in midwest South Dakota were graveled in 1934. Those were the premium twelve-feet-wide roads between towns. On all other roads a film of fine dust sifted down and settled over those who traveled them, blinding anyone who followed too close behind, or who met someone going in the opposite direction. Luckily a man usually had the roads to himself!

White Clay Buttes could be seen for miles across the rolling Dakota prairies; there were few trees and no tall buildings to block the view. The Buttes were a ways off from any real road.

After Charley turned off the dirt road he followed an old trail which had once been a buffalo crossing. He wended his way through cactus and crab grass, played "gotcha" with the tumble weeds blowing in front of his truck. Past clusters of prairie dogs standing sentinel; when they got too close the creatures disappeared under ground into their tunnels.

By dusk the Iowa visitors were as close to White Clay Buttes as they wanted to be. There wasn't much to see anyhow, so Charley turned back, the Iowa folks worrying they'd never make it "back to civilization" before dark.

That trek did more than tantalize the Iowans. It also whet Carrie's appetite for travel. By the 1930's the good people of Lyman County were witnessing a veritable explosion of cars and trucks. There was talk about "oiling" the roads between towns.

"I guess that _was_ a while ago, wasn't it?" asked Charley. "It sure sounds like you'd like to get out of the county again? Then, why don't we up and do it?"

"That'll be the day," answered Carrie. "Talk is cheap. Talk is as far as we'll ever get."

"Now, protested Charley. "I like to travel as much as the next guy, but there's always the chores."

Carrie grumbled to herself, "If it wasn't the chores, it would be something else." But she said out loud, "Maybe we could get someone to do the chores once. Or better yet, maybe we could get up real early, leave before daylight, and come home after dark. The cows could wait that long, couldn't they?

Charley listened. He could tell by the sound of Carrie's voice that she was desperate to see more of the country. Her cousin's remark had really got to her. "You sure stay put out here."

"How about we drive out to see the Badlands?

Our cattle truck ought to work fine, if I fix seats in the back. The kids will love it. Let's talk it up with the Barretts. You talk to his wife, and I'll talk to him.

"Right. I've been thinking we'd ought to do something with the Barretts, ever since I was called in to be midwife when their baby was born. The Barretts would be fun to take along. They have kids the age of ours, plus a few extras! It will be more fun for the kids that way."

"You haul cattle to Sioux city in this truck; so it should be sturdy enough," laughed Jack Barrett, when they talked to him about it.

"The women can pack lunch, and between you and me, Charley, we can ride herd on the kids and see that we don't lose anybody!"

Soon the kids from both families, who made up 3/4 of the country school they all attended, were in on the planning. The excitement grew; the younger ones turning circles at the thought of it all.

"What are the Badlands like, Dad?" they asked.

"High and eerie with bare mountains of sand, with gullies in between. With no trees and very little grass."

Not much life there--maybe a few prairie dogs, and a few birds but they can fly in and out."

"How did the Badlands get that way?" asked Katie, the curious one of their children.

"They are sand dunes twisted this way and that by the wind and rain for thousands of years," explained Charley. "They are streaked with color, as though somebody cleaned a paintbrush and ran with it against the pinnacles. Like nothing you've ever seen before," said Charley.

"Where do the colors come from?" asked Katie the skeptic.

"Well, Katie, they say it's minerals which cause those streaks of color. I've been told the red streaks are from the iron in the soil, and the green streaks from copper, but I don't know for sure. And the white on the ground is alkali."

The day before the trip Barrett brought over seats from an old car body which sat in his yard. "This will give the women a soft place to sit while they are trying to hang on to the young ones," he said.

After the car seats were arranged, the men suspended army blankets across the corners of the stock truck to provide shade for those who rode in the back. "These khaki blankets I brought back from World War I are coming in handy," said Charley. "When the sun goes down, and it cools off, the kids can use them to curl up in."

Early the next morning, as soon as they were loaded, they headed west, driving away from the sun, filled with the excitement that trips to new places with children conjure.

Stashed into the back of the truck were the mothers, and 10 kids. In the front of the truck sat Charley, who drove, and Jack Barrett, his copilot, though he had never been far from home. The children, patrolled by the older boys, dug their toes into the sides of the truck, trying to get high enough to see where they were going. Carrie gave silent thanks that the two oldest of the Barrett boys were old enough not only to be scared about climbing the sides of a truck when it was moving, but also to have authority with the younger ones.

When they reached the county line Charley thought it was time they stopped to have something to quench their thirst. He pulled his rig over to a wide spot along side of the road, where a solitary tree stood.

There the children downed great tin cups of nectar which their mothers made by mixing water with one of the new flavorings purchased from the Watkins Man, the same vendor who'd been peddling vanilla and cinnamon for years. At the first stop they savored the cherry and could hardly wait to try the lime and the grape. To them the nectar was sweet as ambrosia.

Shortly after they climbed back into the truck and were on their way the boys saw what they thought were the Badlands. They beat on the back of the truck window. "Look, look," they shouted. "We can see them. Over there. The Badlands."

Charley pulled the truck over to see what the hullabaloo was all about.

"We're in the Badlands," the children shouted, pointing. "There they are. Over there. The Badlands?"

"No," Charley said. "Boys those are just little bitty pimples of dirt, knobs in the ground. You'll know the Badlands when you see them. Don't worry about that!"

It was noon when they arrived at Cedar Pass, so named because of the grayish cedars which struggled for survival against the wind and the hot sun. The roots of the cedars clung to bits of soil deposited in crevices between rocks. The cedars marked the entrance to the Badlands National Park.

Charley brought his truck to a halt, and the families clamored out. The first reaction of the travelers was that of stunned silence. The lack of plant or animal life left a stillness; a pervasive sense of eeriness, of being in a part of the world perhaps inhabited by evil spirits. The noon day sun was straight over head; as it burned down upon their heads they instinctively shielded their eyes from its glare.

They were caught in a spell, that of being mysteriously plunged into the midst of a surreal painting, surrounded as they were, by pastel-striped, sand-covered peaks in the process of erosion which would undoubtedly continue for another thousand years. For a brief moment each beheld the glory that is the Badlands.

The moment was broken when Charley said, "Me and my brother used to ride horseback out here when we were kids. We saw these peaks when they were nothing but plain sand. We decided to do something about it so the next time we came out we brought cans of paint with us. Yessir, we did a good job, wouldn't you say?"

"Stop it, daddy," said Katie. "If you painted it, show us where you left the paint cans?"

With that the boys, who had eagerly scaled the sides of the stock truck all morning, now saw real peaks to climb. They ran towards the peaks, planning to use a rope as a ladder. "Watch for rattlesnakes," both fathers warned at the same time.

The little girls, content to dig in the sands, decided to take colored sand home as a souvenir. What they didn't wrap to take home stuck to their perspiring skin. Katie observed to her Mother, "Look. We're like pieces of sandpaper."

The glaring sun at noon isn't inviting to those who live with it every day; their first thought is to get away from it. The only shade to be found was in the shadow of the truck, so that's where the picnic lunches were set out, ready for eating. They dined on potato salad, sandwiches, and the first "fryers" of the year. This time they washed it down with nectar made from the lime flavor mixed with water from the five gallon cream can they'd carried from home.

They didn't own a thermos bottle between them, but the adults had coffee in a jug swaddled in canvas. The coffee, more tepid than hot, brought no complaints.

Exploring in the afternoon sun gets old, fast. Despite being outside every day all summer, despite coverings on their heads, they were beginning to sunburn so they loaded up and headed home.

They found the same lone tree along side the road where they had their first morning break. This time they munched on left over sandwiches. They ate what was left of the sandwiches, with the added texture of sifted colored sand from the packages the girls stored next to the sandwiches!

The total distance they had gone was 125 miles, counting both ways! The evening turned cool, just as Charley had said when he explained to the Iowans why he liked Dakota so well. Before they reached home all except the oldest boys were asleep, sprawled around, the khaki colored blankets pulled over their shoulders.

Carrie was the first to notice the light in the window. That's when she realized she had forgotten to extinguish the flame in the kerosene lamp when they left in the morning.

They had been gone from before sunup until after sundown. They had an entire day away from the farm.

HE'S ALL RIGHT NOW

"He's all right now," my father said, of George.
What did he mean, "He's all right now?" It puzzled me.

My brother George was only eight but he could ride a
horse and rope a calf. And cut a cow from out the herd.
Sometimes he'd ride so far away that we'd get scared.
Then dad would call, and then we'd hear, from far away,
His answering tune.
And George could fish, and set a trap.
 He seemed to know when bass would bite...

When George was here, we'd laugh, and shout,
He'd climb and leap and I would clap...
But George took sick . . .

The doctor came, and shook his head.
"There's nothing we can do," he said.
"Just wait, and pray. It's in God's hands."

I couldn't think that God would take him, but

He did.
He's gone. George is not here.
And yet, he's everywhere.

And now I know what father meant
"He's all right now."

OCCUPATIONAL HAZARDS

When the spinster who had been teaching for a half
century at a one-room country school in Willow Township
finally retired, the school board was forced to seek another
qualified teacher. It took a bit of doing. South Dakota
teachers had heard the siren call of higher wages and were
leaving the state by the dozens.

The Board advertised their plight in nearby states. They
got lucky. The lone teacher who answered their plea, Miss
Gracie Bell, had most of the needed credentials, though she
was not yet certified. She also had a mop of red hair, was
"purty as a red carnation blooming in the desert, wee as a
tailor's thimble, and energetic as a pocket gopher caching his
winter's supply of seeds."

Gracie emigrated from North Dakota, a land far enough
away from Jones County, South Dakota, to seem both exotic
and exciting to those who had never been out of the state.
There was about Miss Bell an aura of high adventure which
envelopes those who strike out on their own to travel to a
new part of the country. Miss Bell soon found such
popularity as she had never imagined.

When word got around that the new school mom had
arrived, older brothers, cousins, and sundry single males were
suddenly overcome with a great desire for more book
learning. It followed then that they were willing, even

anxious, to daily escort younger relatives to school. Jones County had never before seen such a whirlwind of activity.

Life had never been like that before for Miss Gracie Bell, either. She was nonplused by all the attention.

But she set to work creating for her students the same aura of excitement. Herself the proven product of a one-room country school the new schoolmom patterned her teaching methods after what she could recall from her own.

Each morning she began by ringing the bell to call the children to task. She used a bronze-colored bill, a replica of the cracked liberty bell. It had coerced generations of South Dakota school children into silence, not only because its sound literally broke sound barriers, but also because of the authority vested in it.

Although there were only 14 students in the white frame one-room country school, and a voice announcing that it was 9:00 o'clock would have sufficed, Gracie preferred the sense of immediacy that ringing the bell provided.

"Opening exercises," the bell declared. First, the salute and pledge to the American flag followed by the singing of the national anthem. Opening exercises followed the same pattern each day, and always included an adventure story read by the teacher to the entire school. Childhood memories rushed back and closed in on Gracie.

Miss Bell's teacher had read aloud when school began each morning, so Gracie knew the books children liked. She loved hearing then, and loved reading them just as much now that she was the one choosing the stories. Uncle Tom's Cabin, Silas Marner, The Five Little Peppers & How They Grew. As she read aloud Miss Bell allowed her mind to wander a little -- she had never actually known anyone by the name of Phronsie but if Phronsie should suddenly knock on the door, Gracie was sure she'd recognize her at once.

The morning, as usual, whizzed by. While the upper grade classes studied South America, the Andes, and the Amazon River, Miss Bell set about teaching reading to lower grade children. With her long ruler she pointed at the sounds on the phonics charts, and drilled the children until each of them knew the "a" sounds by heart. That wasn't good enough for Miss Bell.

She insisted that they also practice *printing* each letter at their desks. Miss Bell pronounced each word slowly, dragging out each letter. "C-at, b-at, f-at, h-at, m-at, p-at, r-at, s-at." Her pupils made few mistakes.

The eyes of the beginning readers glowed with satisfaction; it was heady stuff to be able to read. An extra reward was getting to write their spelling words on the blackboard with chalk!

While the lower grades copied spelling words, Miss Bell turned to the middle grade children, but soon found the whole school listening. How could they do anything else when the conversation was about foreign lands, and of strange animals to be found in strange countries across the ocean?

So engrossed were the children that only Miss Bell noticed the time. Though the wall clock said 10:30 which was recess time, the teacher saw no reason to disturb the children's work. She figured to have their recess 15 minutes recess later. As long as she started school on time each morning, managed two fifteen minute recesses somewhere in between, and closed on time, she reasoned that the children were getting the proper amount of work and play. She answered only to the parents and the county superintendent of schools. Or so she thought.

There came a sudden, persistent knock at the door. Gracie's first thought was, "Now who can that be . . .Oh, can't I even think any more without my thoughts being snatched up?"

A moment later she had collected her wits. The visitor was not one of the young bucks who had serenaded her the night before. It was Mrs. Gabe, wife of the rancher whose land was adjacent to the school grounds.

The rancher's wife had let herself into the building through the cloak room, and there she waited for someone to help her with her problem.

She began tremulously. "Is the school clock broken?" Then she apologetically offered, "I could ask the school board to order a new one for you."

"No," Miss Bell replied. "That won't be necessary. This clock works just fine. Why do you ask?"

"Because," Mrs. Gabe explained, "When I'm working outside I can tell what time it is by when the children are outside for recess. My radio programs come on at 10:15, the same time your recess begins. I listen to Guiding Light and Ma Perkins on the radio every morning. When the programs are over it's time to fix lunch for Mr. Gabe and Seymour, our hired man. This is the third time this week that I missed my programs; I waited until the children came outside for recess, and when they did my programs were already over."

"Oh, dear," said Gracie, "I am really sorry. It seemed foolish to stop in the middle of a lesson just because the clock said 10:15. I didn't realize any one was telling time by when we had recess!"

LEARNING THE COMBINATIONS

During the lunch hour Miss Bell wrote the 45 arithmetic combinations on the blackboard in five columns.

Then she directed them to practice saying the answers to themselves, at first, beginning in the upper left hand corner, then dropping down to the next line. They held up their hands when they thought they were ready to say them out loud, and they gradually gained speed. Saying the answers aloud helped them to learn. Those at their seats could soon catch any errors that were made.

For the younger children she got out match sticks for counting. Soon they were adding and subtracting match sticks and were eager to "say the combinations," too, of which there wer forty-five.

"Children," said Gracie, in her most school mistress voice, "On Friday you are to bring your mother or father to school so you can show them how well you do your tables. Remember to bring a guest."

"Bring someone" is the way the children heard it. They had no trouble getting someone to come. Tom Turnow, a young uncle of two of the students, showed up at nine the next morning.

"Jim and Nancy said you wanted someone from the family so they could show off their multiplication skills," he said. "Well, here I am."

The children took turns haltingly giving answers, improving each time. "Now it's your turn, Tom," the children teased. But Tom was not good at math.

"Miss Gracie," Tom begged, "Let me come to school everyday so I can learn the answers, too."

"Tom," said Miss Gracie sweetly. "After you have signed our guest register,you may go home. You may come back when you are ready to challenge the children. Until then, though, you are going to have to practice."

"Can I practice with you tonight?" he asked.

"Say May I," prompted the children.

"No, I'm afraid I do not have time, thank you," said the teacher firmly.

The contest was on. No other challenge could have worked so well. Docking the children one minute for incorrect answers amazingly stimulated their memories. Jim and Nancy, brother and sister, fought to outdo their own best scores, and one another. The same was true of every student. It wasn't long before there were no challengers from outside the school.

There came a day when Miss Styles, the County Superintendent, knocked on the door. "Who could it be?" asked Megan, one of the twins.

When Miss Bell looked up she saw a stocky, heavy-set woman, dressed all in brown -- brown tweed jacket, brown skirt, and brown oxfords with low heels. She radiated a no-nonsense approach which the children quickly sensed. They bent their heads into their books as though studying hard; no one could have ever seen a quieter, more attentive class.

"Our guest is Miss Styles, County Superintendent of Schools," Gracie explained. "She wants to tell you about Rally Day."

Miss Styles began, "I want you to come to compete with children from all over the county. Rally Day will be on May 2 this year. You may enter spelling, addition and multiplication contests. There will also be athletic contests--running, broad jump, high jump, and baseball throwing."

"The school that wins the most first places will be given a trophy which they can keep in their school for a whole year. If a school earns the trophy three years in a row, they may keep it forever!" She continued, "I can see you have been practicing and if you keep on like this you may very well be among the winners."

Then Miss Styles left, waving a friendly goodbye.

"I know we'll do well," said Miss Bell. "Because you are all such hard workers.

BULL IN THE SCHOOL YARD

The days had been growing shorter and colder since early December, and keeping warm became more important than looking good. Bundled against the cold with parka hood, sweater, coat, snow pants and boots, Miss Bell trudged the two miles to and from school each day. Keeping her company was second grader, Ella Mae, at whose home she boarded. So far, both had avoided frost bite.

Friday afternoon was when the Young Citizen League meetings (YCL) were held. The students took turns presiding as president, taking minutes, and giving imaginary treasurer's reports. Regular chores were also an intrinsic part of the YCL.

Children in 5th through 8th grades took turns bringing coal from the coal shed behind the school. The younger children had a job they relished -- beating chalk dust out of the erasers, managing to get most of the chalk dust on themselves. The taller children were given the job of washing the blackboards, after they had carefully erased around the 45 combinations. That way they could go over them again before they left for home at day's end.

One Friday afternoon, just as they were ready to start for home, there appeared in the school yard a big rust-colored bull, switching his tail as he grazed on the scattered patches of grass that had weathered the recess ball games. The bull stood in their way, half way between the road and the schoolhouse.

Nothing the children nor the teacher did from their safety zone at the schoolhouse door could cause the animal to move. The children knew better than to try to sidle past the ominous-looking animal. Not until Mr. James and his hired hand, Mel, came driving in, did the animal budge.

"Come on, kids. Jump in the truck," ordered Jerry's father, "Old Ferdie has held you hostage long enough." He piled the Hauges, the Robinsons and his own son into his pickup.

"We'll see that old Ferdie gets out of your way, too, teach," called the hired man. With that, Mr. James revved the truck, guided it straight at the imposing animal and gently nudged the animal along. He continued nudging the bull down the road, until the animal began to trot, head tilted to one side against the wind.

When Ellie Mae and Miss Gracie started for home, the bull was no longer in sight. The short days were almost too short; by the time they reached home, the sky was rosy as the setting sun diffused the colors of the sky across the earth.

"Why not dismiss the kids half an hour earlier each day," suggested Ellie's mother when they arrived from school at sundown. "It's pretty cold now that the days are so short, and two miles is far enough to walk even when it's not cold."

Gracie appreciated the suggestion. She took it into consideration, thought it might be a good idea to start letting the children out earlier right after Christmas.

CHRISTMAS PROGRAM

As soon as Thanksgiving was over the entire school began to work in earnest on the Christmas program. At the end of each school day Gracie sat down at the slightly-out-of-tune organ and drummed out Christmas tunes. The children gathered around and sang.

They sang every Christmas song in the *Golden Book of Children's Songs: Up On The House Top, Jolly Old Saint Nicholas, Jingle Bells, Silent Night, Deck the Halls With Bows of Holly, Hark the Herald Angels Sing,* and *Away in the Manger.*

"My mom knows all these songs," bragged the second grader.

"Both my mom and dad know all these songs," echoed the others, "and when we practice them at home we all sing together." It was true. The air for miles around was saturated with the same lilting Christmas melodies.

Every student had a "piece" to learn for the program, which was held on the afternoon before school closed for Christmas vacation. Names were drawn so each child could give and receive one gift.

Special guests were the little brothers and sisters. For them it served as an introduction to school, in effect, their kindergarten! Each was presented with papier mache beads the children had rolled and painted, as well as belts made by folding cellophane wrappers from cigarette packages. Each family received silhouettes of their own children, made with one child holding a flashlight while Miss Bell sketched the profiles. It became a group activity; those who handled scissors well did the cutting; the younger ones helped paste the profile on another sheet which became the frame.

Chain loops made from strips of colored construction paper and glued together were hung in the windows by those tall enough to do it. Trees were hard to come by in central South Dakota, and too expensive to buy so Miss Bell drew a tree on the blackboard with colored chalk.

Then the twin's mother ordered an artificial tree from the Sears Roebuck catalogue and offered to let the school borrow it until Christmas vacation started. The branches were sparse, farther apart than on an authentic tree, and the green color was a hue no respectable tree would wear, but it sufficed. The children strung popcorn for it, and on the day before Christmas vacation they strung cranberries, too.

From clothespins they fashioned candle holders! They painted the holders red and green and glued on short candles.

"Children, each of you can pinch one colored clothes pin onto the branches," directed Miss Bell, "And that will be your very own candle to take home after the program." When the twins' mother saw the decorated tree she exclaimed, "You kids and your teacher made that spindly little tree look downright beautiful. Better not light those candles, though," she warned, "The tree could catch on fire. It looks purty as it is."

The custom was for Santa to pass out gifts at the Christmas party. Despite uncles and older brothers insisting they would make wonderful Santas, Miss Bell claimed that part of the education of the school children was to play the role of Santa Claus. Calvin, the oldest boy in school, the lone eighth grader, dressed like Santa. He handed each little visiting brother and sister an orange, and a candy cane from the sack he carried on his back.

When the erstwhile Santa beamed and said, "Ho, ho ho. And who do we have here?" Calvin's little brother said, "You can't fool me. You're not Santa. I can tell by your shoes. You're my brother. You're Calvin."

STORM

When school resumed in January temperatures were below zero, and got colder every day. One day Mike, the father of the first grade twins, came after his children early. It was only two o'clock. He said, "I'm early because the radio announced that a blizzard is predicted. I'll take the kids who live in my direction, and drop them off at their homes. It's too darn cold for them to walk very far in this weather. You got a ride?"

Gracie replied, "If it's really bad Ella Mae's dad will come for us."

"Well, it's really bad. They'll be here soon. Sure of it."

Gracie and Ellie waited until four o'clock, long after the parents of the other children had come and gone. It looked terrible outside, but without a radio in the school, and no telephones there was no way to get information from the outside. Gracie had to make up her mind whether to stay the night, or face the brutal wind on the way home.

She had half a sandwich left over from lunch; Ellie never finished all the food her mother packed for her, so they'd be all right, at least the first night. They probably wouldn't starve. They began to have a great appreciation for the YCL--there was enough kindling inside the schoolhouse to last for several days.

It was then that Gracie remembered the county superintendent sending around word that they should be prepared to stay at the school in case of storm warnings. She'd made a mental note to take the superintendent's advice, but all she had done about it, so far, was to bring a couple of quilts.

With most of the children gone the schoolroom seemed distressingly quiet. When they looked outside they couldn't see much, decided windows in a school house were designed to let in light instead of to allow those inside to look out. All they could see was that snowflakes were swirling around and visibility wasn't much better than zero. When Miss Bell said they'd better stay the night, Ellie asked, "But what will we do for light?"

The teacher had no answer for that. She'd never been in the schoolhouse after dark. She replied, "I guess we will just have to go to bed, or read by the firelight from the stove, like Abe Lincoln did. Remember?"

The two of them, Gracie and Ellie, played cat and mouse on the blackboard until they were bored. Ellie wound the handle on the phonograph so she could play the records. The records had never sounded so scratchy.

Then they heard a rubbing on the side of the schoolhouse. They both sat very very still, breathing as quietly as they could. Ellie, wide-eyed, clung to Miss Bell and whispered, "Who could that be?"

"I don't know," breathed Gracie.

"Maybe it's someone who needs help," said Ellie. "Maybe we should let them in."

"I-I-I don't think so," breathed Gracie. "Why would anyone be out in a night like this?"

They tried to peek out the windows but the night was so dark they couldn't make out what it was that was rubbing against the schoolhouse. Then they heard a grunt and a bellow, and guessed that it might be the same animal that had visited them during the week!.

Miss Bell sighed. A bull rubbing against the side of the building she could handle. Strange men she couldn't. They must have fallen asleep sometime after their scare because they didn't hear another sound until sometime after daylight when they heard a scraping at the front door.

When they peeked out they saw that snow had drifted across the front porch of the school so that they couldn't possibly have opened the door from the inside. Gabe, the nearby neighbor, whose wife set her clock by the times they were out for recess, had come to their rescue. When he had cleared a path with his snow shovel he rapped on the door and called, "Hey, teach, you okay?"

He wore a red plaid cap with earflaps pulled down. His face was red; his nose whiskers stiff and bristly, thickened by snow and ice. He stamped his feet to shake the snow off his boots, and stepped inside the entry way of the school.

"See you kept that old heater going all night. That's good. Should have known that a North Dakota girl would know enough not to stick her nose outside in weather like this.

"I saw Michaels pick up the school kids yesterday when it was beginning to blizzard. Didn't stop snowing all night. Drifts are more than five feet high in some places. If you're expecting Ellie's dad, don't. I doubt anyone can get through.

"The weather report said it ain't going to let up soon. Ma and I got to thinking about you and the little girl being here all alone. Said I'd better see if you were all right. Have you got enough kindling? Got anything to eat?"

Then he looked at the coal bucket in the corner. It had been full when the storm started. "I better fill your coal bucket. Tell you what, if the weather doesn't clear up pretty soon we'll come and take the two of you to our place. My wife will fix something hot for you to eat."

It was afternoon before Gabe and his hired man came to get them. Gabe introduced Gracie by saying, "This is Seymour. We call him Seemore because he can see farther than anyone else, always knows which corner of the pasture the cattle will be in."

Gabe and Seymour had dug out a sleigh which hadn't been used for years and filled it with straw and blankets for warmth. They all clambered into the sleigh and in no time made the half mile drive to the Gabes.

When Mrs. Gabe saw they had arrived she ladled hot potato soup into bowls for them. Home made bread, fresh from the oven went with it. Food had rarely tasted so good.

110

Mrs. Gabe asked, "What did you two do to keep busy last night? Do you like to play cards? What kind of cards do you play?"

"How about Slippery Ann?" asked Seymour.

"You probably know that game as Hearts," Mrs. Gabe said to Gracie."Where you try to sluff off the queen of spades to somebody else. And try not to take any tricks with hearts in them."

After one game Ellie Mae lost interest in cards, said she'd rather play with the cat. Mrs. Gabe said, "Now that we have four adults. Let's play Whist. If you don't know how, we'll teach you. Men against women."

"I'm an old Whist player," said Gracie. And she was. The women got good cards and beat the men bad.

The men had all kinds of excuses. Gabe said something about "not sitting with the bathtub" which always brought down the house because no one had bathtubs unless you counted the round steel tub filled with hot water from the teakettle to use on a Saturday night.

To change their luck, they said, both Seymour and Gabe walked completely around their chairs. Then they decided they'd better switch partners, "give the women a break."

The radio had so much static they couldn't hear anything that night but the next morning, the third day of the storm, they heard just how bad the storm had been.

The storm had spread across the state and a lot of livestock was lost. Cattle bunched up in fence corners against the wind the first day. By the next day fences didn't mean a thing; the snow had crusted and livestock walked right over the top of the fences.

When Ellie looked out the window she saw the snow was as high as the roof of the barn. It looked as though the roof reached to the ground. Later on in the morning Gracie and Ellie went out "for a breath of fresh air." The bright sun caused a glare so they had to squeeze their eyes shut against it.

Ellie said, "There's the rooster. I heard him crowing this morning."

"Yes, he thinks he's the reason the sun came out," said Mrs. Gabe. "See those chicken scratches on the snow? That's old chanticleer's signature. The snow is packed so hard that old bird doesn't even sink down."

On Saturday morning Seymour said, "Get your things ready. We'll take you girls home today. I think we can get through in the pick up."

On the way they met Jack, Ellie's father, who was just coming after them. Jack said, "I knew Gabes would look out for you. Thank God for good neighbors."

Before the girls went home Seymour directed his conversation to Ellie. He said, "Would you and Miss Bell like to go to the square dance next week?"

Jack said, "You two can go, Seymour, but my daughter is too young for dances. You probably got more than you can handle just escorting Miss Bell. Sure you want to escort someone to a dance who'll be dancing with everybody else all evening?"

Seymour grinned. "I can beat her playing whist. Bet I can step on her toes harder than anyone else can. How about it, Miss Bell?"

"Yes, how about it, Mr. Seymour! Let's get the record straight. We beat you, you didn't beat us," laughed Gracie.

"You're not answering my question, Miss Bell. Would you like to go to the dance in town? Or would you rather teach the combinations to Turnow? Is he still coming to school to get help for his math?"

As it turned out the weather was bad every Saturday night for the month of January. Then on the Saturday closest to Valentine's Day there was a dance and pie social in town. Ladies of all ages were supposed to bring pies to be auctioned. The trick was that no one was supposed to know whose pie they were bidding on.

Gracie made a cherry pie, fitting, she thought, to the occasion. Ellie's mother offered to carry it so no one would know which pie was Gracie's.

"Everybody is trying to get me to tell 'em which pie is teacher's," said Ellie. "But I ain't telling."

Old Fiddler, a drummer, and whoever they could get to pound the ivories, were tuning up when the crowd drifted in.

The girls stood on one side of the room, all dolled up, hoping they'd be asked to dance. Gracie sat demurely by Mrs. Gabe. It was the first time in months that she hadn't worn snowpants and her legs were cold. The boys clustered together at the back of the room, daring each other to ask a girl to dance.

As soon as the music started the girls started dancing, doing fancy steps the guys wouldn't dare try. Married couples were next to get out on the dance floor. A favorite tune was "Alley Cat," great for doing the two-step, a step everyone in the county dared to try to dance.

Soon everyone who wanted to dance was on the floor, high school kids, grade school kids, grandparents. There were always more women who wanted to dance than men who would try. Many an Aunt took to the floor to initiate nieces and nephews into the intricacies of dancing.

Old Fiddler wanted everybody on the floor. He said, "This floor does its own thing. Vibrations from the music, and your own dancing feet make moving around here easy. Even the guy with two left feet can't help but dance. So come on, everybody, give it a twirl."

Gracie had plenty of partners, but Seymour, very assertive, cut in on every dance. He may not have been the best card player in the world, but he could dance up a storm. After the first round Gracie was breathless. She forgot all about the cold.

Then the caller made his announcement: "Folks, we are holding this Firemen's Ball to get a little money to buy badly needed equipment. You've been enjoying the dance so far, haven't you?"

After hoots and whistles of approval, the caller went on. "I've been told that some of you came to square dance. We're going to start as soon as you can get a partner out on the floor. Then, about ten o'clock or so we'll auction off the pies. Now grab your favorite partner, line up along the wall and get into the action."

With the couples lined up, the caller began his call. "First bow to your partner. Then bow to your corner. Now allemande left with your left hand, and right to your partner, and right and left grand; meet your partner and dosey do; and promenade home.

After a few squares, Old Fiddler stopped and the auctioneer began. He said, "I have here before me a variety of pies. Some are marked custard, some apple, some chocolate, and several are marked cherry. Remember the money from the sale of these pies benefits the firemen. With whatever money we take in tonight we will buy new fire fighting equipment.

"I'll start with an apple pie. Mom's apple pie. A favorite of all. What am I offered? Give me fifty cents. Give me a dollar. Going, going, gone. Apple pie like Mom used to make. Sold for a dollar bill. Step right over here, gentlemen. "Don't let anyone else eat with your girl. Spend what it takes to buy her pie. Show her you think enough of her to spend all you got. The fire department needs new equipment. What am I offered?"

Gracie did her best to act nonchalant; several would-be suitors were watching her out of the corner of their eyes. Turnow, Seymour, Mel, and others were bidding on the pie they thought belonged to Gracie. Ellie's father threw in a couple of bids designed to bring the price up. Then Mr. Gabe topped his bid. The younger guys gave up, thinking the pie must be one made by Mrs. Gabe. Besides the price went higher than they could afford.

Finally the auctioneer stopped. He said, "Sold to Mr. Gabe, the highest bidder. "Thank you," said Gabe, "Let Natvig pay for it. I put the bid in for him."

Natvig was the new insurance salesman in town. He was probably earning more money than any of the younger men all put together. Gracie was annoyed with herself for not letting Ellie tell which pie was hers, but she decided to be a good sport about it, to regard it as a good cause.

Natvig looked pleased as punch. The rest of Miss Bell's suitors stood nearby cracking jokes, while Gracie and Natvig ate cherry pie. Gracie did not know Natvig so she remained somewhat aloof, excused herself as soon as possible, and went home, as she had come, with Ellie and her parents.

INSURANCE MAN

School had barely begun on the following Monday when there was another knock at the schoolhouse door. Miss Bell was reading a very exciting part of Uncle Tom's Cabin; she was right where Liza was crossing the river on ice. It wasn't Liza, though, who stood there waiting. It was, in fact, not even a female.

The nattily dressed salesman (navy suit, red striped tie) who thrust a card at Gracie which read "J.J. Natvig, Insurance" bore no resemblance to any of the story-book characters they'd been hearing about. Gracie recognized him at once as the man who had put in the highest bid for the cherry pie she brought to the pie social.

"I'm sorry, sir. School is in session," said the young schoolmistress, handing back Natvig's card. She moved to shut the door, but Natvig's profession had taught him the rewards of persistence. He was not faint of heart. He deftly turned so that the card Miss Bell tried to return fell to the floor.

"Keep it," he said gallantly. "I shall return when you have more time." He tipped his hat, turned on his heel, and walked jauntily down the school steps, got into his new, 1939 Plymouth and shot away.

It was almost 4 o'clock, just before school was out, when Natvig made a second appearance. Hat in hand, he swept it ceremoniously, handing his card to the youngster who came to the door. He announced, "J.J. Natvig, Insurance, at your service. I'd like a few minutes with the school mom, if you please."

"The **teacher's** name is Miss Bell, if you please," she said. "What is it you want?"

"If Madam School-**Teacher** has a little time I would like to explain about an insurance program specifically designed for educators, such as yourself," Natvig said.

"Until school is dismissed, Mr. Natvig, I will not be free to discuss anything with you. The children and I have chores we must finish first," she said.

Taking her comment as an invitation to wait inside the school, Natvig glanced into the mirror hanging on the wall, smoothed his hair, and waited by the window, his eyes following the teacher's every move.

Gracie busily wrote the assignments for the following day on the blackboard. Out of the corner of her eye she supervised the children as they dusted erasers, washed blackboards and swept the hallway. At the same time she noted that the coal buckets needed to be filled.

The chores nearly done, she turned to the insurance man and asked, "Now, what is it you wish to show me?"

Almost as soon as the words were out of her mouth she realized it could be taken the wrong way, and became flustered. She bit her lip. Natvig leered, "Oh, you really want to see it now? Maybe a little later---."

It soon became clear that the salesman hadn't spent the day poring over paper work. He had been enjoying the fruit of the vine, probably in small nips, off and on all afternoon. Nevertheless, he sensed that his comments made Miss Bell uncomfortable. He nodded sagely, and whispered, "Little pitchers have big ears." He then set about grandly opening a brown leather case from which he took out various insurance plans and spread them out on Gracie's desk.

But he kept beating around the bush; he did not get down to the business of explaining insurance plans. Gracie peered at him over the ledger in which she kept attendance records, and admonished him, "I really don't have a lot of time, Mr. Natvig. I'd appreciate it if you'd get right into explaining the pros and cons of your various insurance policies."

Natvig raised his eyebrows and made a slight gesture to indicate that third grader Ellie Mae should leave. He said, "We can discuss things better when we're alone."

Miss Bell's eyes flashed as she replied curtly, "Anything that you wish to discuss with me may be said in front of Ellie Mae. I board with her parents, and we go home together."

"Anybody ever tell you you're beautiful when you're mad," said Natvig admiringly, then changed his tactics. He pointed to the chair next to Gracie's desk, and said formally, "May I sit here?"

"Now this policy," he began, "would be ideal for a young woman all alone in this vast country. It works like a savings account for you. You can pay into it for a limited number of years until such time as you want it, say as when you get married. It could be used for a down payment on your first bedroom set, for instance, or your honeymoon. Oh, there are so many things I can show you," he said earnestly, "if only you had time."

Then suddenly he took her hands in his, bumping against her, and looked soulfully into her eyes. "Gad, you are beautiful," he said. "Don't be mad at me. I can't help myself." He pretended to look penitent.

Gracie rose to her full five feet one inch, cut him off in mid-sentence and said, "I do not need insurance, Mr. Natvig, from you or from anyone else from your company. You may go. **NOW!**

She pointed at the door and stood there, willing him to leave. She was trembling but her voice carried authority and he began to edge towards the door.

"Sure I can't offer you a ride home," he pleaded. Finally he doffed his hat, slipped out the door and into his Plymouth, and roared out of the schoolyard.

The temperature outside had dropped, and Miss Bell and Ellie Mae faced into the wind as they headed home. They were a good mile down the road when Natvig came back, eased his car to a stop, and again offered them a ride. When he saw the stony look on Miss Bell's face he sped away, then suddenly turned around in the middle of the country road, and returned. His eyes were noticeably bleary, his speech was thick. He said, "I'm going your way and you just as well take a ride. B-r-r- It's cold out there, and I would be honored to give two such lovely ladies a ride home."

Ellie Mae's blue eyes beseeched her teacher to accept the offer. The wind and cold had joined forces to penetrate their heavy jackets, and send chills up their spines. The teacher shook her head firmly at the child, and replied, her voice icy as the piercing wind, "No thanks. We have our own transportation."

When he left, his car was weaving down the road from side to side. Ellie Mae questioned, "**Where's** our transportation? Dad said he and Mom were going to an auction today. Are they supposed to be coming after us? They'll be late because Dad said the old timer who was having the sale had lots of junk to bid on."

The walk home was more than two miles and the wind blew more fiercely by the minute. When the teacher and her student reached the driveway they saw Natvig's car parked in front of the house. Ella Mae's parents were no where in sight. Gracie grabbed Ella Mae by the coat collar before she could dash over to Natvig's car, and urgently whispered, "Pretend you don't see him. We'll sneak into the barn and wait until he leaves." Delighted to play hide and go seek Ellie Mae touched her fingers to her lips, her merry eyes dancing.

It was late in the day; the sun hung low in the western sky, streaking the sky with orange and pink. Soon the warmth of the sun, which held the frigid air at bay all day, would be gone, and even though winds die down at the end of the day, it bode to be a nasty evening. And still Ellie Mae's parents didn't show.

The two stood motionless in the barn, and, though protected from the wind, were getting chillier by the minute. Gracie began to wonder if they really could outlast Natvig.

The rattle of the old Ford told them Ella Mae's parents and their hired hand had finally made it home, which gave them the opportunity to dash for the house.

Jack Powers, Ellie's father, leaped out of his car, to see what Natvig was doing there. Natvig, by this time was snoring deeply, periodically snorting and jerking. The car's engine was still running.

Powers shook him, "Wake up you fool--don't you know you can suffocate from carbon monoxide when you leave your engine running?"

There was no waking Natvig. Jack hollered to his hired hand to jump in the Ford and follow him. Then Jack shoved Natvig over, got in beside him, and delivered the would-be salesman to his own home. Jack did not approve of drinking, figured that anything that happened to Natvig was what he deserved for drinking, yet his own conscience wouldn't allow him to leave Natvig to freeze to death.

With the hired man's help they half dragged, half carried Natvig into the old farm house where he lived. They tossed him on his bed, fully clothed, and piled on all the blankets they could find. They built a fire in the pot-bellied stove in his front room to take off the chill. After the fire began to throw off heat, Jack and the hired man left.

There were no telephones in rural South Dakota in those days. It was generally agreed that "phones are always out of order when you need them, and by the time they're fixed you don't need 'em any more." It was fact that telephone wires were broken each winter by the weight of snow. It thus happened that word that Natvig's house had burned down did not get around for a day or two.

Sparks from the stove must have first ignited the kindling wood piled in the corner, and then the flames must have leapt to the wooden floor of the old farmhouse. The premise, at first, was that was that after sleeping off some of the alcohol, Natvig had gotten chilled, gotten up to throw more coal on the fire. Then dozed off again sitting in front of the stove. The combination of the whiskey and the warmth from the fire probably caused him to fall asleep in front of the stove.

When Jack Powers heard that the house had burned he felt terrible. He bemoaned the fact that he had ever had mercy upon Natvig. Said it might have better if he'd just left Natvig in the car, felt he should have stayed with him all night, figured that what he had meant to be a good deed had backfired. He felt he'd fumbled his responsibility and it depressed him. He fumed at himself that he should have left well enough alone.

The house had burned, that was true, but Natvig hadn't. Nor had he frozen to death. Instead he had awakened, felt thirsty, and decided he needed more whiskey. He climbed into his car, headed it east, fell asleep driving, and ran the car off the road.

As it happened someone found Natvig's car in the ditch. Natvig was still alive. The alcohol content in his body probably kept him from freezing to death.

The neighbors banded together and sent Natvig back to relatives in Minnesota, to recuperate. A year or two later Natvig was back, to show off his woman. It was said that the woman, a widow with several children, did not allow alcoholic beverages in her house, and that so remarkably well did she rule that Natvig was never again seen to take a drink.

And Natvig did so well at his insurance business, even collecting for his burnt house, that farmers who were discouraged with their lot seriously recommended that their children consider going into the insurance business.

By the time spring came and Rally Day was next on the agenda, even the third graders knew the addition combinations. The older children practiced on both the multiplication and addition combinations. By May they knew them all by heart. They itched to bring home a trophy!

Spelling contests were also a part of Rally Day, so after other studies were completed Miss Bell allowed the older children to practice spelling words by pronouncing them to one another. The sixth grader and the eighth grader took turns pronouncing words for the other to spell.

Using ancient BLUE CONTEST SPELLERS they learned to spell words for which they did not know the meanings, and could barely pronounce. Day after day they worked at them anyhow. By the time Rally Day came around they'd gone through the book three times.

Miss Bell's students did not win a single outdoor race, but their practice paid off on the spelling and math contests.

The announcement came over the loudspeaker at the end of the day. "First, second, and third prizes in Multiplication have all been won by children from the same school. This same school has also placed first in 6th and 8th grade oral spelling contests."

"I am particularly pleased," said a beaming woman Miss Bell did not know, but who took the loudspeaker from the hands of the announcer, "Because I think of these children as mine. I taught for almost twenty years at the school these children attend."

LAST DAY OF SCHOOL

A lone tree by the section line near the school was claimed by the natives to be the only tree in the county. They told Miss Bell they had been having last day of school picnics around that tree for years.

The day arrived. Each family brought sandwiches, a cake, and one brought potato salad. One mother made her famous angel food cake, using 13 egg whites. No one objected when she said she had to make a gold cake to use up the egg yolks, so she would bring it, too. By the time the picnic ended not a crumb from either cake was left.

It was a custom to have a ball game for the last day of school each year. Visitors against the school kids. "Visitors" were parents, uncles, and hired men.

By now Natvig was out of the picture. Mel and Tom had given up, and only Seymour kept coming around.

At the end of the day, Seymour gathered up the balls and bats and made himself generally helpful. He said to Miss Bell. "What will you be doing this summer?"

"I'll be in North Dakota going to college all summer to pick up the rest of my teacher credits."

"Then I suppose with all those college men hanging around you wouldn't have time for anyone from South Dakota should they happen to drop by?"

"Oh, I dunno," said Gracie, archly. "I dunno. Guess you'll just have to try me and see."

THE LILAC HEDGE

Jakob Neilsen fingered the visored cap thoughtfully, turning it around and around in his work-calloused hands. It was the red CENO FEED cap that the boys in the Farmers Cooperative Grain Elevator had just given him as a retirement present.

The feed cap reminded him of the one he'd worn 50 years earlier when he still lived in South Dakota. At that time he wore it to shade his eyes from the intense glare of the Dakota sun. In those days rural South Dakota had no electricity and most certainly no air conditioned tractor cabs. And now his only granddaughter thought she'd found her one true love and was going to marry and go out there to live!

Only half-listening as Selma read a letter Jake was startled to catch the name Hofsteider, the same name as the folks who'd been their closest neighbors. Memories came flooding back, things he thought he'd long forgotten.

When his family had pulled up stakes the only thing they'd hated to leave behind were the neighbors. And, of course, the lilac hedge they'd tended so carefully. He could remember, as though it were yesterday, the exact moment when they'd decided to quit farming.

The whole summer had been hot, but that day in late July was a real scorcher. It was so hot that the metal loops which buttoned at the shoulders of his striped OSHKOSH overalls sizzled when touched, and circles of perspiration around his armpits stained the sleeves of his light blue denim work shirt.

The wheat had ripened to a golden hardness, and Jakob, anxious to get the crops in, had been in the field since dawn. He felt an urgency to get the grain hauled into the elevator in town. This year, more than ever before, they needed money from the crops, needed it real bad.

They had weathered eight years on the farm. The first four years had been good. Everyone called it "next year" country -- if you didn't make it one year, there was always next year.

First it was the grasshoppers took all the wheat. Then there was the terrible drouth, which didn't let up. Like other farmers he'd had some livestock, a hedge against crop failure, but the water supply was too low to support even a few head of cattle. Well diggers had punctured holes all over the county but there still wasn't enough water at any one place and they'd taken to herding the cattle from well to well.

The wisdom of the old time farmers was that if you could just hang in there and could get a crop every third year, you could make a go of it. After the fourth year of crop failure the Neilsen's clung to a wary hopefulness. This had to be the year the tide would turn. The crops would be good, the hoppers would have gone somewhere else, and Uncle Sammy would guarantee good prices.

When Jake stopped to dump a load of grain into the truck that his 8 year old, freckle-faced son Rudy was manning, he doffed his visored cap hoping to lasso a stray breeze. The tightness of the headband where it pressed against him left his hair wringing wet.

That was when he noticed that the sky was darkening; far to the west, ominous clouds were beginning to gather. There was a time of the year when to see clouds of any kind was to rejoice, but this wasn't the time. Electric storms in this kind of heat spelled disaster.

"Dad, I think it's going to rain," Rudy had told his father, eying the turbulent sky.

"Looks like more than rain, son. These are wicked clouds, rolling and black. We'll cut as much as we can. Maybe, God willing, the storm will bypass us," his father said, sounding doubtful.

Then Jake hastily climbed back into the seat of his red Farmall tractor and began to drive the combine round and round the field, aiming to save it all, trying to do the impossible, before the thunderstorm struck.

The clouds were rolling furiously across the sky by this time, as though hurrying helter-skelter to get to some important event. The sky, which at first had been merely dark, became a livid midnight blue, with a curious gray-green color abutting the edges of the heavens. Only a provident God could change the course of the storm.

As the first huge rain drops tattooed down Jake and Rudy turned off the tractor, leapt into the truck and wheeled it across the field hauling in the wheat they'd combined. By this time hailstones were beating a staccato rhythm on the cab of the truck. Sheets of pelting rain made driving next to impossible, but they made it into a cattle shed where they waited for the storm to let up.

When the storm was over Jakob knew his harvest was over, knew that the life of the farmer was over for him, too. They had nothing left on which to live. They had depended on this crop, this season. It was a last-ditch stand. They had counted on the Almighty to make good on His promise, Whatsoever you ask in My Name.

Jake was strangely quiet, pensive, and he didn't answer the first time Rudy spoke to him. "Dad?" Rudy asked. "Dad?" But he knew by the somber look on his father's face that it was no use to persist.

Finally his dad said, "It's cleared up enough to go to the house. These summer storms don't last long, over as soon as they're started. Let's see if Ma and the little kids are all right."

Jake sounded tired and Rudy recognized a false heartiness in his voice.

Selma Neilsen's eyes met her husband's. Without discussing it they both knew they hadn't given up, they had been knocked out. It wasn't easy to leave the land they'd wrested from the prairie. Only half of their land had been plowed when they got the farm. The fence they'd built of the rocks they'd cleared from the land would endure forever. And no one else had even tried to make lilacs grow in this country--the lilac hedge was atributed to their hard work and persistence.

Hailstones were piled ankle deep in the yard, big as marbles, a few as big as baseballs. The six and seven year old excitedly began to gather them up in buckets, exulting in their size, planning to store them so they'd last forever, planning to make all the ice cream they'd ever want.

Jake had let Selma make the goodbyes to the Hofsteiders; he wasn't any good at farewells, and it hurt too much. There'd been no extra time for writing nor money for postage in those first years, and after a while they had lost contact.

The years had passed quickly; it seemed hardly possible that they had grandchildren old enough to get married.

The letter that Selma was reading was putting such a glow on her face that Jake made an effort to pay more attention. The letter was from the Hofsteiders, after all these years.

"Just thought you'd like to know that we now own the land where you planted the lilac hedge. It still blooms every spring and scents up the countryside. People still come from miles around to admire it. And the stone fence made of the rocks you cleared from the acreage still stands."

"We're finally retiring; couldn't bear to turn the place over to strangers. Our grandson Kenneth, has found a lovely girl at the University of Minnesota who is willing to live on a farm, and we'll be turning the place over to them. Her father's name is Rudy Neilson, a common enough name in these parts."

The letter went on briefly but Jake wasn't listening. The remnant of Jakob's tribe was going home.

"Whatsoever you ask in my name."

THE PATH

He came to this vast land a growing boy
  And watched the sun rise over distant hills,
    And heard the lark sing "Joy of life"
    And saw the gopher scuttle down the trail.

He plowed new fields to seed with corn and grain
  Was blessed to reap such harvests few have known.
    And savored life's reward--intrinsic joy--
The knowlege that his wheat would feed the world.

But then tornadoes wounded, scarred his land
And hailstones, wreaking fury, scourged his crops
And in the wake........he knew despair

He bowed his head in helplessness, and wept
He raged at God until at last he slept.

And then God showed him He was there, was everywhere
  Along the path completely veiled by grass
    Mid long-stemmed flowers, broken stalks,
      and weeds. Was everywhere.

As one by one the silver stars appeared
  Peace enveloped the earth, and crickets chirped.

THE AUCTION

"Caught you red-handed," Everett joshed the pint-sized kid who was thrusting a bright yellow handbill through the screen door.

"Mr. Crouch at the Journal said to stick this flyer between the screen and the front door so it can't blow away, and so you'll see it first thing when you open your door," the boy earnestly explained.

"Well, then let's see what it is that's so all-fired important that you walked all the way out here with it," said Everett picking up the flyer and peering at it.

"Well, I'll be," he said looking closer, "It's Jasper's estate sale." Then, musing aloud he continued, "If I'm not mistaken Jasper came here to live in 19-0-5. He's been living in central South Dakota ever since. That makes it nearly 40 years for Jas."

Then Everett turned to the boy. "Thank you, Sonny. Thank you. You're the Bjerdahl boy, aren't you? Well, you're all right. Tell your dad I said you're a keeper. Tell him you're not as bad a kid as I thought any offspring of his would be!"

"Everett, stop it. That boy doesn't know you're teasing." said Sarah. Turning to the lad she smiled and said, "Don't you pay him any mind, son. Tell him to pick on somebody his own size."

Everett turned to his wife, "He knows I'm joshing." Then, "Sarah, do you wanta take in an auction Saturday? Must be Jasper decided to throw in the towel. I was wondering how long he could hang on--he's been failing ever since his wife passed away. I heard his son was trying to get him to move back east where he lives so he could look in on him now and then. We'd ought to go to the auction so's we can say our goodbyes to Jasper."

Everett handed the handbill to his wife, who looked it over. "I see Elvira's sewing machine is listed. It always sat in her parlor in front of the east window. Jas bought her that machine one Christmas--a Sears Roebuck special. She was real proud of it. Said the treadle wasn't heavy like on her old one; it was so light that her legs didn't hurt when she used it."

And then, after a pause, she added, "Yes, let's go to that sale. I think I might like to bid on that sewing machine myself to remember Elvira by."

So, come Saturday Everett and Sarah found them selves heading for Jasper's farm sale. The weather was warm--it was a drowsy day in early fall. The stubbly grass around Jasper's house was brown and dry, and so was what was left after harvest of the wheat field. Nobody could tell where the lawn ended and the wheat field started. It seemed as though every possible parking space was already filled with vehicles whose owners had parked and then ambled over to size up the farm machinery lined up in neat rows around the yard.

Most of the household items had been placed out of doors, arranged along the sides of the house. Chairs placed here and there made for easy sitting. Otherwise customers with tired feet might go elsewhere.

134

"Looks as though everybody and his dog are here," said Everett, as he and Sarah climbed out of the Pickup. "This could be the social event of the season!" He and Sarah milled about greeting people, and examining the for-sale items, picking up an object here and there to peer at in the sunlight.

"Look at this, Ev," called a neighbor. "Right up your alley. Screws, cans of 'em. Bicycle locks, odds and ends of nails, hinges stacked together. Found this stuff under a "Make me an offer" sign. There's more like this, too."

Sarah spied a box full of buttons, zippers, half-used spools of thread, and needles she fancied. Before she could make up her mind whether she really needed them they were gone. A young mother with a brood of young ones in tow had no such doubts; she still sewed for her family. She tucked the sewing supplies under her arm.

An old timer at the sale strolled up and greeted Sarah and Ev. "Finding anything you want?" he asked.

"I don't see anything I can't live without," said Everett. "But there are a few tools I wouldn't mind calling my own."

Sarah replied, "There's a lot of stuff I don't need and some I wouldn't mind having, if the bidding doesn't get out of sight."

The neighbor continued, "I spose we ought to see what the Prairie Garden Ladies have to offer? They might like a little help getting rid of it!"

The Prairie Garden members, who had been working the lunch counter since early morning, had set up shop in the garage so there'd be shade. They were hot and sweaty, damp tendrils of hair curled against their faces. "We're serving sandwiches, pie, cake and coffee. What'll it be?

135

"What? No fried chicken?" Everett asked, pretending to be dismayed. "The fryers ought to be just right for eating about now."

"The chickens are big enough," explained the ladies, "But last year the chicken got blamed for the ptomaine poisoning. We thought we'd better stick with something that doesn't need refrigeration."

"Won't hardly seem like a country auction without fried chicken," lamented Ev. Spotting a pie he couldn't resist he asked, "What kind of pie you got? I'll have me a piece."

"You guys go ahead and eat," Sarah said, "I'm going to find out when Elvira's sewing machine will be auctioned." Turning to the ladies in the kitchen she said, "Just whistle if you need help -- after the sewing machine is sold."

Sarah joined the group clustered around the machine, which looked a little the worse for wear and tear. The top of the cabinet was water-marked with big stains, where houseplants had been watered.

"Elvira wouldn't be happy about that," said one of the group. "Just like a man. Forgets to water the house plants. When he remembers to water them they are so dry the water goes straight through and ruins the finish of whatever the plants are setting on. It happens all the time."

She went on, "Do you remember the time Jasper and Elvira's daughter Mary Lou sewed right through her finger? She was a little tyke, but bound and determined to use that new machine. She invited our twins over to see her mother's Christmas present. They all wanted to see how it worked.

"First the Mr. showed them how to thread the needle which was complicated, especially for kids to do. Then the kids got to take turns sewing a seam. That's when it happened. Didn't stop Mary Lou none. She's been sewing ever since."

Another said, "Probably couldn't help herself; it was in her blood. Elvira sewed all the time, too. She made all kinds of things out of the sacks the flour came--curtains, dish towels, pillow cases. I think she even made bedsheets until they found the seams irritated them when they tried to sleep."

"Remember how happy we were when the flour mills started printing patterns on the sacks? The County Extension Club had patterns for aprons and dresses. They even had a pattern for a man's necktie. Elvira said she tried making under shorts for Jas but he refused to wear 'em!"

"Is Jas here?" asked one of the ladies. "I haven't seen him. Do you spose it's too soon after his operation for him to be up all day," said another.

"I'm gonna browse some more while the looking is still good," said Sarah, "before the auctioneer starts. Did anybody notice that old wooden coffee grinder? It's gotta be worth something. I'm surprised it hasn't been grabbed up already."

"Antique collectors been calling the newspaper office ever since the hand bill came out. If there's anything worth collecting, they've already got it."

The sound of the auctioneer's mellow voice came through loud and clear. "Reckon you've had time to think over what you want or do not want. What you see here is a life time's accumulation of a good friend, a good neighbor. It's all got to be sold today. Some of the best buys this side of Silver City will be going on the block in the next few minutes. Shall we begin?"

Auctioneering was a family affair. As soon as the bidding on an article was closed the auctioneer's son shouted the name and price of the highest bidder. The auctioneer's wife marked it all down. "Going, going, gone." One after another each item was auctioned.

"Sold" signs adorned most of the equipment and household items sold briskly. People were just beginning to realize how short the fall days had become. By six o'clock the auctioneer figured he'd had all the offers he was going to get and decided to call it a day.

Still Jasper hadn't shown up, though everyone kept expecting him. Everett said, "Somehow, it just don't seem quite right to set a price on what a man has spent years accumulating when he isn't around to see who gets what. I wish Jas would show up."

The crowd had thinned considerable before Jasper arrived. He walked around shaking hands and greeting old friends and neighbors, who all wished him the best. When he came to where Sarah sat he took her hand in his.

"Sarah," he said, "Elvira would be pleased that you got her sewing machine." He hesitated, "The harpsichord was hers, too, and it didn't go. I don't suppose you and Ev have any use for a musical instrument."

Ev said, "I can't carry a tune in a bushel basket. Playing a radio is all I'm able to master." He laughed at his own joke.

Someone offered, "Maybe the band teacher could make use of it. That man can squeeze music out of anything, even high school kids!"

"What about you, Jasper?," asked Ev. "You going to be all right? It can't be easy to watch your life's work divvied up and sold before your eyes."

"Well," Jasper said slowly, "if I had my druthers, I'd be 30 years younger and I'd be staying right here. But that's not the way it is."

"Hear you're going to give city life a whirl?" said Everett. "How you gonna like that?"

"I don't know how I'll take to city life," said Jasper, "with all them people, and all that noise around all the time."

Ev agreed. "They say you can take the boy out of the farm but you can't take the farm out of the boy, and I reckon that's the truth."

"But I'll be near my son and my grandkids, and a man can't have it much better than that."

JENNY COMES CLEAN

Far out in the country, miles from town
Where few passers-by see her ranch
Jenny hangs laundry on wires stretched taut
And held up in the air with a branch.

There she hangs coveralls, blue denim shirts,
Scrubbed clean with ashes and lye
Neatly she clothes-pins them, all in a row
And waits for the hot winds to dry.

Primly she hangs things, precisely arranges
Dresses and aprons, so colors won't fade
Gracing the line next, a young child's clothing
Rompers, and blouses and items handmade.

Then she hies to the attic, with girdles and slips
(And items she couldn't discuss)
She hangs them with care lest a male dare stare
Snatch a peek, sneak a look, raise a fuss.
Causing Jennie to blush.

THE PRAIRIE FIRE

Folks around Draper, South Dakota, still refer to the summer of 1930 as a Scorcher. (Folklore has it that you could fry eggs on the rooftops during August of that year!)

The searing sun turned the treeless plains into a tinderbox; the grasses, curled and brown, lay wilting alongside the road; the drouth-stunted weeds crunched underfoot. An idle flick from a cigarette, a careless spark from a running motor, even the hot sun beating down on a chip of broken glass could ignite the vast prairie turning it into a blazing holocaust.

Morning dawned bright and clear. There was an air of tranquility on the day the prairie fire struck. It was barely past noon when the farmer noted the first faint smell of smoke and, could see, in the distance, along the horizon, the shadowy tracings of a fire.

In the moments it took to reach his tractor he exulted in how much easier it was to plow safety furrows with his new tractor than it had been in the past with a team of horses. With a tractor he could maneuver the dried coulees, could easily cross the rough, untamed prairie.

Round and round the scattered farm buildings the farmer plowed, leaving protective furrows of freshly turned earth. Satisfied that his buildings were safe from fire he thought next to protect his winter's supply of cattle food. The furrows were purple-black and deep, so wide an errant fire could not cross.

As he finished fireproofing his own place, he noticed the wind had switched slightly. Shouting to his wife that he was going to plow around the neighbor's buildings, too, he hurried off, in high gear, cutting through the pasture, heading towards the little cottage where an old couple lived.

They were a little old couple, in their late 70's, stone deaf. They wouldn't have heard about the fire, but by this time they would have smelled it, and seen it, and would have had no way to get out of its path.

The wind, which had increased sharply, began whipping the fire along. Scientists can explain how hot air rises and causes movement which is wind; in the course of a prairie fire, fire begets wind, and when the fire gets a good strong toehold, there's very little that can hold it back.

The farmer could see it coming closer, could see the red tongues of fire consuming the brittle, toast-colored grass.

It was about that time that a neighbor lady from the west came to help. She and her young children, ages four through eight, brought two large cream cans full of water. They were prepared to help beat back the fire.

At almost the same time two rigs of men arrived with barrels of water, and heaps of gunnysacks. Leaping out of the trucks they grabbed the sacks, soaked them in water, and frantically began beating at the fire as it raged in front of them.

The neighbor lady, who hadn't waited to search for gunny sacks, grabbed what she could that wouldn't burn readily. She snatched the heavy denim jeans her eight year old was wearing, doused them in water, and began lashing furiously at the fire which by now was frighteningly near.

Moments later several more rigs of men arrived, all with barrels of water. One of the men, an old timer, looked at the highway, a natural barrier to the fire, and reckoned, gravely, that they would have to start a backfire if they were to break this one's force. He'd experienced many fires, and this one was one of the fiercest.

The wind was flogging the fire into a frenzy. The crackling heat provided a backdrop of sound effects for the treacherous wind. Without a backfire, there could be no stopping this fire.

A backfire was built to consume the combustible materials in the path of a fire, so that it would have no place to go, and would be forced to die. There is a trick to it, a technique, and the old man knew it. He and several others huddled together to protect the flame from the onslaught of the wind, nursing their flame along until it was ready.

With the highway as a safety zone behind them, the men worked, coaxing, channeling, directing their fire towards the big one, until there was nothing left between the two fires to devour.

Taming the rampant fire required all the strength the men had, and even after the wind had died down, and dusk had come, they did not dare to leave.

Wiping sweaty arms across their foreheads, sipping what water was left, they sprawled on the charred earth, wishing it might rain. They were exhausted, but so was the fire.

It wasn't until then that they heard the news about the farmer who had gone to plow the furrows around the neighbor's home. When the capricious fire had turned, it had trapped the farmer. He had jumped from his tractor, and ran back through the fire, protected by leather leggings, remnants of World War I, and his arms, which he used to shield his face.

When he was found he was dazed and incoherent. The neighbors who found him took him immediately to the nearest doctor, thirty miles away. The tractor, in the perverse way of things, was turning circles, as though performing a slow ballet movement. Treatment for burns in those days was vaseline to be slathered on, and gauze bandages. The neighbors transported him, covered him with an apron, and gave him sips of water from a thermos made from a mason jar wrapped in burlap. When they brought him home he was beginning to be lucid.

All that fall neighbors came to help him with the chores, and to haul him to the doctor. The gauze stuck to his burned flesh and tore at the wounds when it was peeled; the odor of rotting flesh left a stench that had to be borne; the days were filled with unceasing pain.

Without the neighbors the work could not have been done. One of them came nightly to do the chores, and to tell tall tales and jokes to make him laugh. He couldn't smile because that caused the blisters on his face to crack and ache, but his big shoulders shook with laughter, and his eyes gleamed.

Winter came, and with the spring, the earth had healed and so had the farmer. The winter snows had blanketed the earth and the melting rains had carried away all traces of the fire that had ravaged it. When the grasses poked through they formed a soft carpet of green. The plowed furrows looked oddly out of place, a vestige, a reminder of things past.

When the gauze and bandages were removed, the fingers were no longer thick from swelling; no longer was there a fear of infection.

When the first green shoots of grain peeked through the ground, the farmer headed into the fields again. His arms were scarred and brown, in stark contrast to the pink-white of his arms above the elbow, where he had always rolled his blue denim shirt sleeves, but his steps were youthful, and plans for the new season began to take form.

It must have been a year later when a magazine salesman found his way to the farmer's home. "Wasn't it somewhere around here," the salesman asked, "where a man got burned trying to plow around an old couple's place?" But the salesman was anxious to sell magazines and didn't wait for a reply. "They say the old couple never realized he was plowing to try to save their place, and I've heard he never told them."

The farmer traded two old batteries for a subscription to a magazine, and shook the salesman's hand when he left.

"Good luck," the farmer said, and added, "Don't bother to stop at the little farm to the east; the old couple who lived there passed on last winter."

*   *   *   *   *   *

The farmer in the story was my father, Helmer Liffengren, of Draper, South Dakota. We had only recently moved to that farm when the prairie fire broke out, and we did not know any of our neighbors well. But, in Dakota, neighbors were a precious commodity, something that one cherished and greatly appreciated.

147

I have written this story not only to pay homage to my father, but to cite the Rankins, The Dowlings, and the others who helped in our time of great need. I would like to go even farther than that: I should like this story to honor good neighbors wherever they may be.

This true story was first published in the May/June, 1993 issue of SOUTH DAKOTA magazine under "Remembering."

About the Author

Louise Liffengren Hullinger grew up in South Dakota and attended rural schools. She graduated from Draper High School in 1942; Teacher's College in Springfield, SD; SD State University, BS in Journalism, 1947; Northeastern, IL, MA in Special Education, 1979.

Taught as rural school teacher, Special Ed teacher and Project Director for LD adults. She was also a free lance writer and reporter for Northern Light.

Book Publications: SPECIAL CHILDREN/SPECIAL FAMILIES (Eterna Press, 1982); A DAY TO CRY (with Mary Grigar, 1994); FIFTY YEARS OF MT. GREENWOOD HISTORY, 1993. She has also written many articles on learning disabilities.

AWARDS: SD State University "Distinguished Alumnus Award" For Outstanding Service To Education, 1979.
"The Caring Servant Award" from Lutheran Church Charities Fund, 1991.
"Volunteer of the Year" from Learning Disabilities Association, IL, 1991.
Faithful Service in Mission & Ministry of Christ's Church, from Northern IL, District LCMS 1994.
Friend of LDA Award from IL, Learning Disabilities Assoc., 1994.
In Recognition of Outstanding Service on behalf of Refugees from Exodus, 1999.

A FEW WORDS FROM THE AUTHOR:

My husband Clifford and I grew up in the South Dakota dust bowl, two towns apart. If it weren't for the shortage of teachers, we may never have met. As it was, his sister Margaret and I met at a teaachers college one summer. It follows that when he came home on furlough his claim was that, "After four years overseas, any girl looked good." We were married in June, 1964. His claim that it was D day is not true!

We have four wonderful children and six grandchildren who have been brainwashed into believing that everything that comes out of S.D. is the greatest, including sunsets and stars. It is not unusual for the third generation of neighborhood children in the Chicago block where we live to swarm into our yard when the SD Uncles come visiting. The boys squeal with delight at the sight of a lariat, and hope to be roped.

In amongst our travels, we go back to South Dakota once or twice a year for a refresher course, since my twin brother still lives there. He now spends half the time in the Black Hills, which he doesn't really like because there are too many trees blocking his view!

Louise Hullinger

Metaphor and Reason in

JUDICIAL OPINIONS

Haig Bosmajian

SOUTHERN ILLINOIS UNIVERSITY PRESS
Carbondale and Edwardsville

Edited by Robert K. Burdette
Designed by Jason Schellenberg
Production supervised by Natalia Nadraga
95 94 93 92   4 3 2 1

Library of Congress Cataloging-in-Publication Data

Haig, Bosmajian A.
    Metaphor and reason in judicial opinions / Haig Bosmajian.
        p.   cm.
    Includes bibliographical references (p.   ) and index.
        1. Judicial opinions—United States—Language.   2. Law—
    United States—Language.   3. Civil rights—United States.
    4. Figures of speech.   I. Title.
    KF211.5.H35   1992
    349.73'014—dc20
    [347.30014]   91-30037
    ISBN 0-8093-1612-9   CIP

The paper used in this publication meets the minimum requirements
of American National Standard for Information Sciences—Permanence of Paper for Printed Library Materials, ANSI Z39.48-1984. ∞

Contents

Preface

In his autobiographical *Of Men and Mountains*, Justice William O. Douglas describes some of the experiences and relationships that influenced him as he was growing up in the Yakima, Washington, area and the Cascade country. At the outset of the book, Douglas observes: "The boy makes a deep imprint on the man. My young experiences in the high Cascades have placed the heavy mark of the mountain on me."

So that the reader can get a partial explanation of how I have come to write this book on language and style in the reasoning of judicial opinions, I take Douglas's "The boy makes a deep imprint on the man" as a starting point. At least on the intellectual level, it probably began in 1945 when as a student at a California community college (then known as Reedley Junior College) I was introduced to the world of philosophy, psychology, sociology, and logic. This new world of ideas created new questions for me about knowledge, justice, and society that I had not been exposed to—not at least through reading John Stuart Mill, Karl Marx, Immanuel Kant, Arthur Schopenhauer, Thomas Jefferson, and others—and discussing them with a professor like Dr. W. Vincent Evans at a community college surrounded by the vineyards and orchards in the San Joaquin Valley. This new world of ideas made a deep imprint on a seventeen-year-old farm boy, who found this heady stuff. When I left Professor Evans's classes in 1947, I was not the same person who had entered two years earlier.

I was introduced in the fall of 1947 to the intellectual excitement at the University of California at Berkeley, where in the Department of Speech I was exposed to a discipline that focused on the analysis of discourse through the study of rhetoric, literature, philosophy, and language. There was Dr. Joseph Tussman, who discussed with us issues related to philosophy, language, and free speech; Dr. David Rynin, who expounded on logic, language, and semantics; Dr. Arnold Perstein, who had us read André Malraux, Richard Wright, Sinclair Lewis, Henrik Ibsen, Ernest Hemingway, Ignazio Silone, and others who had written about universal social, political, and religious issues and controversies.

But the controversies outside the classroom were making an equally significant impression on this eighteen-year-old who saw and heard professors defending their free-speech rights and academic freedom, for this was the frightening time of loyalty oaths and disclaimer affidavits required of tens of thousands of state and federal employees, including teachers. It was the time of McCarthyism, which brought with it investigating committees inquiring into the beliefs, expressions, and associations of professors, writers, artists, and others. In 1949, the year I graduated from the University of California, the state of New York was passing a statute that required teachers to sign a disclaimer affidavit as a precondition of employment. Those who did not sign, who took the position that it was none of the government's business what their beliefs were or whom they associated with, were either fired or not hired. One year later, the state of California required the following oath from its teachers: "I do not advocate, nor am I a member of any party or organization, political or otherwise, that now advocates the overthrow of the Government of the United States or of the State of California by force or violence or other unlawful means; that within the five years immediately preceding the taking of this oath, I have not been a member of any party or organization, political or otherwise, that advocated the overthrow of the Government of the United States or of the State of California by force or violence."

Out of this era of fear and repression came the "silent generation," which was "chilled" into silence as a "pall of orthodoxy" spread over the nation. Principled professors who refused to sign the oath were dismissed. Writers were cited for contempt of Congress, some sentenced to jail terms, because they refused to reveal to government investigating committees their past associations and the names of people the committees labeled un-American. Inquiries were made into the political beliefs of labor leaders, educators, ministers, students, and a host of others. This young college student wondered what had happened to the guarantees of the First Amendment and the Fifth Amendment. Thus developed an interest in one aspect of this book—the freedoms of speech and association.

The other aspect of this work, language and style, developed further as I conducted my dissertation research at Stanford University on the techniques of persuasion used by Hitler and the Nazis. What became evident was that through the power of language, through the control of metaphors, through the power to define others, Hitler relabeled the Jews "bacilli," "vermin," "parasites," and "plague," language that led to a dehumanization of a people and to the "final solution." It did not take long to understand more fully than I had previously that this use of language to label, define, and dehumanize human beings had been used by Americans, individually and institutionally, to metaphorize blacks into "chattels," "savages," and "nonpersons," and "American Indians" into "barbarians," "heathens," and "the uncivilized." My interest and research in the anti-Semitic language of the Nazis, the language of white racism, the language of Indian derision, the language of sexism, and the language of war culminated in the publication of *The Language of Oppression* in 1974. Having seen how language can be and has been used to defend the indefensible (to use George Orwell's phrase), I was brought back to the issue of freedom of speech, for the question became: If language can be used to define people into submission, does such language deserve First Amendment protection? Thus these three interests came together—language, freedom of speech, and the law.

These interests converge again in this book on metaphor in the reasoning of court opinions. While I was teaching several courses whose students were required to read judicial opinions related to First Amendment freedoms, it became evident that as students of rhetoric, we could not ignore the heavy reliance of the courts on the tropes, especially metaphor, metonymy, and personification. This tropology of the law is the focus of this book. However, it has also been my intent that the reader finish the book with a fuller appreciation of the First Amendment's role in this nation's survival as a people striving for "a more perfect union" and "freedom and justice for all." Hence, this is not a book devoted exclusively to identifying the crucial judicial tropes and their relevance and influence. While I have prepared a book directed to students interested in language, rhetoric, free speech, and the law, an effort has been made to keep the book free of legalese and academese, making the book accessible to the educated layperson. It is my hope that the reader, whether student or layperson, will learn not only something about how the tropes have been applied in judicial argument and decision making but also something about the power of figurative language and the centrality of freedom of speech to a nation that claims to be free and democratic.

I have looked at the court opinions not only through the eyes of the rhetorician but also through the mind of a civil libertarian. As I peruse the following passage from Justice William Brennan's opinion in *Keyishian v. Board of Regents* and see the impact of the tropes, I appreciate the arguments culminating in the Court's decision to strike down as unconstitutional New York's oath requirement of teachers:

> Our Nation is deeply committed to safeguarding freedom, which is of transcendent value to all of us and not merely to the teachers concerned. That freedom is therefore a special concern of the First Amendment, which does not tolerate laws that cast a pall of orthodoxy over the classroom. . . . The classroom is peculiarly the "marketplace of ideas." The nation's future depends upon leaders trained through wide exposure to that robust exchange of ideas which discovers truth "out of a multitude of tongues, [rather] than through any kind of authoritative selection."

. . . .

We emphasize once again that "[p]recision of regulation must be the touchstone in an area so closely touching
our most precious freedoms," *N.A.A.C.P. v. Button . . . ;*
"[f]or standards of permissible statutory vagueness are
strict in the area of free expression. . . . Because First
Amendment freedoms need breathing space to survive,
government may regulate in the area only with narrow
specificty." . . . New York's complicated and intricate
scheme plainly violates that standard. When one must
guess what conduct or utterance may lose him his position, one necessarily will "steer far wider of the unlawful
zone. . . ." *Speiser v. Randall. . . .* For [t]he threat of sanctions may deter . . . almost as potently as the actual application of sanctions." . . . The danger of that chilling effect
upon the exercise of vital First Amendment rights must be
guarded against by sensitive tools which clearly inform
teachers what is being proscribed.

The regulatory maze created by New York is wholly
lacking in "terms susceptible of objective measurement."
. . . Vagueness of wording is aggravated by prolixity and
profusion of statutes, regulations, and administrative machinery, and by manifold cross-references to interrelated
enactments and rules.

The tropes in this passage—among others, "laws that cast
a pall of orthodoxy over the classroom"; "classroom is peculiarly the 'marketplace of ideas'"; "discover[ing] truth 'out of
a multitude of tongues'"; "precision of regulation must be the
touchstone"; "First Amendment freedoms need breathing
space to survive"; "steer[ing] far wider of the unlawful zone";
"the danger of that chilling effect"; and "the regulatory
maze"—are an integral part of the argument that the Court
has presented to reach its decision: "We therefore hold that
§ 3021 of the Education Law and subdivisions 1(a), 1(b) and 3
of § 105 of the Civil Service law as implemented by the
machinery created pursuant to § 3022 of the Education law are
unconstitutional." The tropes are not merely "rhetorical flourishes or ornaments," for as Charlotte Linde and others have
reminded us, "People in power get to impose their meta-

phors" and hence must be paid attention, especially when they appear in the opinions of our judiciary, an institution composed of people in power who indeed get to impose their metaphors.

My examination of the tropology of the law is restricted to judicial opinions dealing with First Amendment issues because it is in that area of the law, and not contract law, property law, or environmental law, that I am most qualified to comment. I leave it to others to examine the tropology in judicial opinions in other areas. I leave it to others to make what they will of "yellow dog contracts," "wraparound mortgage," "ripe for adjudication," "at first blush," "floating capital," "heir of the blood," "negative pregnant," and "dead freight."

Further, this work is restricted to tropes and does not deal with that other group of figures of speech, schemes. While schemes (such as antithesis, asyndeton, anaphora, antimetabole, etc.) can be used effectively in adding to the persuasiveness of discourse, they do not have the impact on meaning or conceptualization that tropes do. This is not to say that schemes do not have an influence on our perceptions. While tropes rely for their effectiveness on the change of meaning of a word from its ordinary sense, schemes rely for their effectiveness on unusual sentence structure and word order.

When Lincoln said "and that government of the people, by the people, for the people, shall not perish from the earth," he was relying on the schemes *epistrophe* (repetition of the same word at the end of each successive clause), *asyndeton* (omission of a conjunction where it would ordinarily appear), and *tricolon* (the division of an idea into three harmonious parts, especially three with the same number of syllables). Through the use of schemes, Lincoln has affected our concept of government and its relation to the people. Had he simply said "government of, by and for the people shall not perish from the earth," the important role of people in government would not be impressed upon our thinking to such an extent.

When a speaker relies on *antithesis* (juxtaposition of contrasting or opposite ideas), the listener's perceptions are somewhat affected by the contrast. In his *Letter from Birmingham Jail*, Martin Luther King wrote: "We have waited for more than 340 years for our constitutional God-given rights. The nations of Asia and Africa are moving with jetlike speed toward gaining political independence, but we still creep at horse-and-buggy pace toward gaining a cup of coffee at a lunch counter." Although the nonliteral, tropistic "horse-and-buggy" and "cup of coffee" contribute to the effectiveness of the passage, King has affected, through the antithesis, our perception of how slow progress in achieving civil rights has been in this country. However, important as they are in persuasive discourse, the schemes are not part of this study. I leave that for another day.

The first three chapters are intended to place the subject of the book into context. Why write judicial opinions? Why publish them? Is style important in judicial decision making? What are the functions of tropes, and why does the judiciary rely so heavily on them? The subsequent chapters focus on specific tropes that played important roles in judicial argument. Each of these chapters provides in varying degrees the background of the individual tropes, examples from court opinions to illustrate their widespread integration into judicial argument, and some observations about their appropriateness and effectiveness. What are the origins of these tropes? How have they been integrated into judicial opinions? Are the tropes useful in creating clearer perceptions, or do they confuse and mislead? It is my hope that as a result of being exposed to the role of tropes in judicial discourse, readers will become more critical "listeners" when they are confronted not only by the tropology of the law but also the tropology of politics, religion, advertising, and everyday discourse.

I wish to thank the College of Arts and Sciences at the University of Washington for the College Released-Time Award for Scholarship, which gave me the opportunity to complete this work.

Acknowledgment is due to the following journals in which portions of chapters 3, 4, 7, and 9 first appeared in another form: *Journal of Law and Education, Religious Communication Today, Midwest Quarterly,* and *Free Speech Yearbook 1981.*

Also, my thanks to my wife, Hamida Bosmajian, who as a friend and professor of English critically and patiently listened as I shared with her some of the ideas in this book.

Finally, a belated thanks to my professors of yesteryear, who introduced me to the world of ideas, orthodox and unorthodox.

Introduction

In his commencement oration at Columbia College in 1889, future Supreme Court Justice Benjamin Nathan Cardozo directed his audience's attention to the importance of tropes in politics and religion: "The aphorism of Emerson, 'Churches have been built, not upon principles, but upon tropes,' is as true in the field of politics as it is in the field of religion."[1] It would have been appropriate for the future jurist, who later recognized and emphasized the nexus between style and substance, to apply Emerson's aphorism to the field of law, for tropes have played as important a role in the law as in religion and politics.

Implied in Emerson's claim that churches have been built not upon principles but upon tropes is the assumption that principles and tropes are distinctly separate and that what is built upon tropes is not built on principles. What needs to be recognized at the outset is that important and influential principles in religion, politics, and the law have often been expressed through tropes. At all judicial levels, metaphors, metonymies, personifications, and other tropes appearing in court opinions have attained permanence, have become institutionalized and relied upon as principles, standards, doctrines, and premises in arriving at judicial judgments.

In his 1963 concurring opinion in *Abington School Dist. v. Schempp,* Justice William Brennan, agreeing with the Court that Bible reading and religious prayer in the public schools were a violation of the First Amendment, designated the personfication "the law knows no heresy" as a "principle" that had "recently been reaffirmed in *Kedroff v. St. Nicholas Cathedral.*"[2] In 1966, U.S. District Court Judge Daniel Thomas, in deciding a freedom-of-religion case, asserted that an Arkansas Code section known as the "Dumas Act" violated "what

1

Jefferson termed the 'wall of separation between Church and State." . . . No constitutional principle is more firmly imbedded in our heritage than this separation."[3] The metaphoric "wall of separation" has achieved the status of a judicial "principle."

In 1972, Judge McGowan, in a case involving the rights to assemble and petition, concluded through personfication: "It is difficult to imagine a statute [prohibiting parades or assemblages on the capitol grounds] which could more plainly violate the principle that 'First Amendment freedoms need breathing space to survive [and] government may regulate in the area only with narrow specificity.'"[4] In 1977, Justice Thurgood Marshall, referring to the 1896 *Plessy* decision, declared in his *Bakke* opinion: "We must remember, however, that the principle that the 'Constitution is colorblind' appeared only in the opinion of the lone dissenter. . . . The majority of the Court rejected the principle of color blindness, and for the next 60 years, from *Plessy* to *Brown v. Board of Education,* ours was a Nation where, by law, an individual could be given 'special' treatment based on the color of his skin."[5]

Still other tropological "principles" have contributed to judicial decision making. In 1963, Justice Brennan, delivering the opinion of the Court in *Bantam Books, Inc. v. Sullivan,* argued metaphorically: "Our insistence that regulations of obscenity scrupulously embody the most rigorous procedural safeguards . . . is therefore but a special instance of the larger principle that the freedoms of expression must be ringed about with adequate bulwarks."[6] Twenty-three years later, Justice Harry Blackmun began his dissenting opinion in another censorship case, *Meese v. Keene:* "The Court, in this case today, fails to apply the long-established 'principle that the freedoms of expression must be ringed about with adequate bulwarks.'"[7] The influence of Brennan's metaphorical argument becomes apparent.

If the judicial trope is not a "principle," it can be a "doctrine." When in 1987 the Supreme Court declared unconstitutional the Board of Airport Commissioners of Los Angeles resolution that banned all "First Amendment activities" in the "Central Terminal Area" at the Los Angeles International Airport, Justice Sandra Day O'Connor, delivering the opinion of the Court, several times relied on the tropological "overbreadth doctrine":

> Under the First Amendment overbreadth doctrine, an individual whose own speech or conduct may be prohibited is permitted to challenge a statute on its face "because it also threatens others not before the court—those who desire to engage in legally protected expression but who may refrain from doing so rather than risk prosecution or undertake to have the law declared partially invalid." . . . The *Baggett* Court concluded that abstention would serve no purpose given the lack of any limiting construction, and held the statutes unconstitutional on their face under the First Amendment overbreadth doctrine.[8]

In a 1969 case involving draft deferments and war protesters, Judge Bazelon relied on still another tropological "doctrine": "*Mitchell* does, of course, antedate the discovery and development of the chilling effect doctrine."[9]

Some tropes in judicial opinions appear once or twice and are never heard from again. Others, however, have staying power, become institutionalized and integral to judicial reasoning and decision making. Some of the more permanent tropes, in addition to being labeled principles and doctrines, have become "central tenets" and "standards." Justice John Paul Stevens, delivering the Court's opinion in *F.C.C. v. Pacifica Foundation*, wrote in 1978: "But the fact that society may find speech offensive is not a sufficient reason for suppressing it. Indeed, if it is the speaker's opinion that gives offense, that consequence is a reason for according it constitutional protection. For it is a central tenet of the First Amendment that the government must remain neutal in the marketplace of ideas."[10] This constitutional "tenet" is based on the nonliteral marketplace of ideas, which in turn becomes an integral part of the judicial argument.

In 1943, Judge Learned Hand, in a case involving newsgathering and monopoly, discussing the public interest in "the dissemination of news from as many different sources, and with as many different facets and colors possible," stated: "That interest is closely akin to, if indeed it is not the same as, the interest protected by the First Amendment; it presupposes that right conclusions are more likely to be gathered out of a multitude of tongues, than through any kind of authoritative selection. To many this is, and always will be folly; but we have staked upon it our all."[11] We have staked our all on the nonliteral metonymy "right conclusions are more likely to be gathered out of a multitude of tongues." This metonymy has subsequently appeared again and again in court opinions involving freedom of speech and the press. It has become one of the most repeated figures in the tropology of the law.

When in 1967 the Supreme Court declared unconstitutional New York's teacher loyalty oath, Justice Brennan, delivering the opinion of the Court, cited the following figurative line from the Court's 1963 *NAACP v. Button* opinion, an opinion Brennan had written: "Because First Amendment freedoms need breathing space to survive, government may regulate in the area only with narrow specificity." "New York's complicated and intricate scheme [the oath requirement]," said Brennan, "plainly violates that standard."[12] The nonliteral "breathing space," a subsequently often-cited personification, had become a "standard." The personification became an integral part of a premise of an argument that led to the *Keyishian* decision.

In *NAACP v. Button* (1963), Justice John Harlan, dissenting, alluded to Brennan's "breathing space" in the following content: "It is true that the concept of vagueness has been used to give 'breathing space' to 'First Amendment freedoms,' see Amsterdam, Note, The Void-for-Vagueness Doctrine in the Supreme Court, 109 U. of Pa. L. Rev. 67, but is also true, as that same commentator has well stated, that '[v]agueness is not an extraneous ploy or a judicial deux ex machina.'"[13] The 1960 law-review article referred to by Justice Harlan does not include the "breathing space" personification but does rely on another trope; Amsterdam titles a section of the article "Clearance Space for Individual Freedoms" and then writes: "The primary thesis advanced here is that the doctrine of unconstitutional indefiniteness has been used by the Supreme Court almost invariably for the creation of an insulating buffer zone of added protection at the peripheries of several of the Bill of Rights freedoms. With regard to one class of cases, those involving potential infringement of first amendment privileges, this buffer-zone principle has always been expressly avowed in the Court's opinions and recognized by the commentators."[14]

While the author of the article spoke of a "clearance space" and the "buffer-zone principle," Justice Brennan preferred the "breathing space" personfication. It is one thing to say that First Amendment freedoms need to be protected by creating a buffer zone; it is something else to say that "First Amendment freedoms need breathing space to survive." "Breathing space" brings with it the implications and power of breathing and suffocation, life and death. The importance of the First Amendment freedoms becomes much more crucial through Brennan's personficiation than through the metaphoric "buffer zone."

Other tropes have equally had their lasting influence and impact. Offensive speech receives constitutional protection because there was no "captive audience."[15] Speech may get constitutional protection because its suppression would have a "chilling effect."[16] Because there are "penumbral rights," we have a privacy right that legalized abortions.[17] These are all tropological arguments since they are all based on premises expressed through metaphoric language.

Where one judge argues that the metaphoric "wall of separation between Church and State" is a "constitutional principle," another argues at length that is a "misleading metaphor."[18] We have the anomaly of the public schools being seen as "marketplaces of ideas" while the students in those marketplaces are defined as "captive audiences," the anomaly of students in captivity participating in the "free trade in ideas."

Where one judge says of the Connecticut telephone harassment statute, "The possible chilling effect on free speech . . . strikes us as minor," another judge sees the statute having a "chilling effect" on irate citizens who might wish to telephone their congressmen or on "customers voicing to a seller dissatisfaction with goods or services purchases."[19]

The Constitution itself has been metaphorized into a machine, then personified into a living, organic document. As Lawrence Tribe has pointed out, "In 1888, James Russell Lowell felt compelled to warn that perhaps too many had come to see the Constitution as a machine that would go of itself." Then, in "the early decades of the twentieth century, the metaphor was largely replaced by one that was vibrant and vital: as Woodrow Wilson wrote in 1908, the Constitution is 'not a machine but a living thing.' The Constitution, said Wilson, is 'accountable to Darwin, not to Newton.' Holmes echoed the sentiment in 1914. He said the 'provisions of the Constitution are not mathematical formulas, . . . they are organic living institutions.'"[20] The personifying of the Constitution had already begun in the nineteenth century when Justice John Harlan declared in his dissenting opinion in *Plessy v. Ferguson* (1896) that the "Constitution is colorblind."[21]

More recently, Justice Brennan, in his 1989 *Hazelwood* dissenting opinion, reiterated Judge Goldberg's *Shanley* passage: "It is most important that our young become convinced that our Constitution is a living reality, not parchment preserved under glass."[22] Not only is the Constitution "colorblind" and a "living reality"; it is also, according to Justice Holmes, "an experiment, as all life is an experiment."[23]

This metaphorization and personification of the Constitution have been accompanied by the personification of the law itself, the judicial opinion itself. Judicial opinions have "progeny." "Nothing in *Roe*," said Justice Blackman in his 1989 *Webster* dissent, "or any of its progeny, holds that a State may not effectuate its compelling interest in the potential life of a viable fetus by seeking to ensure that no viable fetus is mistakenly aborted because of the inherent lack of precision in estimates of gestational age."[24] In his decision for some Texas high school seniors who had been suspended for distributing near school premises an underground newspaper they had authored and published, Judge Goldberg wrote: "Even the educational progeny of *Plessy v. Ferguson* . . . held that the manner in which a state operated its public school system *must* be subject to constitutional review."[25] The landmark *New York Times v. Sullivan* has had "progeny,"[26] as has *Tinker v. Des Moines School District.*[27] Still another landmark decision, *Brown v. Board of Education*, has had "progeny."[28] Landmark decisions appear to have the greatest begetting power. The personification of justice, law, the Constitution, and judicial opinions is examined and discussed in Chapter 8.

The tropes have long played an important role in judicial argumentation and decision making, and in the end have influenced our lives as much as, if not more than, tropes found in our political, scientific, literary, and religious discourse. The judicial "marketplace of ideas" may in the end be more important to perceptions of our society than the political "iron curtain." The judicial "wall of separation between Church and State" may be as crucial to the nation's religious behavior as the biblical "The Lord is my Shepherd." The judicial "chilling effect" can influence our lives as much as the literary "We are the hollow men."

Even though the tropes have become doctrines, standards, and principles on which judicial arguments are based, very few jurists and legal scholars have examined the functions and implications of tropes in court opinions. As Judge Richard Posner has pointed out in his *Law and Literature* (1988), "The subject of judicial rhetoric is both rich and comparatively unexplored."[29] The fact that the rhetoric of judicial opinions has not been adequately examined was recognized by Robert Prentice when he wrote in his 1983 article "Supreme Court Rhetoric": "Despite the importance of rhetoric in the shaping of Supreme Court opinions, the subject has received little scholarly attention."[30] While there is a paucity of literature on the rhetoric of judicial opinions, there is still less scholarship dealing with the tropes and their impact on judicial decision making.

The importance of the metaphor in legal discourse, however, began to be recognized and explored by a few legal scholars in the 1980s. For example, in his April 1986 article, "Agon at Agora: Creative Misreadings in the First Amendment Tradition," David Cole examines judicial "misreadings" and discusses the metaphorical change from Justice Holmes's "free trade in ideas" to Justice Brennan's "marketplace of ideas." Cole says of the market metaphor:

> The "marketplace of ideas" soon [after it was introduced by Brennan in 1965] became a well-worn phrase. Its relevance in judicial opinions and law journal articles is attributable in part to its obvious bow to Holmes, but Brennan's revision is significant. Brennan localized the metaphor; he gave the market a sense of place. Brought down from the Holmesian skies, the marketplace of ideas grounds "free trade" in a specific locale and context. . . . The marketplace of ideas connotes diversity and pluralism at ground level without resting on theories of abstract, truth-generating invisible hands.[31]

One year later, a different metaphor was examined in Burr Henly's "'Penumbra': The Roots of a Legal Metaphor." Henly concluded and warned, after tracing the history of this metaphor in judicial decision making: "Beginning with its use by Holmes, the penumbra metaphor has been fuzzy and ambiguous. . . . In the penumbra, judges are, to some extent, free from text and precedent as well as reason. But they are never freed from responsibility, including the responsibility to try to penetrate what Cardozo called 'the mists of metaphor.' Metaphors like 'penumbra' are useful and are even, at some level, inescapable. In the long run, though, they are not a substitute for theory."[32]

The legal concept *standing* was examined by Steven L. Winter in his 1988 article "The Metaphor of Standing and the Problem of Self-Governance." Winter wrote: "The key to understanding—and to unlocking the barrier of standing law—lies in an appreciation that the term 'standing' is a metaphor. Its origin no doubt comes from the physical practices of the courtroom: A court will only hear a participant if he or she *is* standing. 'Standing' is therefore a natural metaphor for when a court will consider a litigant's claim; the metaphor is motivated by our experience."[33] Winter's analysis of the "standing" metaphor leads him to conclude that "the metaphor of 'standing' is a myth that has become '*the* literal truth' and shaped—or misshaped—our thinking about adjudication. It has shaped our thinking about adjudication to conform to two separate 'truths' embedded in the metaphor, and to think about them as one. The first is the 'truth' of individualism: One stands alone; one stands up; one stands apart; one stands out; one stands head and shoulders above the crowd."[34]

The "marketplace" metaphor was once again examined by Steven Winter in his 1989 article, "Transcendental Nonsense, Metaphoric Reasoning, and the Cognitive Stakes for Law": "Our modern understanding of the first amendment is dependent upon the use of the *market* metaphor. The metaphor carries over from the source domain of economic experience certain normative cultural assumptions about the usefulness and value of autonomy and free trade and applies them to the target domain of free speech."[35]

In "Metaphor and Paradox," Thomas Ross states at the outset: "Our metaphors at once obscure and express the paradoxical nature of the pieces of law to which they refer. Left unexamined, they nicely obscure the deep contradictions. But when we really look at our metaphors, we confront our contradictions and we experience paradox."[36] Ross argues that metaphors of law are "figures of speech" that "shatter and reconstruct our realities."[37] What becomes clear is that in the 1980s a few legal scholars began to recognize metaphors such as the "marketplace of ideas," "standing," and "penumbra" as more than ornaments to embellish judicial opinions.

If tropes have been such an important part of judicial argument, why the dearth until the 1980s of scholarship in figurative language and the law? Perhaps the answer lies partly in the way we have perceived what judges do when they write opinions. We see judges as giving "logical" reasons for their judgments through "argument" and through the precise, literal use of language; we associate the judiciary with "logic" and not with the other two elements of the classical trivium, grammar and rhetoric. But this can also be said about our perceptions of scientific discourse. Surely scientists relying on the scientific method are seeking their "truths" through logical reasoning and the precise, literal use of language and symbols. Yet we have significant research and writing related to the metaphors of science.[38] Hence, our perception of judges as individuals relying only on "logic" may not be the explanation for the lack of analysis of tropes in court opinions.

Perhaps the answer lies in the fact that scientists themselves have examined scientific discourse and have found there the significant role of metaphor, while judges have not looked at their opinions for similar reliance on tropes, especially the metaphor. It could be that scientists are more likely to participate in this self-examination; the scientific inquiry and theory based on a scientist's metaphor invites examination and testing by others. The acceptability of the theory may depend on the "accuracy" of the metaphor.

Hugh Petrie, in his "Metaphor and Learning," commenting on Kuhn's observations about the workings of science during scientific revolutions, points out: "During the periods of normal science, puzzles and problems are solved by the use of the accepted paradigm of the moment. Occasionally, such problems or disturbances resist current paradigm efforts to solve them and they become anomalies. The scientist then searches for a new metaphor or model which can remove the anomaly."[39]

One of the characteristics of science is that "its conclusions are tentative, i.e., are not necessarily the final word." A scientist is free to say that his or her theory is tentative, that it might be "wrong." The judge cannot evade making a final judgment. The judge cannot simply say, "I cannot make up my mind in this case" or "This judgment may be wrong, but on the other hand it may be right." As Karl Llewellyn has put it, "The court must decide the dispute that is before it. It cannot refuse because the job is hard, or dubious, or dangerous."[40] Or as Charles Breitel has asserted, Courts must decide the cases presented to them; they have no choice to abstain for any reason. Their unsureness, the difficulty of the case, or the absence of clearly applicable law is no excuse."[41] In science there is a built-in system of self-criticism, ongoing experimentation, which is not built into the judicial decision-making process. We have dissenting opinions, which question the judgment of a court, and we have concurring opinions, which might question the reasoning of the court; and we have a system of appeals. But there is no practice, as in science, of more open, public self-evaluation. Judges do not ordinarily answer questions about their opinions and decisions. And they are reluctant to comment publicly on the reasoning, language, and judgments of their colleagues. This may explain in part why there is such a dearth of literature from judges about the language of opinions, especially the reliance on figurative language.

Judge Frank Coffin, discussing the paucity of this self-examination by judges, states that "for the most part, judges in recent times have largely left to others the writing about their craft and calling. There are ample reasons for this. One is that the judge's code of ethics precludes his writing about what he knows best—the steps he took in arriving at his last or his most widely known decision—for that decision must be judged solely by what he or his court wrote to justify and explain it."[42]

Still another reason for minimal rhetorical self-analysis by judges, especially of their opinions, is suggested by Susan Tiefendrum:

> The distinction between scientific and non-scientific discourse is important to the characterization and differentiation of literary and legal discourse. In legal discourse there is a conventional preference for referential terms. In contrast, literary discourse is characterized by a predominance of metaphor and metonymy. Students of law are taught early in law school to avoid the use of emotive or metaphoric language in legal brief writing. Despite the generally held belief in this convention, metaphors are commonly found in cases. Ironically, the use of metaphor is especially prevalent in the free speech area. For example, Justice Brandeis used the highly charged metaphor of slavery to describe the emotional state of fear: "[I]t is the function of speech to free men from the bondage of irrational fears." Justice Harlan's metaphor in *Cohen v. California* is memorable: "[O]ne man's vulgarity is another's

lyric." Legal language, then, is not the scientific discourse
ideally composed of referential terms that it is thought to
be.[43]

That the judicial opinion has remained rhetorically unexplored is especially surprising and alarming, since (1) several
judges have expressed misgivings in their opinions about the
use of tropes in judicial decision making and (2) the courts
have relied heavily on tropes in arguments justifying their
decisions.

A few jurists have recognized, but only in passing, the
importance, ramifications, and dangers of metaphorical expressions in judicial argument. Justice Cardozo, well known
for his imaginative use of tropes, warned: "Metaphors in law
are to be narrowly watched, for starting as devices to liberate
thought, they end often by enslaving it."[44] Like Justice Cardozo, other Supreme Court justices have been suspicious of
the judiciary's reliance on metaphorical expression in opinions. Referring to the "wall of separation between Church and
State," Justice Stanley Reed warned in his dissenting opinion
in *McCollum v. Board of Education:* "A rule of law should not be
drawn from a figure of speech."[45]

Justice Potter Stewart also saw dangers in the reliance on
metaphors in the law, declaring in his dissenting opinion in
the school-prayer case *Engel v. Vitale,* "I think that the Court's
task is not responsibly aided by the uncritical invocation of
metaphors like the 'wall of separation,' a phrase nowhere to be
found in the Constitution."[46] More recently, Justice William
Rehnquist attacked the "wall of separation" metaphor, referring to it as "Jefferson's misleading metaphor"[47] and contending that "whether due to its lack of historical support or its
practical unworkability, the *Everson* 'wall' has proved all but
useless as a guide to sound constitutional adjudication."[48]

While judges have been declaring that "metaphors in the
law are to be narrowly watched" and that "a rule of law should
not be drawn from a figure of speech," these figures of speech
have remained unexamined with few exceptions. That judicial tropes warrant watching becomes even more evident
when one reads Judge Posner's words: "Many of the stylistic

shortcomings of judicial opinions, and of legal writing generally, could be ameliorated if it were more generally realized
that style is organic to judicial writing, as it is to literature but
not to science; and that in the areas of law that matter—the
areas of disagreement—to divorce style and content is not an
attainable goal."[49]

Griffin Bell, once a judge on the U.S. court of appeals and
later attorney general in the Carter administration, recognized the importance of style in writing judicial opinions:
"Style in judicial writing is an important factor in the growth
of law. The style of an opinion may affect the manner in which
it's interpreted by the reader. It may also govern the frequency
with which the opinion will be cited in other cases and thus
determine the influence the opinion will ultimately have."[50]
This latter observation by Bell is especially pertinent, for what
becomes very clear as one examines the tropes of the law is
that what is often quoted from a court opinion to support a
subsequent decision is the tropological passages.

In 1919, Justice Holmes, dissenting in *Abrams v. United
States*, gave us the influential metaphorical "marketplace of
ideas," although he did not phrase it in exactly those terms.
Holmes wrote: "But when men have realized that time has
upset many fighting faiths, they may come to believe even
more than they believe the very foundations of their own
conduct that the ultimate good desired is better reached by
free trade in ideas—that the best test of truth is the power of
the thought to get itself accepted in the competition of the
market."[51] Whenever *Abrams* is cited, it is usually this passage
from Holmes's dissenting opinion that is quoted. The metaphorical "market" and the "free trade in ideas" have become
influential tropes in American judicial philosophy.

When in *Adler v. Board of Education* (1952) the Supreme
Court upheld the constitutionality of New York's loyalty oath,
Justice William O. Douglas dissented, pointing out the dangers of such oaths: "What happens under the law [requiring
teachers to sign loyalty oaths] is typical of what happens in a
police state. Teachers are under constant surveillance; their
utterances are watched for clues to dangerous thought. A pall
is cast over the classroom."[52] Justice Douglas's metaphorical

"pall" fifteen years later appears in the Court's opinion striking down the New York oath as unconstitutional. Justice
Brennan, delivering the opinion of the Court in *Keyishian* and
referring to safeguarding academic freedom, declared: "That
freedom is therefore a special concern of the First Amendment which does not tolerate laws that cast a pall of orthodoxy
over the classroom."[53] The metaphorical "pall of orthodoxy
over the classroom" has subsequently been cited often in
court opinions dealing with the First Amendment rights of
students and teachers. It has become one of the most influential tropes in judicial decision making.

One of the metonymies relied on heavily by many courts
in deciding First Amendment cases involving speech and
press controversies in the schools appeared in Justice Abe
Fortas's opinion in *Tinker v. Des Moines School Dist.*: "First
Amendment rights, applied in light of the special characteristics of the school environment, are available to teachers and
students. It can hardly be argued that either students or
teachers shed their constitutional right to freedom of speech
or expression at the schoolhouse gate."[54] The metaphoric
"shedd[ing]" and the metonymic "schoolhouse gate" have
provided much First Amendment protection to students and
teachers from judges who when citing *Tinker* invariably quote
this tropological passage.

In 1964, Justice William O. Douglas, in *Griswold v. Connecticut*, argued that "the First Amendment has a penumbra
where privacy is protected from governmental intrusion."[55]
Nine years later, the metaphorical "penumbra" became part of
Justice Harry Blackmun's *Roe v. Wade* opinion asserting that
"the Court has recognized that right of personal privacy . . .
does exist under the Constitution" and that the "roots of that
right" were partially found "in the penumbras of the Bill of
Rights."[56]

All of these tropes—the marketplace of ideas; the wall of
separation between church and state; the pall of orthodoxy
over the classroom; the schoolhouse gate; penumbral rights—
have become integral parts of arguments appearing in judicial
opinions. Sometimes several tropes are "piled one upon another" in a single opinion. In 1972, the U.S. Court of Appeals

for the Second Circuit decided in *James v. Board of Education* for a high-school teacher who had been discharged from his teaching position for wearing a black armband to school to protest against the Vietnam War. Judge Irving Kaufman incorporated into the court's opinion the several tropes that had become crucial in First Amendment cases. Judge Kaufman relied on the "schoolhouse gate" from *Tinker*. Through personfication, he declared that "freedom of expression demands breathing room." He spoke twice of preserving the "marketplace of ideas." He saw the students as a "captive audience"; to punish teachers, he said, "would appear to the students to be sanctioning the very 'pall of orthodoxy,' condemned in *Keyishian*, which chokes freedom of dissent."[57]

When in 1988 the Supreme Court unanimously decided for *Hustler* magazine and against Jerry Falwell, who had sued the magazine to recover damages for invasion of privacy, libel, and intentional infliction of emotional distress, Justice Rehnquist, delivering the opinion of the Court, relied on the "marketplace of ideas" three times, the personification "breathing space" for First Amendment freedoms three times, and the metaphoric "chilling effect" once, along with "fighting words" and several other tropes.[58] The judiciary's heavy reliance on this type of nonliteral language demonstrates that tropes are an integral part of the opinions of the courts.

At one time judges did not have to give reasons for their judgments. Decisions were made without any accompanying discourse explaining the decision. Legal scholar Piero Calamandrei tells us that "in early times the judge was also a priest or soothsayer, who sought aid and inspiration from superstition and magic; he found the motivation for his judgment in the flight of birds or in the palpitating entrails of the sacrifice."[59] Eventually, however, the birds and entrails gave way to decision making of juries and judges relying on verifiable proof and judicial reasoning. About the function and evolution of the court opinion, Calamandrei states:

> The major function of the judicial opinion is an explanatory or, one might say, a pedagogical one. No longer con-

tent merely to command, to proclaim a *sic volo, sic iubeo*
[as I wish, so I command] from his high bench, the judge
descends to the level of the parties, and although still
commanding, seeks to impress them with the reasonableness of the decision and as such it attempts to be as persuasive as it can. Ever since justice descended from
heaven to earth and the idea gained ground that the judge
is a human being and not a supernatural and infallible oracle to be adored, whose authority is beyond question,
man has felt the need of a rational explanation to give validity to the word of the judge.[60]

The reasonableness of the explanation presented in the
opinion may in the end depend on the "reasonableness" of the
tropes used to convey the principles and premises upon
which the arguments are based. To analyze and understand
the reasonableness of the decision, one may have to examine
carefully the tropology of the opinion, with the understanding that the tropes are not merely ornamental flourishes.

Various judges have given a nod of recognition to the
significance of "style" in the persuasiveness of the judicial
opinion and have spoken of the nexus between substance and
style. After asserting that "the style of an opinion may affect
the manner in which it's interpreted by the reader," Judge
Griffin Bell argued that "style must be regarded as one of the
principal tools of the judiciary and it thus deserves detailed
attention and repeated emphasis." The word *style*, Bell reminds us, "comes from the Latin word 'stylus' which was an
ancient writing instrument. One end was used for writing in
wax and the other for erasure by smoothing the wax. Hence,
we have a useful analogy, style is related to writing and
revision—drafting and redrafting."[61]

Emphasizing the importance of style in opinions, Justice
Cardozo declared: "The opinion will need persuasive force,
or the impressive virtue of sincerity and fire, or the mnemonic
power of alliteration and antithesis, or the terseness and tang
of the proverb, and the maxim. Neglect the help of these
allies, and it may never win the day."[62]

Cardozo's position that an effective style is important to a
well-written opinion has been shared by Richard Weisberg,

who stated in his 1979 article "Law, Literature and Cardozo's Judicial Poetics":

> Style inevitably contributes to, and often controls, the present and future meaning of appellate opinions, even those not actually written by the judge who signs them. Cardozo's case clearly demonstrates, particularly given his awareness of the integral place of style in the law, that the effective use of style, as often as "logic," underlies successful appellate advocacy and adjudication. . . . Cardozo realized that the *form of an opinion actively contributes to its correctness;* style thus conceived is an element to be evaluated as part of the correctness of a decision, not as ancillary or merely ornamental element.[63]

The distinctions between style and content, style and logic, have come to be recognized as artificial and inappropriate distinctions. Our language determines to a large extent how we see reality, and tropes especially affect our perceptions and how we see the "truth." Murray Edelman wrote in *Politics as Symbolic Action*: "Thought is metaphorical and metaphor pervades language, for the unknown, the new, the unclear, and the remote are apprehended by one's perceptions of identities with the familiar. Metaphor, therefore, defines the pattern of perception to which people respond."[64] Lakoff and Johnson have placed the greatest importance on the role of the tropes, especially the metaphor, in affecting our perceptions of events, people, concepts, truth, and reality: "In all aspects of our life, not just in politics and love, we define our reality in terms of metaphors and then proceed to act on the basis of the metaphors. We draw inferences, set goals, make commitments and execute plans, all on the basis of how we in part structure our experience, consciously and unconsciously by means of metaphor."[65] As Charlotte Linde has put it, "Whether in national politics or in everyday interaction, people in power get to impose their metaphors."[66]

Considering the power of the judiciary to determine what is legal and what is illegal, what is a crime, and who is to be punished, the tropology of the law especially needs watching. As civil-rights–black-power activist Stokely Carmichael observed in 1967, "It [definition] is very, very important because I believe that people who can define are masters."[67] " 'When I use a word,' " said Humpty Dumpty in *Through the Looking Glass,* " 'it means just what I choose it to mean—neither more nor less.' " " 'The question is,' " said Alice, " 'whether you can make words mean so many different things.' " " 'The question is,' " said Humpty Dumpty, " 'which is to be master—that's all.' "[68]

When the courts speak through their opinions, they speak as "people in power" and "masters," and as such they have the authority to define and to impose their tropes, directly and indirectly. Through the reliance on precedents, the repetitive citation of legal tropes becomes increasingly influential. The written and published opinion, relying on precedents, repeats the tropological arguments, further institutionalizing figuratively expressed principles, doctrines, standards, and premises. The reliance increasingly embeds the repeated tropes in the legal landscape. The figurative phrases, Justice Holmes (who has contributed his share of such phrases) observed, lead to ideas becoming "encysted in phrases and therefore for a long time cease to provoke further analysis."[69]

Confronted with the nexus between style and content, the widespread reliance of the courts on nonliteral language in legal arguments, we are led to heed the advice of James Bradley Thayer: "Law is not so unlike all other subjects of human contemplation that clearness of thought will not help us powerfully in grasping it. If terms in common legal use are used exactly, it is well to know it; if they are used inexactly, it is well to know that, and to remark just how they are used."[70]

1

The Functions of the Judicial Opinion

We don't have money at the Court for an army
and we can't take ads in the newspaper, and
we don't want to go out on a picket line in our
robes. We have to convince the nation by the
force of our opinions.

—JUSTICE TOM CLARK[1]

Before turning to an examination of the tropes
and their application in judicial decision making, a review of
the history and purposes of the judicial opinion and its
publication is called for, since an understanding of the tropology of the law is related to the development of the law and its
reliance on principles, premises, and precedents, or *stare
decisis*.

The difficulties arising from judicial decisions without
opinions was recognized by Chief Justice Earl Warren when
he wrote in *Jacobellis v. Ohio* (1964), in which the Court decided
that the film *Les Amants* was not obscene: "This Court hears
cases such as the instant one not merely to rule upon the
alleged obscenity of a specific film or book but to establish
principles for the guidance of lower courts and legislatures.
Yet most of our [obscenity] decisions since *Roth* have been
given without opinion and have thus failed to furnish guidance."[2] While explaining to the parties involved why a case is
decided as it is, the opinion, as Karl Llewellyn has observed,
"has in addition a central forward-looking function which
reaches far beyond the cause at hand: the opinion has as one if
not its major office to show how like cases are properly to be
decided in the future."[3] The principles and premises promul-

gated in the opinion bring continuity, stability, and predictability to judicial decision making. It has not always been so.

Piero Calamandrei tells of an ethnologist's witnessing a judicial procedure practiced by a tribe on the banks of an African lake: "When a dispute arose the two litigants were tied to stakes set up on the shore at an equal distance from the water and left there to await judgment. Before long the judge, an elderly alligator experienced in this work, appeared from out of the water and looking over the situation slowly crawled toward one of the stakes. The litigant who was eaten lost his case (with costs)."[4] This reliance on "chance" to arrive at judicial decisions appears in Burma where "suits have been determined by the parties being burned with a candle, equal in size and both lighted at once; and he whose candle outlasts the other is adjudged to have won his case. In Borneo, the two parties are sometimes represented by two shellfish on a plate, which are irritated by pouring on some lime juice, and the one first moving settles the guilt or innocence (according to the arrangements made) of the owner."[5]

Human beings in dispute have not always had their differences settled by judges writing judicial opinions to explain and justify their decisions. For centuries, controversies and disputes, guilt or innocence, were not decided by arcane principles and close reasoning appearing in published opinions.

In England before the Norman Conquest, "there were no judges in our sense of the word, no attorneys, no policemen, and from the vantage of the twentieth century, no rational method by which the allegations of either plaintiff or a defendant could be proved 'beyond a reasonable doubt.'"[6] In the twelfth century, "when Henry II came to the throne there was no clear distinction between civil and criminal law. Crime was a wrong against an individual, to be remedied by either blood or money. Trial by battle, compurgation and the ordeal were still used as methods of deciding cases."[7] In effect, compurgators were character witnesses who were simply there to avow that the defendant was a person to be believed, not to provide testimony regarding the lawless action with which the defendant was charged. In criminal cases, guilt or innocence was decided by compurgation or the ordeal.

Throughout ancient Europe, "in trial by battle, the accuser and accused fought in mortal combat to determine the guilt or innocence of the suspected person. In the trial by fire, the accused walked bare-footed over red hot iron plow-shares, or coals of fire, carried a red hot iron in his hand, or walked through flames, clad in a suit of wax, spread over woolen cloth, known as the 'trial of the waxen shirt,' because if he was unhurt by the fire and the wax was unmelted, he was considered innocent, but otherwise was adjudged guilty."[8]

Trial by ordeal "existed long before the common law and indeed long before Christianity. Trial by ordeal was regarded as an appeal to God to decide the guilt or innocence of the accused and might take various forms. Ordeal by fire or boiling water was common. This involved burning or scalding the prisoner's hands and bandaging them. The bandages were removed after three days, when guilt would be established if the hands had not healed."[9] There were still other ordeals to determine guilt or innocence: trial by Eucharist, trial by the cross, and judgment of the bier.[10]

Today, the person who contends that he or she has been libeled may go to the judicial system for a peaceable settlement of the issue. However, as Lois Forer has observed, "The libel suit for vindication of reputation was alien to early English law. It developed as a less lethal alternative to the duel fought by gentlemen in the defense of their 'honor.' Judicial combat, in which a duel was used in lieu of a criminal prosecution was abolished in 1818."[11]

Determining the guilt or innocence through the entrails of a sacrifice, trial by fire, trial by boiling water, and other divinatory practices was eventually replaced by the decision making of judges who were obligated to give reasons for their judgments. The judicial opinion, however, did not come with the earliest record keeping of judicial proceedings. The judgments of the courts in thirteenth-century England were not accompanied with opinions providing the reasons for the decision. As Arthur Hogue points out, the royal plea rolls were records kept solely for use in "royal administration, and the king was particularly interested in knowing who owed him money and how much." "But the reasoned opinion of the justices employed in arriving at the decision was not considered of value in the thirteenth century. The decision alone was recorded. Even after the beginning of reporting and the making of those unusual volumes known as *Yearbooks*, the modern doctrine of *stare decisis* could not develop because uniform reports of cases could not be widely distributed until the beginning of printing in the fifteenth century."[12]

In his classic work *A History of English Law*, W. S. Holdsworth characterizes the *Yearbooks* as "the law Reports of the Middle Ages" and describes them as "the most important source of, and authority for, the mediaeval common law." Excepting the plea rolls, the *Yearbooks* are "the only first-hand account we possess of the legal doctrines laid down by the judges of the fourteenth and fifteenth centuries."[13] While the reasoning behind the judgments appearing in the *Yearbooks* was hardly developed, with the coming of these records, the concept of the precedent was established. In 1315, Justice William of Bereford is recorded as responding to counsel Herle's "Sir, we should recover only the place and the hedge where the sallows were growing" with "You have never yet seen in this Court an assignment of waste upheld in respect to sallows, and we shall not make such a precedent; and so we give judgment that you take nothing by your writ."[14] Holdsworth has cited passages from the *Yearbooks* to support his contention that "we can see from the early Year Books that a considered decision was regarded as laying down a general rule for the future. 'The judgment to be given by you,' said Herle in argument in 1304, 'will be hereafter an authority in every *quare non admisit* in England.'"[15]

We have moved from trials by ordeal to judicial judgments without explanation to judicial judgments based on principles and the beginnings of the concept of precedents. With the *Yearbooks* we are presented with rudimentary judicial argument and discourse. "With the beginning of the Year Books," observes Carleton K. Allen in his *Law in the Making*, "we can form some notion of the practical workings of precedents in the courts. Decisions are cited often enough to show that both Bench and Bar consider them a relevant part of argument."[16]

As was recognized by the original "opinion" writers, if one is to have an efficient system of law based on precedents, a written record is needed. In his discussion of the origin of the judicial opinion, Judge Emlin McClain explained: "The Year Books . . . show what was decided, not as adjudications important between the parties, but as precedents to be considered in other cases. . . . The whole conception was that which is still familiar to us of a judge trying a case in the light of all the information as to the previous law attainable and ruling on new questions by applying to them principles already recognized, his rulings being preserved for the use by other judges. This was the development of the doctrine of precedence. This was the recognition of law made by the judges."[17]

The authors of the *Yearbooks* are unknown. The earliest notes of the court proceedings were made by apprentices in French, as William Bolland tells us in his in-depth work *A Manual of Year Book Studies*, "for their own private purposes. Now these notes were notes of what happened in the Common Bench, of the arguments, the objections, the rulings and judgments used and taken and made."[18] Eventually, copies of these notes were produced in the *Scriptoria* and sold. Bolland describes the reproduction process and the problems of inaccuracy accompanying the process:

> In these Scriptoria will be gathered men who can write with reasonable rapidity and legibility, but whom the testimony of their work prevents us from crediting with much more than this. What happens then? Someone, we may suppose, will read the reporters' notes aloud. The scribes will follow with their pens the spoken words as accurately as they can, consistently with not taking overmuch trouble, and, one would imagine from what results they produced, never worrying themselves about getting a word which they had not caught overcertainly repeated; but they will not set down what the reader read, unless, and it is not a very improbably supposition, he was inclined to make slips as they were. A word will be misheard for another word that has a similar sound but a quite different meaning, and the wrong word will go down. That it happens to make nonsense is not the business of

the scribes; at any rate they do not take it to be. . . . And
so from inaccuracy of hearing, from carelessness, from inability or neglect to follow the reader with the closeness
necessary for accurate reproduction, we get a series of
first varients from the same set of original notes. Each
scribe has produced a version different from the original
version and different from the versions of his fellows.[19]

The *Yearbooks* come to us in French, for in the twelfth
century French was the language used in legal proceedings.
As Pollock and Maitland point out in *History of English Law,* "If
we must choose one moment of time as fatal, we ought to
choose 1166 rather than 1066, year of the assize of novel
disseisin rather than the year of the Battle of Hastings. Then it
was that the decree went forth which gave to every man
dispossessed of his freehold a remedy to be sought in a royal
court, a French-speaking court. Thenceforth the ultimate
triumph of French law terms was secure."[20] Pollock and
Maitland provide us with a list of French words that became
part of the English legal language, words such as *obligation,
debt, guarantee, trespass, assault, arson, burglary, lien, grant,
easement, marriage, judges, jurors, counsel, defendant, evidence,
verdict, sentence, pardon, execution.*[21]

Late in the fifteenth century, several years after William
Caxton introduced printing in England, William Machlinia
began printing the *Yearbooks*. While the authorship of earlier
Yearbooks remained unknown, the law reporters of the six-
teenth, seventeenth, and eighteenth centuries put their
names to the private sets of reports they printed and sold. As
Walker and Walker indicate, "At first the private reports were
scarcely fuller than the Year Book reports had been. Very
soon, however, many sets of private reports become far more
detailed, reproducing much of counsel's arguments and virtually the whole of the judgment."[22] In 1865, the Council of
Law Reporting was established to publish the reports of the
courts and to this day, while the Law Reports are not an
official publication in England, "they are the series of reports
to which counsel should refer when citing a case which is
reported in the Law Reports."[23]

The first publication of American judicial decisions occurred in 1789. The first colony in the "New World" was established in 1607, but it was almost two centuries later that the first published court opinions began to appear in the newly created nation. Samuel Eliot Morison has pointed out that "legal development is probably the least known aspect of American colonial history. Judicial opinions were not recorded in the colonies, no year books were issued, and the printed material for legal and judicial history have been so scanty as to preclude the more cautious historians from dealing with this important side of colonial life."[24]

As Francis Aumann tells us, in 1789 Ephraim Kirby of Connecticut "made a permanent place for himself in the annals of American law when he published in Lichfield, his *Reports of Cases Adjudged in the Superior Court and Court of Errors of the State of Connecticut from the Year 1785 to May, 1788* (1789). This work was the first fully developed volume of law reports published in the United States."[25]

Until the beginning of the eighteenth century, executive and judicial government, as one writer declared in 1829, "was what might truly be called *primitive*. No trace can be found of law as a science or profession. The judges left the ploughed field for the bench, when occasion called, and found reason and common sense a very sufficient substitute for Pandects and Year Books. In the piety of their hearts they adopted the law of Moses for their criminal code, and in civil litigation the common law of England was made, as far as their slender means of information would permit, the rule of their decision."[26]

A former dean of the Yale Law School, Grant Gilmore, has said plainly that "it is pointless to speak of an 'American law' before the 1800s."[27] Gilmore demonstrates the nexus between the dearth of published opinions and the lack of a legal system: "There can hardly be a legal system until the decisions of the courts are regularly published and are available to bench and bar. Even in the seaboard colonies, where the practice of law had, during the eighteenth century, become professionalized, there were no published reports; consequently there was nothing which could rationally be called a legal system."[28]

By 1820, "a substantial body of American legal materials had accumulated. The decisions of American courts, state and federal, were being published."[29] In 1790, the first collection of Pennsylvania court decisions were being published. In 1793, the first collection of Vermont court decisions was published. Aumann tells us that "while Connecticut was the first American state to print judicial decisions, this work was done . . . as a private venture. New York and Massachusetts were the first states to order official publication of decisions. New Jersey followed this practice in 1806 and South Carolina in 1811."[30]

As for the Supreme Court, the first collection of the *United States Reports* appeared in 1790, although these reports were not known by that title until 1874; prior to 1874, the reports were named for the official reporters, such as Dallas (1790–1800), Cranch (1801–15) and so on. Early reporting of Supreme Court decisions followed the English tradition, the reporters working "at their own expense and for their own profit and prestige," as David O'Brien observes in *Storm Center: The Supreme Court in American Politics*. As noted by O'Brien, the practice of having the Supreme Court decisions published by the Government Printing Office is relatively recent: "For most of the nineteenth century, the Reporter could practice law before the Court or serve as a judge in a lower court. In publishing the Court's decisions, the Reporter could advertise his legal services as well. Until the chief judgeship of Taft, the Reporter continued to engage in this semiprivate enterprise and supplemented his salary by negotiating contracts with publishers and by selling to the public the *United States Reports* (containing the final opinions of the Court). In 1922, Congress established the present arrangement: the Reporter's salary is fixed by the justices and paid by the government, and the Government Printing Office publishes the *United States Reports*."[31]

During the first three decades of the 1800s, there was such an increase in the number of published volumes of court decisions that there were those who complained of the "vast and increasing multiplication of reports as well as law treatises."[32] There were others, however, who saw the need for and value of the published judicial reports. One writer in 1828 stated several reasons for the publication of the reports:

> Of the importance of it to our personal rights we cannot form too great an estimate. It secures the judiciary, by every possible motive, to the faithful administration of justice . . . when they know that their opinion may be severely scrutinized by the ablest men of their own, and perhaps of coming ages; when they reflect that those opinions will be either made the basis of further adjudications, or rejected as inconclusive and false; above all, when from fear of error they are led, as in this country they almost universally are, to write their opinions at length, and themselves prepare them for the press, they have every inducement, interested and disinterested, which can possibly be crowded upon the mind, to be laborious, accurate, and impartial. Let then our legal decisions be brought, as extensively as may be, before the public; for nothing can tend more unerringly to the faithful administration of justice.[33]

During the twentieth century, a variety of views have been presented by judges, attorneys, and others about the purpose of and need for the judicial opinion. Why do we need an opinion at all? Jerome Frank stated: "Often when a judge decides a case he simultaneously publishes an essay, called an opinion, explaining that he used an old rule or invented a new rule to justify his judgment. But no matter what he says, it is his decision which fixes the legal positions of the litigants. If Judge Brilliant decides that Mr. Evasion must pay the federal government $50,000 for back taxes or that Mrs. Goneril is entitled to nothing under the will of her father, Mr. Lear, the contents of the judge's literary effusion makes not one iota of practical difference to Mr. Evasion or Mrs. Goneril. Opinion or no opinion, opinion-with-a-new-rule-announced or opinion-with-old rules-proclaimed—it is all one to the parties whose contentions he adjudicated."[34]

Some scholars have emphasized that the function of the judicial opinion is to persuade the judge's audience that he or she has made the correct decision. Stevenson states that the judge, having examined the facts, researched the authorities, and reached a decision, must go on to decide the "question of what information he should present to his readers to persuade them of the rightness of his conclusion." As Stevenson sees it, "The purpose of the written opinion is not, after all, for the judge to arrive at a conclusion. He has already done that. Rather, it is for him to protect his conclusion and his reasons for holding it to those audiences who need to know about it. . . . The written opinion is not a set of notes written by a judge for his own use. Rather, it is a persuasive essay directed outward toward specific audiences. Thus the writer's task is to select that information which is necessary to accomplish his rhetorical purpose."[35]

Three purposes of the published opinions are presented by Mark Franklin, who states that they are "evidence that rational procedures were used to reach the decision. They satisfy the public's wish to have justice done. They give the losing party, despite his disappointment, the feeling that he has had his day in court. They become part of an accumulation of case law that will guide future judges."[36]

The reasoned opinion, says Calamandrei, is there in part "to persuade the losing party that the judgment against was the inevitable conclusion of a logical process and not the result of oppressive and arbitrary improvisations. Even counsel for the losing party may find in the reasoned opinion the arguments that had previously escaped his attention and that convince him of the error of the position he had sustained." Further, the judicial opinion "has a more strictly juridical use, that of enabling the parties to determine whether or not there may lie within the reasoning on which the judge bases his decision any of those defects that make the decision susceptible to revision on appeal."[37]

As Calamandrei sees it, there is still another facet to the judicial opinion: "Rather than a preliminary study made by the judge to enable him to decide justly, the opinion is generally the expression of a soul-searching reappraisal made by the judge to convince himself that he has decided justly. Its purpose is to establish by logic the validity of a decision actually based on sentiment; it is the realization of the sense of justice, the demonstration of the *ratio scripta* that the judge prepares for his own peace of mind as much as for the parties, corroborating a discovery born of his intuition."[38]

While Stevenson's assertion that the purpose of the opinion is not "for the judge to arrive at a conclusion" may be accurate in some instances, there are judges and legal scholars who have argued that the opinion functions as a step in reaching the decision. Judge Frank Coffin, of the U.S. Court of Appeals for the First Circuit, emphasizes in his *Ways of a Judge* the relationship between the thinking-through and the writing of an opinion: "A remarkably effective device for detecting fissures in accuracy and logic is the reduction to writing of the results of one's thought processes. . . . Somehow, a decision mulled over in one's head or talked about in conference looks different when dressed up in written words and sent out into the sunlight." Sometimes, says Judge Coffin, an opinion "will simply not do" or an opinion "simply won't write," and "the act of writing tells us what was wrong with the act of thinking."[39]

Similarly, Robert Leflar draws a relationship between the process of writing the opinion and the eventual decision arrived at by the judge: "One function [of judicial opinions] that is recognized both by detached students of the judicial process and by opinion writers themselves is that the necessity for preparing a formal opinion assures some measure of thoughtful review of the facts in a case and of the law's bearing upon them. Snap judgments and lazy preferences for armchair theorizing as against library research and time-consuming cerebral effort are somewhat minimized." Leflar points out other functions of the opinion, the most immediate "to explain to parties and their counsel what is being done in their case." The opinion "is the appellate judges' and courts' major communication, almost their sole communication, with society. It is their interpretation of themselves to practicing lawyers, to trial judges, to law teachers, to laymen. . . . Opinions are the principal vehicle for judicial communication."[40]

Drawing on his personal judicial experience, Justice Roger Traynor of the California Supreme Court discusses the importance of the writing of the opinion: "In sixteen years I have not found a better test for the solution of a case than its articulation in writing, which is thinking at its hardest. A judge, inevitably preoccupied with the far-reaching effect of an immediate solution as a precedent, often discovers that his tentative view will not jell in the writing. He wrestles with the devil more than once to set forth a sound opinion that will be sufficient unto more than the day."[41]

Others have suggested that the judicial opinion is there to protect the judge. Speaking to the American Bar Association in 1902, Judge Emlin McClain declared: "The desire of a judge deciding a case to vindicate the result which he reaches so that he shall not be chargeable with incompetence or partiality, is commendable; but where it is not customary to make any such explanation, the administration of justice is quite as effectual without as with it."[42] Sixty years later, Glendon Schubert wrote: "It seems evident that the whole point of the opinion-writing ritual is to provide acceptable rationales which will protect the justices from personal criticism—and even from personal responsibility—for their decisions."[43]

Still another function of the judicial opinion is its contribution to the continuity of society. John Reid, professor of law at New York University, said in 1963: "The heart of the common law system is the written judicial opinion. It is both the working tool of lawyers and the building block of judges. Until the dawn of the age of legislation and the rise of administrative agencies, it performed most of the tasks Americans ask of their law. It was the measure of continuity and the barometer of change. The judicial opinion serves many men in many ways. It is a test tube for sociologists, a slide rule for jurisprudents, a mine lode for novelists."[44] The continuity theme was also noted by Leflar: "It is a function of law to grow; growth enables law to satisfy a changing society's new needs instead of restricting and strangling them, and a common law judge's opinions must yield this growth. It is also a part of law's function to maintain the society's historic and traditional continuity with its past, and it is the writer of appellate opinions who in our system is principally responsible for maintaining this continuity."[45]

Writing an opinion and publishing an opinion are different matters. While the writing may be needed to compel the
judge to produce a more carefully thought-out, rigorous opinion, publication is not. Stevenson has pointed out that the "act
of writing down a conclusion is an excellent way for a judge to
clarify his own thinking." But "if the only purpose of written
opinions were to help a judge decide a case intelligently, there
would be no need to publish them."[46]

The publication of judicial opinions implies an audience.
Justice James Hopkins of the New York Supreme Court, Appellate Division, begins his article "Notes on Style in Judicial
Opinions" with the assertions that "1. Judges write opinions
for an audience" and "2. The opinion, as an expression of
judgment, is an essay in persuasion. The value of an opinion
is measured by its ability to induce the audience to accept the
judgment."[47] Judge George Rose Smith of the Arkansas Supreme Court, asking the question "For whom are opinions
written—the litigants, the lawyers in the case, the bar as a
whole, the trial court, the public, the newspapers, posterity?"
answers: "No inflexible answer is possible. . . . He [the judge]
realizes, not always consciously, that at times it is vital for the
impact of his words to hit a particular target, which may be
one or more of the groups just mentioned. Much of the art of
being persuasive lies in knowing who it is that must be
convinced."[48]

Judge Smith observes that on occasion the opinion writer
may seriously have to consider fellow judges as the audience:
"Where a decision-making conference invariably precedes
the preparation of the opinion, a judge writes primarily to
persuade his own colleagues. This may happen when he
believes with heart and soul that his position is right, but he
knows that his majority is shaky. Here persuasiveness must
midwife the opinion if it is to come into existence at all."[49]

Asking the question "Why an opinion at all?" Judge Smith
responds: "Above all else to expose the court's decision to
public scrutiny, to nail it up on the wall for all to see. In no
other way can it be known whether the law needs revision,
whether the court is doing its job, whether a particular judge
is competent. A secondary reason, well stated by Traynor, is

that there is no test of a decision equal to the discipline of having to compose an opinion. Without written opinions judicial mistakes would proliferate beyond knowing and beyond knowability."[50]

In his survey, which included forty-six judges, Thomas Marvell reports in *Appellate Courts and Lawyers*:

> The judges were asked who they would like to impress when writing opinions. Half said they do not care—or at least are not conscious of caring—about impressing anybody but themselves. Judges, thus, view themselves as very self-willed and are not likely to abandon their own reasons for those they believe would impress others. This does not mean, however, that they write only for themselves, for they have in mind very definite audiences, which differ from case to case. They wish to give the losing parties the impression that the court has considered their arguments—wishes them "to feel they've had a good run for their money," as one judge said. Likewise, when reversing a lower court judge, they wish to show that his positions had been considered. On the lawmaking side, they try to make opinions and precedents serviceable to the lawyers and judges who must use them.[51]

In addition to keeping in mind the losing parties and other judges, the opinion writer considers, Marvell reports, public reaction, especially press reaction. These are kept "in mind when wording opinions (as opposed to when reaching decisions); judges may leave out language that could lead to attacks, or explain the holding with extra care so that the press does not misinterpret it." Marvell found that "by far the most important audience is the opinion writer's colleagues; he may tailor his opinion to get their votes or simply to please them."[52]

Chief Justice Joseph Weintraub of the New Jersey Supreme Court has recognized the several audiences of the opinion writer: "The aim of writing is communication. A writer has something to say. How he says it depends upon the audience he must reach. The judicial opinion is beamed primarily to the lawyer and the trial judge—fellow technicians. Yet opinions may interest persons untutored in elementary concepts and legal shorthand. The litigant of course is interested, but he can look to counsel for explanation of the assumptions all lawyers understand." According to Justice Weinbraub, the extent of the public interest in the case may determine the language of the opinion: "The general public . . . depends upon the fourth estate for its comprehension. Unless the reporter is trained in the law, and usually [he] is not, he may miss the point or express it in terms which lead his audience to wonder how a high court could reach conclusions so quaint or forbidding. The opinion writer may therefore consider whether the case is of sufficient public interest to warrant discourses framed for lay comprehension."[53]

Professor Walter Gibson asked twenty-five state supreme court and U.S. court of appeals judges attending an appellate judges seminar in 1960, "To whom do you write your opinions?" Some of their answers: "for posterity"; "for the bar"; "for the legislature to show that new legislation is needed to clean up the common law mess in the general area"; "for law students, both today's and tomorrow's"; "for the readers of *The New York Times*, or comparable local newspapers"; "for the writing judge, to satisfy himself that his decision is right"; "for the losing lawyer or for the lawyers and parties in the case"; "sometimes for my brother judges, so that I can get a majority of the court to go along with me in the decision."[54]

For whomever the judges write their opinions, the "opinions are the principal vehicle for judicial communication."[55] Judges do not have so readily available the means of communication to which legislators have access: "Law made by legislators is in a measure explained to the people by the legislative debates and reports that precede its enactment. They are directed as much to the electorate generally as to fellow-legislators. Further explanations may come in later campaigns for reelection. For judge-made law the only comparable explanation is the judicial opinion."[56]

We have moved from the ancient practices of deciding disputes and complaints by relying on chance, divine intervention, and ordeals to judgments from judges who simply decided and gave no reasons (or a minimal number of reasons) for their decisions to judges presenting opinions written with a variety of audiences in mind and the intent to persuade them of the reasonableness of the decisions. The judge's choice of language and style may in the end determine whether the opinion and decision are perceived as persuasive and acceptable. Indeed, the language and style may ultimately determine whether the principles and doctrines stated in an opinion are subsequently cited by other courts.

A judicial system relying on precedents requires by its very nature citation from prior opinions and as such has led to the reiteration of legal concepts, expressed through figurative language, that have become the bases for legal decisions. The language and style of the opinion become an integral part of the process that ends with the announcement of the decision. Of the crucial role of language and style in judicial opinions, of the relationship between substance and style, Leflar has written: "Some judges argue that literary style has little or nothing to do with the quality of opinions, that style is 'dressing' merely, and that the functions of opinions are served wholly by their substantive content. This simply does not make sense. For one thing, every judge has a writing style, whether he knows it or not. . . . Whatever it is, it determines how effectively the substantive content of opinions is conveyed; in fact, it determines whether there really is a usable substantive content, and what that content is."[57]

2

Style and Tropes

In his classic *Law and Literature* Justice Benjamin Cardozo emphasized the inseparability of substance and form, contending that substance and form are "fixed into a unity":

> We are merely wasting our time, so many will inform us, if we bother about form when only substance is important. I suppose this might be true if one could tell where substance ends and form begins. Philosophers have been trying for some thousands of years to draw the distinction between substance and mere appearance in the world of matter. I doubt whether they succeed better when they attempt a like distinction in the world of thought. Form is not something added to substance as a mere protuberant adornment. The two are fused into a unity.[1]

"The argument strongly put," said Cardozo, "is not the same as the argument put feebly any more than the 'tasteless tepid pudding' is the same as the pudding served to us in triumph with all the glory of the lambent flame. The strength is born of form and the feebleness that is born of the lack of form are in truth qualities of the substance. They are tokens of the thing's identity. They make it what it is."[2]

This integral relationship between substance and form, content and style, thought and language, has been observed by judges and novelists, rhetoricians and historians. The essence of style, said Stendhal, "is to add a given thought all the circumstances calculated to produce the entire effect which the thought ought to produce."[3] In his essay "The Language of Statemen," Louis Halle speaks of "winged words" elevating the ideas and arguments in our political discourse. After discussing Lincoln's Gettysburg Address as poetry, Halle declares: "The elements of a high order, enshrined in language by our greatest leaders, are not represented only by such attitudes as those of compassion and magnanimity that we may think of as constituting the content of the Second Inaugural Address. They are also represented by the rhythmic forms into which inspired language falls, by the shapes its phrases take, and by the harmony of its sounds. At the highest level, then, as perhaps at the lowest too, thought and language are inseparable."[4]

Commenting on the literary qualities of the Declaration of Independence, Carl Becker observed that "the primary purpose of the Declaration was to convince a candid world that the colonies had a moral and legal right to separate from Great Britain."[5] To achieve this purpose, Jefferson was very careful in his wording and phrasing. Of Jefferson's style, Becker states: "Having something to say, he says it, with as much art as may be, yet not solely for the art's sake, aiming rather at the ease, the simplicity, the genial urbanity of cultivated conversation. The grace and felicity of his style have a distinctly personal flavor, something Jeffersonian in the implication of the idea, or in the beat and measure of the words."[6]

More recently, Judge Richard Posner has argued that style does matter in judicial discourse and has concluded that "judicial opinions (and briefs . . .) are unavoidably rhetorical [in the sense of persuasive], and in much the same way literature is."[7] In his discussion of the style of judicial opinions, Posner focuses on Justice Holmes's dissent in *Lochner v. New York* and especially "the most famous sentence in Holmes' dissenting opinion": "The Fourteenth Amendment does not enact Mr. Herbert Spencer's Social Statics." Posner recognizes the significance and impact of Holmes's use of figurative language:

> The absurdity of the idea that the Constitution would enact a book with a weird title, written by an Englishman, lends emotional force to the sentence and—my essential point—operates as a substitute for proof. Holmes has

made Spencer's book the metaphor (broadly defined; technically the figure of speech employed is not metaphor but
metonymy) for the philosophy of laissez-faire. And metaphors, because of their concreteness, vividness, and,
when they are good, unexpectedness, are more memorable than their literal equivalents. This is one reason why
the dissent in *Lochner* not only contributed to the shift of
opinion that culminated many years later in the repudiation of "Lorchnerism" but also became the symbol of opposition to the judicial philosophy reflected in the
majority opinion.[8]

Compare Posner's position on the role of style and metaphor in judicial opinions with those of M. I. Sastri, who
contends that there is no place for symbolism and metaphor
in "technical writing": "Another charge that is often leveled
against legal prose is that it lacks embellishments, such as
metaphor. The charge is without merit because symbolism, by
definition, has no place in technical writing."[9]
It is now well established that the tropes, especially the
metaphor, are not simply rhetorical flourishes and ornaments
used to embellish discourse. We have come a long way from
the position of Thomas Hobbes, who declared in *Leviathan*:
"In Demonstration, in Councell, and all rigorous search for
Truth, Judgement does all; except sometimes the understanding have need to be opened by some apt similitude; and then
there is so much use of Fancy. But for Metaphors, they are in
this case utterly excluded. For seeing they openly professe
deceit; to admit them into Councell, or Reasoning were
manifest folly."[10] We have come a long way from John Locke's
denigration of figurative language:

> If we would speak of things as they are, we must allow
> that all the art of rhetoric, besides order and clearness, all
> the artificial and figurative application of words eloquence
> hath invented, are for nothing else but to insinuate wrong
> ideas, move the passions, and thereby mislead the judg-
> ment, and so indeed are perfect cheat; and therefore how-
> ever laudable or allowable oratory may render them in
> harangues and popular addresses, they are certainly, in

all discourses that pretend to inform or instruct, wholly to
be avoided and, where truth and knowledge are concerned, cannot but be thought a great fault either of the
language or person who makes use of them.[11]

Contrast Hobbes's attack on metaphor and Locke's denun-
ciation of the "figurative application of words" with Lakoff
and Johnson's position that "our ordinary conceptual system,
in terms of which we both think and act, is fundamentally
metaphorical in nature" and that "human thought processes
are largely metaphorical."[12]

Kenneth Burke tells us at the outset of his discussion of
the "four master tropes," "I refer to metaphor, metonymy,
synecdoche, and irony. And my primary concern with them
here will be not with their purely figurative usage, but with
their role in the discovery and description of 'the truth.'"[13] Or
as Lakoff and Johnson have put it, "New metaphors, like
conventional metaphors, can have the power to define reality."[14] Through metaphors, whether political, economic, judicial, or everyday expression, we define and redefine our
"realities" and our "truths."

While metaphors can and do "generate new knowledge
and insight," as Max Black declared, and play a role "in the
discovery and description of 'the truth,'" as Burke stated, and
"can have the power to define reality," as Lakoff and Johnson
contended, this master trope must be carefully scrutinized,
especially since it can affect our perceptions of knowledge,
truth, justice, and reality. Philosopher Monroe Beardsley
warned: "The trouble with metaphors is that they have a
strong pull on our fancy. They tend to run away with us. Then
we find that our thinking is directed not by the force of
argument at hand, but at the interest of the image in our
mind."[15] Recognizing the dangers of metaphorical talk,
Beardsley stated: "Because of its very complexity, its multi-
plicity of meaning, a metaphor is hard to control—to keep
from saying things you don't want to say, along with the
things you do want to say." Second, "It is not only meanings
that sometimes tend to run away with us in metaphor. It is
thinking itself. A metaphor can be extremely helpful to

thought, when it suggests an analogy that opens up new lines of inquiry; but if the image is strong and colorful, it can fasten itself upon us and control our thinking too rigidly."[16]

Others who like Beardsley recognize the important role of the tropes in our public and private discourse and are also aware of the difficulties we can get into have given us warnings. As Warren Shibles expressed it, "Without being conscious of metaphor and one's metaphors, one becomes their captive."[17] Or as one of George Eliot's characters in *Middlemarch* says, "'We all of us, grave or light, get our thoughts entangled in metaphors, and act fatally on the strength of them.'"[18] Stephen Ullman, recognizing the importance of style and the figures of speech, also warned us of the pitfalls of "misleading figures of speech": "By unthinkingly and mechanically repeating the same image, we may in the end forget that it is metaphorical; moreover our feelings for the tenor may be affected by those for the vehicle. The figurative element in such expressions as Juggernaut, Moloch, Armageddon, 'cordon sanitaire', 'doodle-bug', Axis, Iron Curtain, and others has, in various ways, undoubtedly coloured the emotional attitude of many people to the objects and ideas in question."[19] Lakoff and Johnson warned: "Political and economic ideologies are framed in metaphorical terms. Like all other metaphors, political and economic metaphors can hide aspects of reality. But in the area of politics and economics, metaphors matter more, because they constrain our lives. A metaphor in a political or economic system, by virtue of what it hides can lead to human degradation."[20]

Agreeing with Lakoff and Johnson that we "live by metaphors," Milner Ball, recognizing the power of metaphoric language, asserts:

Preemptive metaphors may be imposed upon us by those in power or may simply have ascended through an undetected evolutionary cultural process. When such colonization of the mind occurs in conjunction with adherence to the belief that truth is objective and absolute, then the ruling metaphors—more dangerous because unrecognized as metaphor—come to define what is considered to be true, and we have what Richard Rorty refers to as the "freezing over of culture." Without access to alternative metaphors, we act and think on the basis of limited comprehension masquerading as the whole truth.[21]

The use of illness and disease metaphors in political discourse clearly demonstrates just how powerful and dangerous metaphoric expressions can be. Susan Sontag discusses the metaphorical uses of tuberculosis, the plague, syphilis, and especially cancer in political persuasion:

> Now, to liken a political event or situation to an illness is to impute guilt, to prescribe punishment. This is particularly true of the use of cancer as a metaphor. It amounts to saying, first of all, that the event or situation is unqualifiedly and unredeemingably wicked. It enormously ups the ante. Hitler, in his first political tract, an anti-Semitic diatribe written in September 1919, accused the Jews of producing "a racial tuberculosis among nations." Tuberculosis still retained its prestige as the overdetermined, culpable illness of the nineteenth century. . . . But the Nazis quickly modernized their rhetoric, and indeed the imagery of cancer was far more apt for their purposes.[22]

As I have pointed out in *The Language of Oppression*, the Nazis relied heavily on the disease and illness metaphors in their attacks on the Jews, Communists, and other "enemies." The Nazis spoke of the "Jewish bacillus," "the Bolshevist poison," "the Jewish plague," "the Jewish parasites," and the "Jewish cancer."[23] As to the cancer metaphor, Sontag points out that "no specific political view seems to have a monopoly on this metaphor. Trotsky called Stalinism the cancer of Marxism; in China . . . the Gang of Four have become, among other things, 'the cancer of China.' John Dean explained Watergate to Nixon: 'We have a cancer within—close to the Presidency—that's growing.' The standard metaphor of Arab polemics—heard by Israelis on the radio every day for the last twenty years—is that Israel is 'a cancer in the heart of the Arab world' or 'the cancer of the Middle East.'"[24]

The disease, illness, and microorganism metaphors were exploited by Ronald Reagan in his attacks on communism and the Soviet Union. Conferring in 1984 with nineteen conservative and religious leaders, Reagan vowed to fight the "communist cancer."[25] During a 1982 conference with some eastern Caribbean leaders, Reagan spoke of the "virus" Marxism,[26] and in 1983 he labeled the Soviet Union an "evil empire," telling the National Association of Evangelicals in Orlando, Florida, regarding communism that Christians are "enjoined by Scripture and the Lord Jesus to oppose it with all our might."[27] The insidiousness of the "cancer," "virus," and "bacillus" metaphors lies in the fact that they all invite extermination. As Lowenthal and Guterman have explained, "The micro-organism seems to combine all the various enemy qualities in the highest degree. It is ubiquitous, close, deadly, insidious, it invites the idea of extermination, and, most important, it is invisible to the naked eye — the agitator expert is required to detect its presence."[28]

In his discussion of the Nazis' redefinition of the Jews as "vermin," "bacilli," and "lice," Thomas Friedman brings to our attention the devastating implications of this metaphorization:

> Then, in an act that might be considered almost poetic were it not so horrifying and grotesque, the Nazi administrative apparatus captured the spirit of the metaphor its propagandists had devised. It contacted the chemical industries of the *Reich*, specifically the firms that specialized in "combatting vermin." Simply, it requested that these manufacturers of insecticides produce another delousing agent, one a bit stronger than the product used for household ticks and flies, but one that would be used for essentially the same purpose. The companies complied. Thus was *Zyklon B* created. The gas, used in a milder form for occasionally fumigating the disease-ridden barracks where other victims were penned, killed millions of men, women, and children. Obscenely clinging to the metaphor they had accepted, the Nazis herded their Jewish victims into gas chambers of death that were disguised as "showers" and "disinfectant centers." What the bureaucrats ac-

complished, the propagandists had made psychologically possible.[29]

What becomes clear is that while some metaphors can "generate new knowledge and insights" and help us in our search for truth and understanding, others can lead to distortion and inhumanity, and can frustrate us in our endeavors to define reality accurately and humanely. When Justice Fortas introduced into judicial argument the metonymic "It can hardly be argued that either students or teachers shed their constitutional right to freedom of speech or expression at the schoolhouse gate,"[30] he was speaking no less figuratively than George Bush when he denounced Saddam Hussein as Hitler. When Justice Jackson argued that the compulsory flag salute was unconstitutional by declaring that "if there is any fixed star in our constitutional constellation, it is that no official, high or petty, can prescribe what shall be orthodox in politics, nationalism, religion, or other matters of opinion or force citizens to confess by word or act their faith therein,"[31] he spoke no less figuratively than the Nazis when they metaphorically dehumanized Jews. For good or ill, the metaphor is a powerful means of communication and persuasion. When people in power effectively impose denigrating and dehumanizing metaphors on others, the fault is not in the metaphor but in ourselves.

Clearly, we are attracted to tropes. We tend to remember them; we find them in phrases and sentences that would soon be forgotten had the tropes not been used. Most of the phrases and sentences we remember from speeches, advertisements, literature, and court opinions include the figurative schemes and tropes:

> Man does not live by bread alone.
> Religion is the opium of the people.
> A page of history is worth a volume of logic.
> Law is an ass, an idiot.
> Speak softly and carry a big stick.
> Ye cannot serve God and Mammon.
> The law knows no heresy.

Ich bin ein Berliner.
The only thing we have to fear is fear itself.
You can take Salem out of the country, but you can't
     take the country out of Salem.
A specter is haunting Europe—the specter of
     communism.
The Lord is my shepherd.
Man is born free, and is everywhere in chains.
Now is the winter of our discontent.

Less memorable but still figurative are the numerous tropes we use in everyday conversation. Many are dead metaphors and have become clichés. Some students "ace" their exams, while others just "bomb"; some students are "cool," and others are "jocks"; some students "brownnose," and some professors are "hard-nosed"; others are "long-winded"; "once in a blue moon" some of us are "blue"; some people are "green with envy," and the naïve are just "green"; cowards are "yellow"; crooks are sometimes caught "red-handed"; some debaters get caught red-handed using a "red herring."

In our judicial system the judge may be "the court" or "the bench," the tropological language freeing the human being sitting in judgment from prejudice, emotion, and bias. Judges and attorneys speak of "the cutting edge of the law," "grandfather clauses," "fishing expeditions," "colorable claims," and "unclean hands." Thomas Ross begins his 1989 article "Metaphor and Paradox," "We live in a magical world of law where liens float, corporations reside, minds hold meetings, and promises run with the land. The constitutional landscape is dotted with streams, walls, and poisonous trees. And these wonderful things are cradled in the seamless web of law."[32] As Ross indicates, "Our metaphors are truly magical in their mystery and power. We do not simply choose them. We do not fully understand how we get meaning from them. We are neither their master nor their servant. Their power is the power to shatter and reconstruct our realities."[33]

Why do we use metaphors at all? Why do we not restrict ourselves to literal language? What functions do tropes perform in explanatory and persuasive discourse? Andrew Ortony presents three hypotheses:

One hypothesis is that a metaphor provides a compact way of representing the subset of cognitive and perceptual features that are salient to it. A metaphor allows "chunks" of information to be converted or transferred from the vehicle to the topic. The second is the "inexpressibility" hypothesis, which states that a metaphor enables us to talk about experiences which cannot be literally described. The third is the hypothesis that, perhaps through imagery, metaphor provides a vivid and, therefore, memorable and emotion-arousing representation of perceived experience. These functions obviously implicate cognitive processes, but they are intended to explain what motivates the use of metaphors in communication.[34]

Max Black asked, "Why stretch and twist, press and expand, concepts in this way? Why try to see A as metaphorically B, when it literally is not B?" Black answered, "Well, because we *can* do so, conceptual boundaries not being rigid, but elastic and permeable; and because we often need to do so, the available literal resources of the language being insufficient to express our sense of the rich correspondences, interrelations, and analogies of domains conventionally separated; and because metaphorical thought and utterance sometimes embody insight expressible in no other fashion."[35]

Beardsley tells us that there are two points to notice about metaphors: "First, metaphors are compact—they are able to condense a number of statements into one, and present them in a single bundle. That is what makes them interesting and illuminating." Second, "besides the great potential richness of meaning in metaphor there is also its creativity. Metaphors give us new meanings, enlarge the capacity of our language to express subtle differences and name qualities of the world for which we may hitherto have no words. Hence, a well-chosen metaphor is likely to catch on, and stay with us, becoming part of the language, since it shows us how to say something we recognize to be worth saying."[36] However, as Beardsley points out, eventually the once creative metaphor ends as a cliché, a dead metaphor that "is no metaphor at all."

Discussing the functions of metaphors, Pollio, Barlow, Fine, and Pollio state: "One of the first and probably most obvious functions of figurative language is that it is often used to express an idea or feeling for which there is no clear or unique expression already available in the language. In this sense, metaphor provides the possibility for talking about things, events or ideas we have never before talked about nor perhaps even thought of." Regarding the power of metaphor, they write: "An historical analysis of metaphoric usage might help to highlight the particular interests and ideas of a particular historical period or epoch. Thus, an age often can be defined in terms of its salient metaphors and such metaphors not only influence the subject areas to which they are applied but may also help shape the problems and solutions of that age. 'As a form of comparative analysis the, metaphors can structure inquiry, establish relevance and provide an interpretive system.'"[37]

This impact that metaphors can have on defining an age and the problems and solutions of an age has been recognized by various authors. Roland Bartel discusses the implications of the American "melting pot of the world," along with Winston Churchill's "iron curtain," presented in his speech at Fulton, Missouri, on March 5, 1946, and the "domino theory" that appeared in the Vietnam War era with its "hawks" and "doves."[38] Judith Best, applying the metaphorical technique to teaching, asks: "Who ever learned of Socrates' metaphor of the cave and forgotten it? Who has ever read Burke and forgotten 'the flies of a summer'? Who has read Machiavelli and forgotten the lion and the fox? Who could forget Nietzsche's criticism of the liberals when it is presented as God is dead and the liberals' picnic on God's grave? A metaphor allows us to see the universal in the particular. It involves us." In answer to her question "Why do students believe that political theory must be an arcane and difficult subject?" Best offers a generalization: "Most minds find abstract reasoning alien. Most minds are at least initially hostile to abstraction, and have a deep-rooted preference for the concrete and particular."[39]

Since so much of the law revolves around abstractions and recondite concepts, David Rumelhart's observations on figurative language are especially relevant: "Nearly always, when we talk about abstract concepts, we choose language drawn from one or another concrete domain. A good example of this is our talk about the mind. Here we use a spatial model to talk about the things that are clearly nonspatial in character. We have things 'in' our minds, 'on' our minds, 'in the back corners of' our minds. . . . It is quite possible that our primary method of understanding nonsensory concepts is through analogy with concrete experiential situations."[40]

Murray Edelman argued that "language does not mirror an objective 'reality,' but rather creates it by organizing meaningful perceptions abstracted from a complex, bewildering world." He writes that "metaphor pervades language, for the unknown, the new, the unclear, and the remote are apprehended by one's perceptions of identities with the familiar."[41]

I. A. Richards agreed that the greater the abstraction, the greater the reliance on metaphor. After contending that "we cannot get through three sentences of ordinary fluid discourse without" metaphor, Richards stated:

> Even in the rigid language of the settled sciences we do not eliminate or prevent it without great difficulty. In the semi-technicalised subjects, in aesthetics, politics, sociology, ethics, psychology, theory of language and so on, our constant chief difficulty is to discover how we are using it and how our supposedly fixed words are shifting their senses. In philosophy, above all, we can take no step safely without unrelaxing awareness of the metaphors we, and our audience, may be employing; and though we may pretend to eschew them we can attempt to do so only by detecting them. And this is the more true, the more severe and abstract the philosophy is. As it grows more abstract we think increasingly by means of metaphors that we profess *not* to be relying on. The metaphors we are avoiding steer our thought as much as those we accept.[42]

What Richards said about metaphors in philosophy applies equally to judicial opinions whence we get the reasons for guilt or innocence, freedom or imprisonment, life or death. Paraphrasing Richards, in law especially we can take no step safely without an unrelaxing awareness of the metaphors employed by the judiciary. Nonliteral language is often needed to explain the abstraction, in philosophy or law, that cannot be conveyed as effectively and persuasively through literal language. Through incorporation of tropes into legal opinions, what is abstruse and obscure becomes concrete and comprehensible. Through personification, what is inanimate takes on human qualities and becomes perceivable. Through metonymy, we may create new perspectives by substituting one word or phrase for another because of a preexisting relationship.

In his discussion of the expository and emotive functions of legal fictions, Lon Fuller acknowledges the persuasive influence of the metaphor on the speaker and the audience. Following his observations about the expository fictions, he writes:

> But a metaphor may be used for the sake of its emotive power, as when the suggestion of government operation of the liquor industry is described as a proposal "to put a beer towel over Uncle Sam's arm." And so it is with the legal fictions designed to dissuade from a course of conduct; the emotive legal fiction seems to be intended rather to induce conviction that a given legal result is just and proper. We may therefore call emotive fictions "persuasive fictions," bearing always in mind that the author of the fiction may be as much influenced by its persuasive power as his audience.[43]

When the Supreme Court decided in *Johnson v. Texas* (1989) that Johnson's public burning of the American flag was constitutionally protected, Chief Justice Rehnquist dissented, stating metonymically at the outset of his opinion: "In holding this Texas statute unconstitutional, the Court ignores Justice Holmes' familiar aphorism that 'a page of history is worth a volume of logic.'"[44] Rehnquist's adherence to the aphoristic metonymy is reflected in his contention that "for more than 200 years, the American flag has occupied a unique position as the symbol of our Nation, a uniqueness that justifies a governmental prohibition against flag burning in the way respondent Johnson did here." Having committed himself to the "page of history," Rehnquist established the direction of his reasoning, leading to the conclusion: "I would uphold the Texas statute as applied in this case."[45] When three justices (Justices White and O'Connor joined in Rehnquist's dissent) treat the metonymy as a principle, attention must be paid to the trope. One is taken back to the Emerson aphorism "Churches have been built, not upon principles, but upon tropes" cited by Justice Cardozo, who went on to say that the aphorism "is as true in the field of politics as it is in the field of religion."[46] Rehnquist's reliance on Holmes's metonymy is but one more demonstration that Emerson's aphorism could be rewritten: The law has been built not upon principles but upon tropes, or more precisely, tropological principles.

3

The Metaphoric "Marketplace of Ideas"

The metaphoric "marketplace of ideas" has been one of the most often cited and influential tropes in judicial decision making. It has been invoked by judges defending the fairness doctrine and attacking library censorship, by judges defending the freedom of association and attacking orthodoxy in the classroom. In 1965, Justice Brennan introduced to the parlance of the judiciary the metaphoric marketplace of ideas concurring in *Lamont v. Postmaster General* in which the Supreme Court declared unconstitutional a postal regulation that required the postmaster general to detain unsealed foreign mailings of "communist political propaganda" and not to deliver the mailings until receipt of a postcard from the addressee indicating desire to receive the materials. Brennan, in his defense of the right to receive, declared: "The dissemination of ideas can accomplish nothing if otherwise willing addressees are not free to receive and consider them. It would be a barren marketplace of ideas that had only sellers and no buyers."[1]

Two years later, in 1967, Justice Brennan, delivering the opinion of the Court in *Keyishian v. Board of Regents*, arguing that the New York teachers loyalty oath had no place in our educational system, asserted, "The classroom is peculiarly the 'marketplace of ideas.'"[2]

In 1969, Justice White, in *Red Lion Broadcasting Co. v. F.C.C.*, upholding the constitutionality of the fairness doctrine, declared, "It is the purpose of the First Amendment to preserve an uninhibited marketplace of ideas in which truth will ultimately prevail, rather than to countenance monopolization of that market, whether it be by the Government itself or a private licensee."[3]

When in 1972 the Supreme Court decided that the Students for a Democratic Society (SDS) could not be denied official recognition as a campus organization by the president of Central Connecticut College, Justice Powell said: "The college classroom with its surrounding environs is peculiarly the 'marketplace of ideas,' and we break no new constitutional ground in reaffirming this Nation's dedication to safeguarding academic freedom."[4]

The library has also been designated a marketplace of ideas. In 1972, when a U.S. district court in Massachusetts decided that the Chelsea, Massachusetts, School Committee could not ban from the school library an anthology of writings by adolescents containing an "offensive" poem, Judge Tauro concluded that "the library is 'a mighty resource in the marketplace of ideas.'"[5] In 1982, when a U.S. district court in Maine decided against the Baileyville School Committee, which removed the book *365 Days* from the high school library, Judge Cyr argued: "Public schools are major marketplaces of ideas, and the first amendment rights must be accorded all 'persons' in the market for ideas, including secondary school students . . . seeking redress of state action banning a book from the 'warehouse of ideas.'"[6]

When the Supreme Court unanimously decided for *Hustler* magazine and against Jerry Falwell, who claimed invasion of privacy, libel, and intentional infliction of emotional distress as a result of a "parody" portraying him in a drunken rendezvous with his mother in an outhouse, Chief Justice Rehnquist invoked the "market" metaphor several times. To support his position that "at the heart of the First Amendment is the recognition of the fundamental importance of the free flow of ideas and opinions on matters of public interest and concern," Rehnquist cited Holmes's 1919 *Abrams* dissenting opinion in which Holmes had stated: "The ultimate good desired is better reached by free trade in ideas — that the best test of truth is the power of the thought to get itself accepted in the competition of the market." In pointing out that a statement made "with knowledge that it was false or with reckless disregard of whether it was false or not" may be held defamatory, Rehnquist went on to say: "False statements of fact are particularly valueless; they interfere with the truth-seeking function of the marketplace of ideas, and they cause damage to an individual's reputation that cannot easily be repaired by counterspeech, however persuasive or effective." But then, arguing that "offensiveness" was not enough to prohibit speech, Rehnquist quoted from *F.C.C. v. Pacifica* "It is a central tenet of the First Amendment that the government must remain neutral in the marketplace of ideas."[7]

Again in 1989, the marketplace of ideas was brought to bear when the Supreme Court decided to give constitutional protection to flag burner Gregory Johnson. Justice Brennan wrote: "The First Amendment does not guarantee that other concepts virtually sacred to our Nation as a whole—such as the principle that discrimination on the basis of race is odious and destructive—will go unquestioned in the marketplace of ideas." This metaphoric phrasing was followed with still another: "We decline, therefore, to create for the flag an exception to the joust of principles protected by the First Amendment."[8]

After Johnson was given First Amendment protection, Congress passed the Flag Protection Act of 1989, followed by more flag burnings. Again the Supreme Court held that the prosecution of the flag burners was inconsistent with the First Amendment. Justice Stevens (with whom Justices Rehnquist, White, and O'Connor joined) declared in a dissenting opinion: "What makes this case particularly difficult for me is what I regard as the damage to the symbol that has already occurred as a result of this Court's decision to place its stamp of approval on the act of flag burning. A formerly dramatic expression of protest is now rather commonplace. In today's marketplace of ideas, the public burning of a Vietnam draft card is probably less provocative than lighting a cigarette. Tomorrow flag burning may produce a similar reaction."[9]

While the marketplace of ideas has become one of the most enduring metaphors in the law, there have been some questions about the continued relevance, validity, and applicability of the metaphor as applied in contemporary First

Amendment opinions. Writing in the *Harvard Law Review*, Jerome Barron stated in 1967: "Our constitutional theory is in the grip of a romantic conception of free expression, a belief that the 'marketplace of ideas' is freely accessible. But if ever there were a self-operating marketplace of ideas, it has long ceased to exist."[10]

When Justice Holmes introduced the competitive laissez-faire market into First Amendment legal discourse in 1919, he did not use the phrase "marketplace of ideas"; he spoke of the "free trade in ideas" and "the competition of the market."[11] And while this is the judicial origin of the metaphoric "market," some legal scholars have concluded that John Milton in his *Areopagitica* (1644) and John Stuart Mill in *On Liberty* (1859) were the forerunners of the marketplace theory. For example, in 1978, C. Edwin Baker wrote "The classic marketplace of ideas model argues that truth (or the best perspectives or solutions) can be discovered through robust debate, free from governmental interference. Defending this theory in *On Liberty*, John Stuart Mill argued that three situations are possible."[12] In 1989, Baker, in *Human Liberty and Freedom of Speech*, identified the marketplace of ideas with Milton and Mill; at the outset of his chapter entitled "The Classic Marketplace of Ideas Theory," Baker quoted from Milton's *Areopagitica*: "And though all the winds of doctrine were let loose to play upon the earth, so Truth be in the field, we do injuriously, by licensing and prohibiting to misdoubt her strength. Let her and Falsehood grapple: who ever knew Truth put to the worst [*sic*], in a free and open encounter."

Baker then began his chapter: "John Milton's imagery received possibly its best elaboration by John Stuart Mill. . . . According to this classic theory, truth is discovered through its competition with falsehood."[13] In a footnote Baker stated: "I refer to Mill to exemplify the marketplace theory because he provides its best formulation."[14] A careful reading of the Milton quote should give the reader an indication that he is not talking about the economics or competition of the market; the quote refers to "Truth be in the field," to misdoubting "her strength," letting "her and falsehood grapple," and finally Truth winning in a "free and open encounter." This and almost all the other images in Milton's *Areopagitica* convey an armed battle, not buying and selling in the marketplace.

Other legal scholars have inadvertently cited Milton and Mill as the sources for the theoretical marketplace of ideas. In 1984, Stanley Ingber wrote, "Scholars and jurists frequently have used the image of a 'marketplace of ideas' to explain and justify the first amendment freedoms of speech and press. Although this classic image of competing ideas and robust debate dates back to English philosophers John Milton and John Stuart Mill, Justice Holmes first introduced the concept into American jurisprudence in his 1919 dissent in *Abrams v. United States.*"[15]

In 1987, David Kretzmer identified the marketplace metaphor with John Stuart Mill: "The best known, and probably most widely quoted, argument in favor of freedom of expression is John Stuart Mill's truth argument. . . . A second Millian premise is that a wide market of ideas does indeed contribute to the gain of knowledge. This premise requires empirical proof. While it is theoretically conceivable that in the long run the truth will indeed always prevail, there is no lack of historical evidence to show that in the short run false views are often the most saleable goods in the market of ideas."[16] Marc Franklin and Robert Trager put it even more directly: "The marketplace of ideas, first enunciated by Milton and later developed by Mill, was recognized in American law by Justice Oliver Wendell Holmes."[17]

Chief Justice Rehnquist has also identified the "marketplace" metaphor with Mill's *On Liberty* and Milton's *Areopagitica*. In a 1980 dissenting opinion, Rehnquist wrote: "The view apparently derives from the Court's frequent reference to the 'marketplace of ideas,' which was deemed analogous to the commercial market in which a laissez-faire policy would lead to optimum economic decisionmaking under the guidance of the 'invisible hand.' See, e.g., Adam Smith. Wealth of Nations (1776). This notion was expressed by Mr. Justice Holmes in his dissenting opinion in *Abrams v. United States* . . . wherein he stated that 'the best test of truth is the power of the thought to get itself accepted in the competition of the market. . . .' See also, e.g., *Consolidated Edison v. Public Ser-*

vice Comm'n . . .; J. Mill, *On Liberty* (1858) [*sic*]; J. Milton, *Areopagitica, A Speech for the Liberty of Unlicensed Printing* (1644)."[18]

Not only does Rehnquist erroneously identify the metaphoric marketplace of ideas with Milton and Mill; the Chief Justice also mistakenly attributes Jefferson's first inaugural address as a source for the marketplace metaphor: "If the complaint of those who feel the Court's opinion does not go far enough is that the 'only test of truth is its ability to get itself accepted in the marketplace of ideas'—the test advocated by Thomas Jefferson in his first inaugural address, and by Mr. Justice Holmes in *Abrams v. United States . . .*—there is no reason whatsoever to limit the protection accorded commercial speech to 'truthful, non-misleading, noncoercive' speech."[19]

The assertions of the Chief Justice and legal scholars notwithstanding, John Milton, John Stuart Mill, and Thomas Jefferson, it must be emphasized, never did use or rely on the marketplace metaphor in the works cited above. While both Milton and Mill had Truth and Falsehood competing, more accurately battling, it was not in the marketplace. In his *Areopagitica* Milton argues against the British licensing act that required publications to receive the imprimatur of the government censor before publication, and all through his speech Milton relies on tropes, creating images of combat, physical encounters, and war, not buying and selling. Early in the "speech," Milton asserts: "And yet, on the other hand, unless wariness be used, as good almost kill a man as kill a good book; who kills a man kills a reasonable creature, God's image; but he who destroys a good book, kills reason itself."[20] This is followed a page later with "We should be wary therefore what persecution we raise against the living labors of public men, how we spill the seasoned life of man, preserved and stored up in books; since we see a kind of homicide may be thus committed, sometimes a martyrdom; and if it extend to the whole impression, a kind of massacre, whereof the execution ends not in the slaying of an elemental life, but strikes at that ethereal and fifth essence, the breath of reason itself; slays an immortality rather than a life."[21]

One of the most famous lines from the *Areopagitica* has Truth and Falsehood involved in physical combat, not in some laissez-faire commercial transaction in the marketplace: "And though all the winds of doctrine were let loose to play upon the earth, so Truth be in the field, we do injuriously by licensing and prohibiting to misdoubt her strength. Let her and Falsehood grapple; who ever knew Truth put to the worse in a free and open encounter? Her confuting is the best and surest suppressing."[22] A few lines later, Milton further develops the combat metaphor to support his argument:

> When a man hath been laboring the hardest labor in the
> deep mines of knowledge, hath furnished out his findings
> in all their equipage, drawn forth his reasons as if it were
> a battle ranged, scattered and defeated all objections in
> his way, calls out his adversary into the plain, offers him
> the advantage of wind and sun, if he please, only that he
> may try the matter by dint of argument; for his opponents
> then to skulk, to lay ambushments, to keep a narrow
> bridge of licensing where the challenger should pass,
> though it be valor enough in soldiership, is but weakness
> and cowardice in the wars of Truth.[23]

In fact, Milton appears to reject the "marketplace" metaphor when he writes: "Truth and understanding are not such wares as to be monopolised and traded in by tickets, and statutes, and standards. We must not think to make a staple commodity of all the knowledge in the land, to mark and license it like our broadcloth and our woolpacks."[24]

Clearly, Milton's "combat" metaphors convey a different process than Holmes's "free trade in ideas" and "competition of the market." As David Cole has correctly observed, his "wrestling match" aside, "Holmes' test recalls and misreads Milton's vision of the struggle between truth and falsehood; Milton's wrestling match becomes Holmes' trading market. The directness of the encounter is lost in the translation; popular acceptance replaces raw strength as the test for truth."[25]

While Mill does not rely as heavily on the more violent combat-war-battle tropes as Milton, neither does the author of

On Liberty suggest a marketplace in his classic chapter "On the Liberty of Thought and Discussion." Mill's language tends towards the battle—adversaries tropes, not trading-buying-selling. Mill writes: "Let the opinions impugned be the belief in a God and in a future state, or any of the commonly received doctrines of morality. To fight the battle on such ground, gives a great advantage to an unfair antagonist."[26] More graphically: "It is a piece of idle sentimentality that truth, merely as truth, has an inherent power denied to error, or prevailing against the dungeon and the stake."[27] Further, "Heretical opinions, on the other hand, are generally some of these suppressed and neglected truths, bursting the bonds which kept them down, and either seeking reconciliation with the truth contained in the common opinion, or fronting it as enemies."[28] Finally, "Truth, in the great practical concerns of life, is so much a question of the reconciling and combing of opposites, that very few have minds sufficiently capacious and impartial to make the adjustment with an approach to correctness, and it has to be made by the rough process of a struggle between combatants fighting under hostile banners."[29]

As for Rehnquist's claim that the "marketplace of ideas" was "the test advocated by Thomas Jefferson in his first inaugrual address," one looks in vain for any allusion to the marketplace in the first inaugural address, delivered in 1801. In fact, Jefferson's tropes convey physical encounters, not marketplace trading. "During the contest of opinion through which we have passed," said Jefferson, "the animation of discussions and of exertions has sometimes worn an aspect which might impose on strangers unused to think freely and to speak and to write what they think; but this being now decided by the voice of the nation, announced according to the rules of the Constitution, all will of course arrange themselves under the will of the law, and unite in common efforts for the common good." Jefferson spoke of "that religious intolerance under which mankind so long bled and suffered" and continued: "During the throes and convulsions of the ancient world, during the agonizing spasms of infuriated man, seeking through blood and slaughter his long-lost liberty, it is not wonderful that the agitation of the billows should reach even this distant and peaceful shore." And perhaps the most famous line from Jefferson's inaugural: "If there be any among us who would wish to dissolve this Union or to change its republican form, let them stand undisturbed as monuments of the safety with which error of opinion may be tolerated where reason is left free to combat it."[30]

Four years earlier, Jefferson had used similar combative language in his famous "Preamble to the Virginia Act for Establishing Religious Freedom" in which he rejected the bad-tendency test: "That it is time enough for the rightful purposes of government for its officers to interfere when principles break out into overt acts against peace and good order; and finally, that truth is great and will prevail if left to herself; that she is the proper and sufficient antagonist to error, and has nothing to fear from the conflict unless by human interposition disarmed of her natural weapons free argument and debate; errors ceasing to be dangerous when it is permitted freely to contradict them."[31]

As one reads the tropes incorporated into the arguments presented by Milton, Mill, and Jefferson in these classic works, it becomes evident that truth was not to be found through "a free trade in ideas" or in the marketplace. The tropology of Milton, Mill, and Jefferson involved combat, war, weapons, battles—all of which create different "realities" than Holmes's "free trade in ideas" and "competition of the market." David Cole has gone further, distinguishing between Holmes's metaphors and the metaphoric "marketplace of ideas," which did not arrive on the judicial decision-making scene until 1965 when Justice Brennan stated in his *Lamont* concurring opinion: "It would be a barren marketplace of ideas that had only sellers and no buyers."[32]

Cole sees the following distinctions between the Holmes and Brennan metaphors: "Brennan localized the metaphor; he gave the market a sense of place. Brought down from the Holmesian skies, the marketplace of ideas grounds 'free trade' in a specific locale and context. . . . The marketplace of ideas, in Brennan's figuration, conjures up the Greek 'agora,' the central meeting place for exchange. These ancient Greek marketplaces were much more than models of market efficiency. Localed at the center of town, they functioned as public assemblies as well as markets; all hawkers, criers, buyers, and sellers were admitted. The marketplace of ideas connotes diversity and pluralism."[33]

While the metaphoric marketplace of ideas has been widely invoked by the courts, there is a serious question of its validity, its applicability as a principle upon which to base First Amendment decisions. In his 1984 article "The Marketplace of Ideas: A Legitimizing Myth" in which he discusses the need to reevaluate the assumptions upon which the marketplace metaphor is based, Stanley Ingber explains: "In our complex society, affected by both sophisticated communication technology and unequal allocations of resources and skills, the marketplace's inevitable bias supports entrenched power structures or ideologies. . . . This critique of the marketplace of ideas has led to the unsurprising conclusion that protection of expression alone does not guarantee an environment where new ideas, perceptions, and values can develop. A diversity of perspectives first requires a corresponding diversity of social experiences and opportunities. Consequently, in spite of the rhetoric surrounding it, freedom of speech by itself cannot ensure a diverse and interactive marketplace of ideas."[34]

D. Edwin Baker, while noting that "the Supreme Court steadfastly relies upon a marketplace of ideas theory in determining what speech is protected," recognizes that "the assumptions on which the classic marketplace of ideas theory rests are almost universally rejected today. Because of this failure of assumptions, the hope that the marketplace leads to truth, to even the best or most desirable decision, becomes implausible."[35] Baker argues that "the adequacy of the marketplace of ideas must be reconsidered if one rejects the assumption of objective truth and assumes that people's perspectives and understanding are chosen or created rather than 'discovered.'" Further, "The classic [marketplace] model also requires that people be able to use their rational capacities to eliminate distortion caused by the form and frequency of message presentation and to find the core of relevant information or argument. This assumption cannot be accepted."[36] Having discussed these and other assumptions, Baker says: "Given that the assumptions underlying the classic marketplace of ideas theory are so clearly incorrect, one wonders why the theory has had such popularity and so many advocates."[37]

Even Chief Justice Warren Burger seemed to recognize the inapplicability of the marketplace metaphor to the realities of contemporary society. Delivering the opinion of the Court in *Miami Herald Publishing Co. v. Tornillo* (1974), Burger acknowledged the arguments that monopolies had taken over where once there was a free market: "A true marketplace of ideas existed [at the time the First Amendment was enacted in 1791] in which there was relatively easy access to the channels of communication. . . . The obvious solution, which was available to dissidents at an earlier time when entry into publishing was relatively inexpensive, today would be to have additional newspapers. But the same economic factors which have caused the disappearance of vast numbers of metropolitan newspapers, have made entry into the marketplace of ideas served by the print almost impossible. . . . The First Amendment interest of the public in being informed is said to be in peril because the 'marketplace of ideas' is today a monopoly controlled by the owners of the market."[38]

While Burger acknowledged the difficulty of getting access to the market, he also stated: "However much validity may be found in these arguments, at each point the implementation of a remedy such as an enforceable right of access necessarily calls for some mechanism, either governmental or consensual."[39] A unanimous Court held that the *Miami Herald* could not be required to print a reply of a political candidate who had been attacked in the newspaper. In a world admittedly made up of monopolies and conglomerates, we still cling to the nostalgic metaphoric "marketplace of ideas."

When in 1919 Justice Holmes spoke of the "free trade in ideas" and the test of truth as "the power of the thought to get itself accepted in the competition of the market," he was not alluding to the conglomerate supermarkets of today. The market in Holmes's world carried with it connotations of buyers and sellers intermingling at a place set aside in a town for small farmers and tradespeople to bargain, trade, buy, and sell. The *market*, according to the first definition in *The Oxford English Dictionary*, is "the meeting or congregating together of people for the purchase and sale of provisions or livestock, publicly exposed, at a fixed time and place; the occasion, or time during which such goods are exposed for sale; also, the company of people at such a meeting."[40] The *market*, *Webster's Third New International Dictionary* tells us, is "a meeting together of people at a stated time and place for the purpose of traffic (as in cattle, provisions, or wares) by private purchase and sale and usually not by auction." Then *marketplace* is defined as first, "an open square or place in a town where markets or public sales are held," and second, "a sphere in which intangible values (as ideas) compete for acceptance."[41] Literally, we have never had a marketplace where ideas were bought and sold. As for the commercial marketplace where people meet in the open squares to traffic in "cattle, provisions, or wares," where there is an intermingling of people, a place of bargaining, trading, buying and selling—that marketplace in the town square has all but disappeared from the American scene.

I remember going as a youth to "free markets" where farmers and tradespeople set up their stalls and tables to sell their produce and wares. There was actually a "meeting or congregating together of people" who talked and bargained with one another. The consumer in this market dealt directly with the farmer and seller. Today we neither see the farmer, who is probably a conglomerate, nor converse with the owner of the supermarket. We silently push the grocery cart through the aisles, filling it with prepackaged goods priced by people we will never meet. In the free marketplace in the square we talked, argued about the value of the goods and produce, the quality of the wares. Today one does not bargain or negotiate with the supermarket personnel; the goods are displayed and priced, and there are no sounds of the old marketplace. The tumult and talk of the old market have been replaced by carefully selected soothing music, subliminal messages, and commercial announcements coming through the supermarket public address system.

In 1970, when the California Supreme Court decided in *In re Kay* to give constitutional protection to several persons who had heckled then Congressman Tunney during a speech at a July Fourth celebration, the court spoke of the "happy cacophany of democracy": "Political campaigns, athletic events, public meetings and a host of other activities produce loud, confused or senseless shouting not in accord with fact, truth or right procedure to say nothing of not in accord with propriety, modesty, good taste or good manners. The happy cacophany of democracy would be stilled if all 'improper noises' in the normal meaning of the terms were suppressed."[42] The loud, confused, and sometimes senseless shouting, the "happy cacophany" in the market in the square, has been stilled and is nonexistent in the supermarket. The market of today does not have the elements that go into making a marketplace as it existed earlier in the twentieth century when Holmes spoke of the "competition of the market."

Another difficulty with the marketplace metaphor is that it leads us to perceive ideas as commodities to be bargained for, things to be bought and sold to those who will pay the highest price. But it is questionable that speech, the expression of ideas, should be metaphorized into a consumer item. After the Supreme Court decided against Murray Kaplan in *Kaplan v. California*, one of the five obscenity decisions of June 21, 1973, Kaplan petitioned for a rehearing, asserting in his petition that he was "perplexed by the Court's wide-ranging analogies between governmental suppression of books and films and regulations of securities, trading stamps, natural resources, bear-baiting, and the like. Petitioner never argued, nor does he believe, that booksellers should be any more immune from consumer protection legislation than should any other businessman. . . . But this Court has said time and again . . . that Government cannot treat alledgedly obscene books and films the same way it can treat trading stamps or heroin."[43]

The American Library Association (ALA) in its *amicus curiae* brief also questioned the Court's comparison of regulation of books and ideas to the regulation of narcotics and garbage. "To equate the reading of books," said the ALA, "with the disposal of garbage and sewage [as Chief Justice Burger had done] . . . is to demean the great meaning of the First Amendment. A long and undeviating line of cases establishes that allegedly obscene books cannot be treated like gambling paraphernalia or narcotics, nor, it is respectfully submitted, may they be equated with garbage and sewage." Quoting from Justice Frankfurter's 1959 concurring opinion in *Smith v. California,* the ALA brief continued: "There is an important difference in the scope of power of a state to regulate what feeds the belly and what feeds the brain. . . . The balance that is struck between [the general principle that awareness of what one is doing is a prerequisite for the infliction of punishment] and the overriding public menace inherent in the trafficking in noxious food and drugs cannot be carried over to balancing the vital role of free speech as against society's interest in dealing with pornography."[44]

Fourteen years earlier, in a case dealing with marketing and disseminating the news, Frankfurter had argued that there was a distinction between selling ideas and selling wares: "A free press is indispensible to the workings of our democratic society. The business of the press, and therefore the business of the Associated Press, is the promotion of truth regarding public matters by furnishing the basis for an understanding of them. Truth and understanding are not wares like peanuts or potatoes. And so, the incidence of restraints upon the promotion of truth through denial of access to the basis for understanding calls into play considerations very different from comparable restraints in a cooperative enterprise having merely a commercial aspect."[45]

Frankfurter was reiterating what John Milton had said three centuries earlier, relying on much the same language used by Milton in his *Areopagitica*: "Truth and understanding are not such wares as to be monopolised and traded by tickets, and statutes, and standards. We must not think to make a staple commodity of all the knowledge in the land, to mark and license it like our broadcloth and woolpacks."[46] Milton's "truth and understanding are not such wares," like "broadcloth and woolpacks," become Frankfurter's "truth and understanding are not wares like peanuts or potatoes." If Frankfurter's position, expressed through metonymy, that "there is an important difference in the scope of power of a state to regulate what feeds the belly and what feeds the brain" is to be accepted, then the applicability of the marketplace metaphor to First Amendment decisions diminishes considerably.

The validity of the marketplace metaphor is further diminished by the fact that the laissez-faire found in the town square is absent in today's marketplace of ideas. For decades, certain types of speech have been prohibited from the marketplace: offensive speech, obscene speech, insulting speech, libelous speech, speech that constitutes a clear and present danger, and speech that constitutes a clear and probable danger. When in 1942 the Supreme Court decided in *Chaplinsky v. New Hampshire* that "fighting words" were not protected by the First Amendment, the unanimous Court declared: "There are certain well-defined and narrowly limited classes of speech, the prevention and punishment of which have never been thought to raise any Constitutional problem. These include the lewd and obscene, the profane, the libelous, and the insulting or 'fighting' words—those which by their very utterance inflict injury or tend to incite an immediate breach of the peace. It has been well observed that such utterances are no essential part of any exposition of ideas, and are of such slight social value as a step to truth that any benefit that may be derived from them is clearly outweighed by the social interest in order and morality."[47]

No similar prohibitions existed in the old market where commercial goods of "slight social value" may have been bought and sold freely to those who had the money to pay. In the marketplace of ideas, however, we have the courts banning from the market offensive and indecent language, language that is "no essential part of any exposition of ideas." The laissez-faire of the old market has been significantly restricted in the marketplace of ideas. While one had always been free to sell "snake oils" in the commercial market, the courts have placed restrictions on the speech "on sale" in the marketplace of ideas.

In the old market in the square, new, even strange and unfamiliar wares being offered for sale at one stall were placed next to the stall offering familiar, tested items; the unusual, unorthodox product appeared next to the orthodox. In the commercial market, when threats are made against the establishment of an entrepreneur, there is usually police protection for the goods and personnel. In the marketplace of ideas the same protection has not always been available to the speaker, the seller, of unsettling, unorthodox ideas. In 1949, a university student, Irving Feiner, standing on a box delivering a speech on a street corner in Syracuse, New York, was arrested and charged with violating a disorderly-conduct statute after he refused to stop speaking as ordered by the police. In his speech Feiner said, among other things: "Mayor Costello [of Syracuse] is a champaigne-sipping bum; he does not speak for the Negro people." "President Truman is a bum." "The American Legion is a Nazi Gestapo." "The Negroes don't have equal rights; they should rise up in arms and fight for their rights."[48] One of the angry men in the audience said to one of the police officers on the scene, "If you don't get that son of a bitch off, I will go over and get him off there myself." The police ordered Feiner to stop speaking, and when he refused, he was arrested.

When the case reached the Supreme Court, the vote was 6–3 against Feiner. The dissenting justices, Black, Douglas, and Minton, expressed concern that the police had not protected the speaker. In the words of Justice Black, "Here the policemen did not even pretend to try to protect petitioner [Feiner]. According to the officers' testimony, the crowd was restless but there is no showing of any attempt to quiet it; pedestrians were forced to walk into the street, but there was no effort to clear a path on the sidewalk; one person threatened to assault petitioner but the officers did nothing to discourage this when a word might have sufficed. Their duty was to protect petitioner's right to talk, even to the extent of arresting the man who threatened to interfere. Instead, they shirked that duty and acted only to suppress the right to speak."[49]

Here, some of the "buyers" threatened the speaker, and the speaker was not given police protection in the marketplace of ideas. Surely, in the commercial market the seller, the entrepreneur, would receive police protection from threats coming from angry buyers dissatisfied with the seller's products. In the commercial marketplace the seller is protected; in the marketplace of ideas the seller cannot always count on similar protection.

The public high school, so often described by the courts as especially a marketplace of ideas, became the focus of a controversy in 1984 when a teacher at Madison High School in Maine "began planning an all-day 'Symposium on Tolerance' in reaction to the tragic drowning of a Bangor homosexual by three Bangor high school students. Tolerance Day, as the program became known, was designed to bring to the school representatives of some dozen different groups who have experienced prejudice in society."[50] As news of Tolerance Day reached the public, school administrators and school-board members received phone calls and visits from people who were critical of the appearance of Dale McCormick, a lesbian who had agreed to speak at Tolerance Day as part of the symposium. "Some callers suggested that picketing might occur on the day of the program, and some parents threatened to keep their children out of school, or to attend school themselves to monitor the symposium. A few of the phone calls warned the Board to expect bomb threats against the school and sabotaging of the school furnace if the program were held."[51] Within a few days, the school board met and voted unanimously to cancel Tolerance Day at Madison High School. The teacher who planned the symposium, McCormick, and a student contended that the school officials had violated their constitutional rights by canceling the Tolerance Day symposium and went to court to seek injunctive relief.

When the case reached the Supreme Judicial Court of Maine, it was decided that the school board had not violated any constitutional rights by its actions. In so deciding, the court asserted twice that the board's cancellation of Tolerance Day did not impermissibly restrict the marketplace of ideas.

First, "We stress that in this case there is no indication that the Board was attempting to 'cast a pall of orthodoxy over the classroom' . . . or to restrict impermissibly the marketplace of ideas within the high school." Then the court argued that the cancellation "did not infringe on the rights of teacher Solmitz and did not impermissibly restrict the free marketplace of ideas at Madison High School."[52] In fact, however, Tolerance Day, itself a one-day marketplace of ideas, was shut down. Had commercial marketplaces received similar threats from the citizenry who did not like the products being sold, it is highly likely that police protection would have been available to protect the seller of the goods. At Madison High School the seller was silenced.

The metaphoric marketplace of ideas is also misleading because in the old marketplace there was equality of access to consumers and equal facilities to display one's goods and wares. Today, no such equality exists in the ideas market. Jerome Barron recognized this inequality when he wrote in 1967:

> The "marketplace of ideas" view has rested on the assumption that protecting the right of expression is equivalent to providing for it. But changes in the communications industry have destroyed the equilibrium in that marketplace. While it may have been still possible in 1925 to believe with Justice Holmes that every idea is "acted on unless some other belief outweighs it or some failure of energy stifles the movement at its birth," it is impossible to believe that now. Yet the Holmesian theory is not abandoned, even though the advent of radio and television has made even more evident that philosophy's unreality. A realistic view of the first amendment requires recognition that a right of expression is somewhat thin if it can be exercised only at the sufferance of the managers of mass communications.[53]

As Barron sees it, the metaphoric marketplace should have been "buried" long ago: "The Justices of the United States Supreme Court are not innocently unaware of these contemporary social realities, but they have nevertheless failed to give the 'marketplace of ideas' theory of the first amendment the burial it merits. Perhaps the interment of this theory has been denied for the understandable reason that the Court is at a loss to know with what to supplant it."[54]

The dangers of metaphoric talk that Beardsley has warned against seem to apply especially with the metaphoric marketplace of ideas. Beardsley states that the "metaphor is hard to control—to keep from saying things you don't want to say." Further, "A metaphor can be extremely helpful to inquiry; but if the image is strong and colorful, it can fasten itself upon us and control our thinking too rigidly."[55] The metaphoric marketplace of ideas "hides aspects of reality," as Lakoff and Johnson would put it.[56] The metaphor brings with it the nostalgic feelings associated with a marketplace that no longer exists, either in the commercial world or in the world of ideas.

This influential judicial metaphor is not just a "rhetorical ornament" but a trope that has affected the way we think of the process we use in our society to determine who does and who does not receive constitutional protection. The fictional marketplace of ideas has led us to believe that we actually do have a process that resembles the marketplace, which brings with it all kinds of positive connotations of choice, individualism, and community. But we mislead ourselves, for with the coming of monopolies, mergers, and conglomerates, that old nostalgic marketplace has been replaced.

Zechariah Chafee, Jr., has argued that one of the obstacles "to the automatic emergence of truth from the contest" is that the means of communication are owned by people who basically have the same views. In his *Blessings of Liberty,* Chafee states that he could "no longer think of open discussion as operating like an electric mixer, which is the impression left by Milton and Jefferson—run it a little while and truth will rise to the top with the dregs of error going down to the bottom."[57] Of course, neither Milton nor Jefferson suggested the mixer metaphor, with the "dregs of error going down to the bottom." Milton and Jefferson had Truth holding weapons, fighting in a conflict with Error, the antagonist. There was no place in their metaphoric world of battle for an electric mixer. Chafee then states that there "are at least three obstacles to the automatic emergence of truth from the contest," and after discussing the first obstacle (the means of communication being owned by people who basically have the same views), Chafee turns to the second obstacle, using still a different metaphor, the sifter: "Is it any longer possible to discover truth amid the clashing blares of advertisements, loud-speakers, enormous headlines, gigantic billboards, television screens, party programs? To sift the truth from all these half-truths drenched with emotion seems to demand a calmness beyond anybody's time and money."[58] The "drenched" half-truths would indeed have difficulty passing through the sifter.

Chafee then proceeds to give us still another metaphor, which he finds more useful: "An utterly different metaphor is helpful to me in picturing what goes on while the conflicting statements of individuals are getting transformed into a satisfactory basis for public action: a bay with thousands of waves, piling up on the shore and then pulling back, sometimes higher, sometimes lower. We know that the tide is either coming in or going out, but we do not have a tide-table. The immeasurable motion appears aimless, but time will show the main course of the sea." "One thing I am sure of," continues Chafee, is "that an alteration of our opinions very rarely comes right after an argument in which we have vigorously taken one side."[59]

The misunderstandings and creation of confused "realities" resulting from the misleading metaphoric marketplace of ideas become especially apparent when the metaphor is applied to the educational environment. While the public schools are the one segment of our society that has been viewed by the courts as especially a marketplace of ideas, some lower-court judges and Supreme Court justices have argued that this marketplace may constitutionally deny to its consumers, the students, certain books and ideas since those books and ideas are available elsewhere. For example, the four dissenting Justices (Burger, Powell, O'Connor, and Rehnquist) in the school-library censorship case *Island Trees v. Pico* argued, through Chief Justice Burger's dissenting opinion, "If parents and students cannot convince the school board that book removal is inappropriate, they have alternative sources to the same end. Books may be acquired from book stores, public libraries, or other alternative sources unconnected with the unique environment of the local public schools."[60]

Then again, Rehnquist, with whom Burger and Powell joined, presented in his dissenting opinion the same argument. The students' right to receive, said Rehnquist, was not violated by the removal of the books from the school library because those books were readily available elsewhere. "Students are not denied books by their removal from a school library. The books may be borrowed from a public library, read at a university library, purchased at a bookstore, or loaned by a friend."[61] Such an argument would never be tolerated if it was applied in the commercial marketplace. No farmer would be prohibited from selling produce in the marketplace simply because that produce was available elsewhere.

Other judges, however, have rejected this resources-available-elsewhere argument. For example, just before they asserted that "a library is a mighty resource in the free marketplace of ideas," two courts argued that "restraint on expression may not generally be justified by the fact that there may be other times, places, or circumstances for such expression."[62] This position would be more consistent with the metaphoric marketplace than the position of the dissenting justices in *Island Trees*, arguing that the availability of a book at a bookstore or from a friend led to the conclusion that the school board's book banning was not a violation of the students' constitutional rights.

In spite of the inconsistencies in the application of the misleading metaphoric marketplace and its questionable applicability to contemporary communication processes, the Supreme Court, as noted by C. Edwin Baker, "steadfastly relies upon a marketplace of ideas theory in determining what speech is protected. Marketplace imagery (competition of ideas, the value of robust debate) pervades Court opinions and provides justification for their first amendment 'tests.'"[63] In 1989, in their separate dissenting opinions in the flag-burning case *Texas v. Johnson,* Justices Rehnquist and Stevens invoked the metaphoric "market" to support their position that the burning of the American flag was not a form of communication protected by the First Amendment. Rehnquist argued: "The American flag, then, throughout more than 200 years of our history, has come to be the visible symbol embodying our Nation. It does not represent the views of any particular party, and it does not represent any particular political philosophy. The flag is not simply another 'idea' or 'point of view' competing for recognition in the marketplace of ideas. Millions and millions of Americans regard it with an almost mystical reverence regardless of what sort of social, political, or philosophical beliefs they may have."[64]

Justice Stevens, comparing flag burning with the defacing of public property, wrote: "The creation of a federal right to post bulletin boards and graffiti on the Washington Monument might enlarge the market for free expression, but at a cost I would not pay. Similarly, in my considered judgment, sanctioning the public desecration of the flag will tarnish its value."[65] While Rehnquist withdraws the American flag from the competition of the marketplace of ideas, Stevens expresses his unwillingness to pay the "costs" to "enlarge the market for free expression."

Justice O'Connor, in her dissenting opinion in *Shapero v. Kentucky Bar Ass'n.* (1988), referred specifically to the metaphoric aspect of the marketplace of ideas and then placed a "constitutional fence" around the marketplace: "Attorney advertising generally falls under the rubric of 'commercial speech.' Political speech, we have often noted, is at the core of the First Amendment. . . . One reason for the special status of political speech was suggested in a metaphor that has become almost as familiar as the principle it sought to justify." After citing the "free trade in ideas" and the "competition of the market" passages from Holmes's opinion in *Abrams,* O'Connor writes: "Traditionally, the constitutional fence around this metaphorical marketplace of ideas had not shielded the actual marketplace of purely commercial transactions from governmental regulation."[66] Her metaphoric fence around the metaphoric marketplace of ideas adds still another question as to just how free and open the market is.

The continued reliance on the marketplace metaphor has interfered with the creation of other more appropriate tropes that would more accurately reflect the contemporary realities of our society. The constant invocation of the metaphor has misled us into a passive acceptance of the trope that is no longer relevant. The outdated metaphor distorts our perception of reality. The laissez-faire world of Holmes's opinion exists today in neither the commercial nor the idea marketplace. As Benno Schmidt has indicated in his *Freedom of the Press vs. Public Access*: "Despite the seeming multitude of mass communications media, most citizens in the United States experience monopoly newspapers, a small number of television stations that are dominated by network programming, and a larger number of radio stations broadcasting largely interchangeable programs with a minimum of concern for public affairs."[67] As the figures provided by Schmidt indicate, the competition in the market is nil: "The number of cities with competing newspapers has shrunk dramatically during this century. The percentage of American cities that are served by newspapers and have more than one paper fell from about 60 percent in 1910 to less than 4 percent in 1972. . . . By 1968, '[O]f the 1500 cities served by a daily newspaper, 85.6% were one-newspaper towns. Although another 150 were served by two dailies, these dailies were under single ownership. Thus, 95% of our communities at the beginning of 1968 had newspapers that were controlled by a single owner.' "[68] "The typical American," Schmidt observes, "lives in a city served by a newspaper that is a local monopoly and is owned by the same interests that control one of the local television stations."[69]

In *Miami Herald Publishing Co. v. Tornillo,* Chief Justice Burger wrote: "The elimination of competing newspapers in most of our large cities, and the concentration of control of media that results from the only newspapers being owned by the same interests which own a television station and a radio station, are important components of this trend toward concentration of control of outlets to inform the public."[70] The Chief Justice indicated in a footnote: "One-newspaper towns have become the rule, with effective competition operating in only 4 percent of our large cities."[71]

When Justice Holmes introduced his metaphoric "the ultimate good desired is better reached by free trade in ideas—that the best test of truth is the power of the thought to get itself accepted in the competition of market," he was not referring to the noncompetitive market described by Schmidt and Burger. It is illusory to continue relying on Holmes's 1919 metaphor in a society where one-newspaper cities are now the rule, where publishing companies are merged into conglomerates, where commercial television networks might just as well be merged since their news and entertainment programs are clones of one another.

New realities require new metaphors. Wendell Wilkie once observed that "a good catchword (in most cases a metaphor) can obscure analytical thinking for fifty years."[72] Fifty years have passed since Holmes applied the rules of the commercial market to the world of ideas. It is time to heed Jerome Barron's 1967 advice and give the metaphoric marketplace of ideas the burial it merits.

4

The Metaphoric "Wall of Separation" between Church and State

"The wall of separation between church and state"—no other metaphor has been discussed by Supreme Court justices as extensively as this "wall." While numerous other tropes—penumbral rights, chilling effect, captive audience, marketplace of ideas, color-blind Constitution—have played an important role in judicial decision making, their figurative nature has not been highlighted as much as that of the wall of separation. Further, no other judicial metaphor has been so directly defended and challenged by the justices, who have been conscious that they are relying on a metaphor that has had a great impact on court decisions related to church-state issues, especially the establishment clause of the First Amendment.

In 1947, Justice Black, a defender of the metaphoric wall, declared in the Court's opinion in *McCollum v. Board of Education*: "The majority in the *Everson* case, and the minority as shown by quotations from the dissenting views in our notes 6 and 7, agreed that the First Amendment's language, properly interpreted, had erected a wall of separation between Church and State."[1] Later in the same opinion Black wrote: "For the First Amendment rests upon the premise that both religion and government can best work to achieve their lofty aims if each is left free from the other within its respective sphere. Or, as we said in the *Everson* case, the First Amendment has erected a wall between Church and State which must be kept high and impregnable."[2]

73

In *McCollum*, Justice Frankerfurter had delivered an opinion in which three other justices joined, arguing that the
Champaign, Illinois, practice of bringing religious teachers
into the public schools on a weekly basis to offer religious
education for students who wished to participate in such a
program was a violation of the establishment clause. At the
outset of his opinion, Frankfurter raises the question of what
the wall separates: "We are all agreed that the First and
Fourteenth Amendments have a secular reach far more pene-
trating in the conduct of Government than merely to forbid an
'established church.' But agreement, in the abstract, that the
First Amendment was designed to erect a 'wall of separation
between church and State,' does not preclude a clash of views
as to what the wall separates. . . . We cannot illuminatingly
apply the 'wall-of-separation' metaphor until we have considered the relevant history of religious education in America,
the place of the 'released time' movement in that history, and
its precise manifestation in the case before us."[3]

By the time Frankfurter gets to the two concluding paragraphs of his opinion, the commitment to the metaphoric wall
is clearly established. "Separation means separation," Frankfurter asserts, "not something else. Jefferson's metaphor in
describing the relationship between Church and State speaks
of a 'wall of separation,' not a fine line easily overstepped."[4]
The opinion ends with "We renew our conviction that 'we have
staked the very existence of our country on the faith that complete separation between the state and religion is best for the
state and best for religion.' If nowhere else, in the relation between Church and State, 'good fences make good neighbors.'"[5]

Two decades later, Justice Black was reiterating this defense of the wall. Dissenting in *Board of Education v. Allen*, he
stated:

> The First Amendment's prohibition against governmental
> establishment of religion was written on the assumption
> that state aid to religion and religious schools generates
> discord, disharmony, hatred, and strife among our peo-
> ple, and that any government that supplies such aids is to
> that extent a tyranny. And I still believe that the only way

to protect minority religious groups from majority groups in this country is to keep the wall of separation between church and state high and impregnable as the First and Fourteenth Amendments provide. The Court's affirmance here bodes nothing but evil to religious peace in this country.[6]

The metaphoric wall received a strong defense from Justice Stevens in 1976 when the Court in *Wolman v. Walter* held constitutional that part of an Ohio statute authorizing the state to provide nonpublic schools with books, standardized testing, and other services but held unconstitutional that portion of the statute relating to instructional materials and equipment and field-trip services. Stevens, concurring in part and dissenting in part, defended the metaphoric wall:

This Court's efforts to improve on the *Everson* test have not proved successful. "Corrosive precedents" have left us without firm principles on which to decide these cases. As this case demonstrates, the states have been encouraged to search for new ways of achieving forbidden ends. What should be a "high and impregnable" wall between church and state, has been reduced to a "blurred, indistinct, and variable barrier." The result has been, as Clarence Darrow predicted, harm to "both the public and the religion that [this aid] would pretend to serve."[7]

Then in 1980, when the Court in *Committee for Public Education and Religious Liberty v. Regan* held constitutional a New York statute that authorized "the use of public funds to reimburse church-sponsored and secular nonpublic schools for performing various testing and reporting services mandated by state law," Justice Stevens dissented, again arguing for the wall of separation: "Rather than continuing with the sisyphean task of trying to patch together the 'blurred, indistinct, and variable barrier,' described in *Lemon v. Kurtzman*, I would resurrect the 'high and impregnable wall between church and state' constructed by the Framers of the First Amendment."[8]

While the majority of justices defended the metaphoric wall in *McCollum*, Justice Reed dissented, pointing out that at Jefferson's University of Virginia there were regulations indicating that students were expected to attend religious worship: "Thus, the 'wall of separation between church and state' that Mr. Jefferson built at the University which he founded did not exclude religious education from that school. The difference between the generality of his statements on the separation of church and state and the specificity of his conclusions on education are considerable. A rule of law should not be drawn from a figure of speech."[9]

Justice Stewart expressed his dismay over the Court's reliance on the metaphoric wall in two school-prayer cases. In 1962, Stewart, dissenting in *Engel v. Vitale* where the Court declared unconstitutional the recitation in the public schools of a prayer composed by the state of New York, declared: "I think that the Court's task, in this as in all areas of constitutional adjudication, is not responsibly aided by the uncritical invocation of metaphors like the 'wall of separation,' a phrase nowhere to be found in the Constitution."[10] One year later, in another school-prayer case, *Abington School Dist. v. Schempp,* Stewart again declared his aversion to the wall metaphor: "The short of the matter is simply that the two relevant clauses of the First Amendment cannot accurately be reflected in a sterile metaphor which by its very nature may distort rather than illuminate the problem in a particular case."[11]

Justice Rehnquist has been most outspoken in his criticism of the metaphoric wall, devoting a large part of his dissenting opinion in *Wallace v. Jaffree* to an attack on the wall. In two successive paragraphs he contends that the wall metaphor is useless: "Whether due to its lack of historical support or its practical unworkability, the *Everson* 'wall' has proved all but useless as a guide to sound constitutional adjudication." In the following paragraph: "The 'wall of separation between church and state' is a metaphor based on bad history, a metaphor which has proved useless as a guide in judging."[12] At the outset of his dissenting opinion, Rehnquist begins his attack: "It is impossible to build constitutional doctrine upon a mistaken understanding of constitutional history, but unfortunately the Establishment Clause has been expressly freighted with Jefferson's misleading metaphor for near forty years."[13]

The metaphoric wall has also been attacked and defended outside the Court by scholars, theologians, and others. Robert Hutchins, critical of the metaphor, wrote: "The wall has done what walls usually do: it has obscured the view. . . . The wall is offered as a reason. It is not a reason; it is a figure of speech."[14] On the other hand, Harold Fey, former editor of the *Christian Century*, has defended the metaphor: "The term 'wall' as Jefferson used it means a distinction, a limitation, a definition of fields of competence and authority. . . . It clarifies rather than confuses thought, and it encourages rather than discourages dialogue between citizens."[15]

The metaphoric wall initially became part of the judicial reasoning of the Supreme Court in 1879 in the polygamy case *Reynolds v. United States*. Delivering the opinion of the Court, Justice Waite quoted from Thomas Jefferson's 1802 letter to the Danbury Baptist Association in which Jefferson wrote:

> Believing with you that religion is a matter which lies solely between man and his God; that he owes account to none other for his faith or his worship; that the legislative powers of the Government reach actions only, and not opinions, I contemplate with sovereign reverence that act of the whole American people which declared that their Legislature should "make no law respecting an establishment of religion or prohibiting the free exercise thereof," thus building a wall of separation between Church and State.

Justice Waite then asserted: "Coming as this does from an acknowledged leader of the advocates of the measure, it may be accepted almost as an authoritative declaration of the scope and effect of the amendment thus secured."[16]

It is ironic that the next time Jefferson's high wall of separation was incorporated into a Supreme Court opinion was *Everson v. Board of Education* in which the Court concluded that state funds could be used to reimburse parents of chil-

dren attending parochial schools for the students' transportation costs. While Justice Black cited *Reynolds* and referred to
Jefferson's "wall," he concluded: "The First Amendment has
erected a wall between church and state. That wall must be
kept high and impregnable. We could not approve the slightest breach. New Jersey has not breached it here."[17] In what
subsequently became one of the often-quoted passages from
Everson, Black wrote:

> The "establishment of religion" clause of the First Amend-
> ment means at least this: Neither a state nor the Federal
> Government can set up a church. Neither can pass laws
> which aid one religion, aid all religions, or prefer one
> religion over another. Neither can force nor influence a
> person to go to or to remain away from church against his
> will or force him to profess a belief or disbelief in any reli-
> gion. No person can be punished for entertaining or pro-
> fessing religious beliefs or disbeliefs, for church
> attendance or non-attendance. No tax in any amount,
> large or small, can be levied to support any religious ac-
> tivities or institutions, whatever they may be called, or
> whatever form they may adopt to teach or practice reli-
> gion. Neither a state nor the Federal Government can,
> openly or secretly, participate in the affairs of any reli-
> gious organizations or groups or *vice versa*. In the words
> of Jefferson, the clause against establishment of religion
> by law as intended to erect "a wall of separation between
> church and state."[18]

The four dissenting Justices in *Everson,* speaking through
Justice Rutledge's opinion, citing Virginia's religious-freedom
statute authored by Jefferson, asserted that they could not
"believe that the great author of those words, or the men who
made them law, could have joined in this decision. Neither so
high nor so impregnable today as yesterday is the wall raised
between church and state by Virginia's great statute of religious freedom and the First Amendment, now made applicable to all the states by the Fourteenth. New Jersey's statute
sustained is the first, if indeed it is not the second breach to be
made by this Court's action."[19]

While the origin of the controversial metaphoric wall has been most closely identified with Thomas Jefferson, Roger Williams referred to the church-state "wall" in his 1644 *Mr. Cotton's Letter Lately Printed, Examined and Answered*, 158 years before Jefferson wrote his famous letter to the Baptists of Danbury, Connecticut.

> The faithful labors of many witnesses of Jesus Christ, extant to the world, abundantly proving that the church of the Jews under the Old Testament in the type, and the church of the Christians under the New Testament in the anti-type, were both separate from the world; and that when they have opened a gap in the hedge or wall of separation between the garden of the church and the wilderness of the world, God hath ever broke down the wall itself, removed the candlestick, and made His garden a wilderness, as at this day. And that therefore if He will ever please to restore His garden and paradise again, it must of necessity be walled in peculiarly unto Himself from the world; and that all that shall be saved out of the world are to be transplanted out of the wilderness of the world, and added unto his church or garden.[20]

Mark Dewolfe Howe has discussed what he sees as the difference between Williams's wall and Jefferson's wall, arguing that Williams's wall was there because of "the dread of worldly corruptions which might consume the churches if sturdy fences against the wilderness were not maintained" and that Jefferson's wall was there because of his "deep anxiety that the liberties of individuals would be endangered if a wall of separation did not stand between them and the state."[21] According to Howe, "The principle of separation epitomized in Williams' metaphor was predominantly theological. The principle summarized in the same figure when used by Jefferson was primarily political." In his discussion of these two walls, Howe argues that the Supreme Court has relied too heavily on Jefferson's wall in its reading of the First Amendment freedom-of-religion clause.[22]

It is clear that Williams recognized the need for the separation of church and state. All through his *Bloudy Tenent* he states his belief in this separation: "Magistrates can have no more power than the common consent of the people shall betrust them with. The spiritual and civil sword cannot be managed by one and the same person. The punishments civil which magistrates inflict upon church for civil crimes are lawful and necessary."[23] Williams quoted approvingly from Martin Luther: "The government of the civil magistrate extendeth no further than over the Bodies and Goods of their Subjects, not over their Soules."[24]

It appears that while some Supreme Court justices have been looking at the wall from Jefferson's side, they were still aware of the "garden" on the other side. In *Reynolds v. United States*, Chief Justice Waite cited Jefferson's Danbury letter and the reference to the "wall of separation." This citation from Jefferson's letter was followed with a recognition that "Congress was deprived of all legislative power over mere opinion," that is, religious opinion, a position that surely was in keeping with Williams's view of the wall.[25]

The state's entrance into Williams's "garden" was clearly prohibited in *United States v. Ballard*, a 1944 case involving what the U.S. Post Office claimed were "fraudulent" religious claims. At the outset of the Court's opinion, Justice Douglas provides the following background:

> Respondents were indicted and convicted for using, and conspiring to use, the mails to defraud. . . . The false representations charged were eighteen in number. It is sufficient at this point to say that they covered respondents' alleged religious doctrines or beliefs. They were all set forth in the first count. The following are representative:
>
> that Guy W. Ballard, now deceased, alias Saint Germain, Jesus, George Washington, and Godfre Ray King, had been selected and thereby designated, by the alleged "ascertained masters," Saint Germain, as a divine messenger; and that the words of "ascended masters" and the words of the alleged divine entity, Saint Germain, would be transmitted to mankind through the medium of the said Guy W. Ballard.

that Guy W. Ballard, during his lifetime, and Edna
W. Ballard and Donald Ballard had, by reason of supernatural attainments, the power to heal persons of ailments
and diseases and to make well persons afflicted with any
diseases, injuries, or ailments, and did falsely represent to
persons intended to be defrauded that the three designated
persons and the ability and power to cure persons of those
diseases normally classified as curable and also of diseases
which are ordinarily classified by the medical profession
as being incurable diseases; and did further represent that
the three designated persons had in fact cured either by
the activity of one, either, or all of said persons, hundreds
of persons afflicted with diseases and ailments;

. . . .

At the time of making, all of the afore-alleged representations were false and untrue and were made with the
intention on the part of the defendants, and each of them,
to cheat, wrong, and defraud persons intended to be defrauded, and to obtain from persons intended to be defrauded by the defendants, money, property, and other
things of value and to convert the same to the use and the
benefit of the defendants, and each of them.[26]

Noting that "the Circuit Court of Appeals held that the
question of the truth of the representations concerning respondents' religious doctrines or beliefs should have been
submitted to the jury," Justice Douglas responded: "We do not
agree that the truth or verity of respondents' religious doctrines or beliefs should have been submitted to the jury.
Whatever this particular indictment might require, the First
Amendment precludes such a course, as the United States
seems to concede." Then drawing on a personification that
appeared in an 1872 Supreme Court decision, *Watson v. Jones,*
Douglas wrote: "'The law knows no heresy, is committed to
the support of no dogma, the establishment of no sect.' . . .
The First Amendment has a dual aspect. It not only 'forestalls
compulsion by law of the acceptance of any creed or the
practice of any form of worship' but also 'safeguards the free
exercise of the chosen form of religion.' . . . It [the First
Amendment] embraces the right to maintain theories of life

and of death and of the hereafter which are rank heresy to followers of the orthodox faiths. Heresy trials are foreign to our Constitution. Men may believe what they cannot prove."[27]

Through *Ballard* the Court was reaffirming that the state cannot breach the wall into Williams's "garden." The wall that Williams built was the same wall that Jefferson constructed, the only difference being that each man was looking at the wall from a different side of the rather solid barrier.

Whichever view one has of the wall, the metaphor has become a crucial and controversial one in judicial opinions related to church-state relations. While Justice Stewart reminds us that the wall metaphor is "nowhere to be found in the Constitution," we need to be further reminded that neither is the "marketplace of ideas" found in the Constitution. Yet both metaphors have become "standards" and "principles" used by the courts in reaching First Amendment decisions.

As for Justice Reed's questioning in *McCollum* of the role of metaphor and figures of speech in reaching judicial decisions, we need to bear in mind Justice Reed's figurative language in a few of his opinions, such as his dissenting opinion in *McCollum*: "Actually, however, future cases must run the gantlet not only of the judgment entered but of the accompanying words of the opinions. . . . The prohibition of enactments respecting the establishment of religion do not bar every friendly gesture between church and state. . . . The Constitution should not be stretched to forbid national customs in the way courts act to reach arrangements to avoid federal taxation."[28] Literally, of course, cases do not "run the gantlet," and the Constitution cannot be "stretched." In *McCollum* Justice Reed asserts that "a rule should not be drawn from a figure of speech," and yet he reaches his decision through the use of several arguments based on the tropes, including metaphor and personification.

One year earlier, Justice Reed, in *Johansen v. United States*, did not hesitate to rely on a metaphoric wall constructed in a different context: "The Federal Employees Compensation Act . . . was enacted to provide for injuries to Government employees in the performance of their duties. It covers all employees. . . . It was a legislative breach in the wall of sovereign immunity to damage claims and it brought to Government employees the benefits of the socially desirable rule that society should share with the injured employee the costs of accidents incurred in the course of employment."[29] While Reed relies on the metaphoric "legislative breach in the wall of sovereign immunity" to support his 1951 *Johansen* decision, one year later he rejects the metaphoric "wall of separation between church and state" on the basis of his newfound principle that "a rule of law should not be drawn from a figure of speech." Clearly, Justice Reed could not escape the tropology of judicial decision making.

When the Supreme Court decided in *Zorach v. Clauson* (1952) that New York's "program which permits its public schools to release students during the school day so that they may leave the school buildings and school grounds and go to religious centers for religious instruction or devotional exercises" was constitutional, Justice Jackson concluded in his strongly worded dissenting opinion with a reference to the condition of the wall of separation: "The wall which the Court was professing [in *McCollum*] to erect between Church and State has become even more warped and twisted than I expected."[30]

Justice Black, also dissenting in *Zorach*, defended the metaphoric wall but also recognized the attacks on the wall: "Probably few opinions from this Court in recent years have attracted more attention or stirred wider debate. Our insistence on 'a wall between Church and State which must be kept high and impregnable' has seemed to some a correct exposition of the philosophy and a true interpretation of the language of the First Amendment to which we should strictly adhere. With equal conviction and sincerity, others have thought the *McCollum* decision fundamentally wrong and have pledged continuous warfare against it."[31]

Over the years, various justices have waged their "warfare" against *McCollum*, attacking the wall in that decision by bringing forth other metaphors. In 1969, delivering the opinion of the Court in *Walz v. Tax Commission*, Chief Justice Burger, arguing that New York's exemption of church property from state taxes was constitutional, relied not on the metaphoric wall but on other less solid metaphoric barriers.

Burger argued that "the course of constitutional neutrality in this area cannot be an absolutely straight line."[32] "Adherence to the policy of neutrality that derives from an accommodation of the Establishment and Free Exercise Clauses has prevented the kind of involvement that would tip the balance toward government control of churches or governmental restraint on religious practice."[33]

When he was not figuratively drawing lines or weighing constitutional values, Burger was drawing "boundaries to avoid excessive entanglement": "No perfect or absolute separation is really possible; the very existence of the Religion Clauses is an involvement of sorts—one that seeks to mark boundaries to avoid excessive entanglement."[34] Then, mixing his metaphors, Burger wrote: "With all the risks inherent in programs that bring about administrative relationships between public education bodies and church-related schools, we have been able to chart a course that preserved the autonomy and freedom of religious bodies while avoiding any semblance of established religion. This is a 'tight rope' and one we have successfully traversed."[35]

When Burger says that "the course of constitutional neutrality in this area cannot be an absolutely straight line" and that the religion clauses seek "to mark boundaries to avoid excessive entanglement," his metaphors suggest a weaker, less discernible barrier between church and state, much weaker than the metaphoric wall of separation.

The "entanglement" metaphor became a major element in the 1971 *Lemon v. Kurtzman* decision in which the Court held unconstitutional the state aid provided to church-related elementary and secondary schools in Rhode Island and Pennsylvania. Burger, referring to the religion clauses, first asserted: "Candor compels acknowledgement . . . that we can only dimly perceive the lines of demarcation in this extraordinary sensitive area of constitutional law." Turning then to his three-part test, which eventually came to be known as the "three-pronged *Lemon* test," Burger wrote: "Every analysis in this area must begin with consideration of the cumulative criteria developed by the Court over many years. Three such tests must be gleaned from our cases. First, the statute must have a secular legislative purpose; second, its principal or primary effect must be one that neither advances nor inhibits religion . . . ; finally, the statute must not foster 'an excessive government entanglement with religion.' "[36]

Having presented the three-part test with its metaphoric entanglement component, Burger further undermined the metaphoric wall of separation: "Judicial caveats against entanglement must recognize that the line of separation, far from being a 'wall,' is a blurred, indistinct, and variable barrier depending on all the circumstances of a particular relationship." Having said this, Burger, it seems, felt compelled to explain: "This is not to suggest, however, that we are to engage in a legalistic minuet in which precise rules and forms must govern. A true minuet is a matter of pure form and style, the observance of which is itself the substantive end. Here we examine the form of the relationship for the light that it casts on the substance."[37] Through his metaphoric mélange, Burger not only minimized the wall but replaced it with figurative entanglements, lines, and blurred, indistinct, and variable barriers. All of this, however, "is not to suggest . . . that we are to engage in a legalistic minuet."

Burger concluded his opinion with the two pervading metaphors in his opinion: "The Constitution decrees that religion must be a private matter for the individual, the family, and the institutions of private choice, and that while some involvement and entanglement are inevitable, lines must be drawn."[38] While Burger's "entanglement" and "lines" metaphors kept state money from being used to pay part of the salaries of teachers employed in nonpublic schools, these metaphors presented images of permissible intrusions that the metaphoric wall did not. One problem that arises is the troublesome task of drawing figurative "lines" through figurative "entanglements" to determine whether there is "excessive government entanglement with religion."

The entanglement metaphor carries with it less assurance that church-state matters will be kept separate. *Entanglement* is derived from *tangle*, which means "to mix together or intertwine in a confused mass; to snarl. 2. To involve in hampering or awkward complications; entangle." *Tangle*, as a noun: "1. a confused intertwined mass. 2. A jumbled or confused state or conditoin. 3. a state of bewilderment."[39] The *Oxford English Dictionary* tells us that while the etymological history of *tangle* is not clear, it can be traced back to a "a general term for the larger seaweeds" and is probably of Norse origin, derived from the Norse *tang*, which is "a collective name for large coarse seaweeds."[40]

Whereas the "wall of separation" is a structure that cannot be breached easily without detection, agreement cannot be determined so easily about what constitutes "excessive government entanglement." As indicated by the definition of *tangle*, it brings with it confusion, complications, and bewilderment, characteristics not associated with the metaphoric wall. The chaos and disorderliness that comes with entanglement creates significant difficulty in determining just what government actions and policies constitute entanglement, minimal entanglement, some entanglement, or excessive entanglement.

The three parts of the *Lemon* test, subsequently metaphorized into three "prongs," became important criteria in deciding church-state cases. For example, in 1977, Justice Blackmun, in *Wolman v. Walter*, asserted that "the mode of analyses for Establishment Clause questions is defined by the three-part test that has emerged from the Court's decisions."[41] "In the present case, we have no difficulty with the first prong of this three-part test."[42] Blackmun, like Burger, referred to a less than substantial wall: "We have acknowledged before, and we do so again here, that the wall of separation that must be maintained between church and state 'is a blurred, indistinct, and variable barrier depending on all the circumstances of a particular relationship.' . . . Nonetheless, the Court's numerous precedents 'have become firmly rooted,' . . . and now provide substantial guidance."[43]

By 1982, although the wall of separation between church and state, according to Burger, was a "useful figurative illustration to emphasize the concept of separateness," it was the *Lemon* test that was applied in deciding the controversey involved in *Larkin v. Grendel's Den, Inc.* In declaring unconstitutional a Massachusetts law that "premises . . . located within a radius of five hundred feet of a church or school shall not be licensed for the sale of alcoholic beverages if the governing body of such church or school files written objection thereto," Burger said that the wall metaphor was "a useful figurative illustration to emphasize the concept of separateness. Some limited and incidental entanglement between church and state authority is inevitable in a complex modern society . . . , but the concept of a 'wall' of separation is a useful signpost. Here that 'wall' is substantially breached by vesting discretionary governmental powers in religious bodies."[44] While the " 'wall' of separation is a useful signpost," in the end the *Lemon* test was used to decide this case.

In 1985, Justice Rehnquist delivered an especially strong attack on both the wall of *Everson* and the three prongs of *Lemon*. He dissented in *Wallace v. Jaffree,* in which the Court declared unconstitutional Alabama's statute: "At the commencement of the first class of each day in all grades in all public schools the teacher in charge of the room in which each class is held may announce that a period of silence not to exceed one minute in duration shall be observed for meditation or voluntary prayer, and during any such period no other activities shall be engaged in."[45] After presenting his view of the historical background of the establishment clause, Rehnquist concluded that "there is simply no historical foundation for the proposition that the Framers intended to build the 'wall of separation' that was constitutionalized in *Everson.*"

With his own reliance on the tropes, Rehnquist attacked the metaphoric wall as it had never been attacked in any other Supreme Court opinion; Rehnquist called for abandonment of the metaphoric wall:

> Notwithstanding the absence of a historical basis for this theory of rigid separation, the wall idea might well have served as a useful albeit misguided analytical concept, had it led this Court to unified and principled results in Establishment Clause cases. The opposite, unfortunately, has been true; in the 38 years since *Everson* our Establishment Clause cases have been neither principled nor unified. Our recent opinions, many of them hope-

lessly divided pluralities, have with embarrassing candor conceded that the "wall of separation" is merely a "blurred, indistinct, and variable barrier," which "is not wholly accurate" and can only be "dimly perceived." . . .

Whether due to its lack of historical support or its practical unworkability, the *Everson* "wall" has proved all but useless as a guide to sound constitutional adjudication. It illustrates only too well the wisdom of Benjamin Cardozo's observation that "[m]etaphors in law are to be narrowly watched, for starting as devices to liberate thought, they end often by enslaving it." *Berkey v. Third Avenue R. Co.*, 244 N.Y. 84, 94, 155 N.E. 58, 61 (1926).

But the greatest injury of the "wall" notion is its mischievous diversion of judges from the actual intentions of the drafters of the Bill of Rights. The "crucible of litigation," . . . is well adapted to adjudicating factual disputes on the basis of testimony presented in court, but no amount of repetition of historical errors in judicial opinions can make the errors true. The "wall of separation between church and state" is a metaphor based on bad history, a metaphor which has proved useless as a guide to judging. It should be frankly and explicitly abandoned.[46]

Having thus attacked the metaphoric wall of separation, Rehnquist then immediately turned his attack on the three-pronged *Lemon* test: "The Court has more recently attempted to add some mortar to *Everson's* wall through the three-part test of *Lemon v. Kurtzman* . . . , which served at first to offer a more useful test for purposes of the Establishment Clause than did the 'wall' metaphor. Generally stated, the *Lemon* test proscribes state action that has a sectarian purpose or effect, or causes an impermissible governmental entanglement with religion." Tracing the background of *Lemon*, Rehnquist found that *Lemon* had "inherited the purpose and effect elements from *Schempp* and *Everson*, both of which contain the historical errors described above. . . . Thus the purpose and effect prongs have the same historical deficiencies as the wall concept itself: they are in no way based on either the language or intent of the drafters."[47]

Rehnquist then proceeded to argue the weaknesses of the *Lemon* test, prong by prong. Toward the end of his opinion, Rehnquist asserted that the Court's perception "has been clouded not by the Constitution, but by the mists of an unnecessary metaphor." "If a constitutional theory has no basis in the history of the amendment it seeks to interpret, is difficult to apply and yields unprincipled results, I see little use in it. The 'crucible of litigation' . . . has produced only consistent unpredictability, and today's effort is just a continuation of 'the sisyphean task of trying to patch together the "blurred, indistinct and variable barrier"' described in *Lemon v. Kurtzman*. . . . We have done much straining since 1947, but still we admit that we can only 'dimly perceive' the *Everson* wall. . . . Our perception has been clouded not by the Constitution, but by the mists of an unnecessary metaphor."[48]

In language and style, what stands out in this paragraph is the fact that what Rehnquist has quoted from previous opinions are the tropes: the "crucible of litigation"; the "sisyphean task of trying to patch together the blurred, indistinct and variable barrier"; the "*Everson* wall"; perception clouded by the "mists of an unnecessary metaphor." This paragraph especially exemplifies Judge Bell's observation that "the style of an opinion may affect the manner in which it is interpreted by the reader. It may also govern the frequency with which the opinion will be cited in other cases and thus determine the influence the opinion will ultimately have."[49]

Further, while Rehnquist earlier in the opinion gives credit to Justice Cardozo for "metaphors in the law are to be narrowly watched" by citing Cardozo's *Berkey* opinion, Rehnquist does not cite *Berkey* as the source for the "mists of metaphor." In *Berkey* Cardozo had written the following two sentences: "The whole problem of the relation between parent and subsidiary corporations is one that is still enveloped in the mists of metaphor. Metaphors in law are to be narrowly watched, for starting as devices to liberate, they end often by enslaving it."[50]

Also, Rehnquist devotes a significant part of his dissenting opinion to an attack on the metaphoric wall of separation, a metaphor the majority did not mention in its opinion. In deciding that the Alabama statute providing for "voluntary prayer" was a violation of the establishment clause, the majority relied on the *Lemon* test, not the *Everson* wall. In devoting such a large portion of his dissenting opinion to an attack on the metaphoric wall, Rehnquist apparently was leading up to his attack on the three-pronged *Lemon* test, arguing that the latter was no more useful than the former.

Having attacked both the metaphoric wall and the three-pronged test, declaring that "the purpose and effect prongs have the same historical deficiencies as the wall concept itself," Rehnquist concludes that the Alabama statute is constitutional and that "nothing in the Establishment Clause of the First Amendment, properly understood, prohibits any such generalized 'endorsement' of prayer."[51]

Rehnquist's objections to the *Lemon* test notwithstanding, the three-pronged test became an integral part of the judicial opinions of judges at various levels deciding establishment clause cases. When in 1987 the Supreme Court declared unconstitutional Louisiana's "Creation Science" Act, which forbade the teaching of the theory of evolution in public elementary and secondary schools unless accompanied by instruction in the theory of "creation science," Justice Brennan, delivering the opinion of the Court, relied on the three-pronged test: "The Court has applied a three-pronged test to determine whether legislation comports with the Establishment Clause. First, the legislature must have adopted the law with a secular purpose. Second, the statute's principal or primary effect must be one that neither advances nor inhibits religion. Third, the statute must not result in an excessive entanglement of government with religion. . . . State action violates the Establishment Clause if it fails to satisfy any of these prongs."[52] The Louisiana act, said Brennan, violated the first prong: "In this case, the petitioners have identified no clear secular purpose for the Louisiana Act." Also, "Because the primary purpose of the Creationism Act is to endorse a particular religious doctrine, the Act furthers religion in violation of the Establishment Clause."[53]

The district courts and the courts of appeal adopted the three-pronged test and applied it to a variety of establishment-clause cases. In 1983, the U.S. District Court for New Mexico declared unconstitutional a New Mexico statute providing that "each local school board may authorize a period of silence not to exceed one minute at the beginning of the school. This period may be used for contemplation, meditation, or prayer, provided that silence is maintained and no activities undertaken."[54] In deciding that the statute was a violation of the establishment clause, the court stated: "In the recent past, the Supreme Court has considered a number of cases touching upon issues similar to those in this case. These cases have resulted in a three-prong analysis which may be stated as follows: '[T]o pass muster under the Establishment Clause the law in question first must reflect a clearly secular legislative purpose, second, must have a primary effect that neither advances nor inhibits religion, and third, must avoid excessive entanglement with religion.'"[55] Then, prong by prong, the district court proceeded to conclude that the statute was a violation of the establishment clause.

In applying the three-pronged test in *Kaplan v. City of Burlington* (1988), a U.S. district court in Vermont held that the city had not violated the *Lemon* test is granting a permit for the placement of a menorah in the Burlington City Hall Park during Hanukkah. Before turning to its application of the three-pronged test, the court stated: "In *Lemon v. Kurtzman*, the Supreme Court conceded that its reference to a 'wall of separation' between church and state . . . had been an unwise choice of metaphors. '[T]he line of separation, far from being a "wall," is a blurred, indistinct, and variable barrier depending on all the circumstances of a particular relationship.'"[56] Having accepted this "disintegration" of the wall, the court proceeded to argue that the placement of the menorah in the city park did not violate any of the three prongs of the *Lemon* test. As for the first prong, "By isolating the government act in question, it is clear that the act does not violate the first prong of the *Lemon* test. The City has a secular purpose, clearly, in allowing expression of all sorts—artistic, political, religious, controversial—in a public forum."[57] As for the third prong, the court argued that there was no excessive governmental entanglement in the placement of the menorah, the court dismissing the entanglement argument since the city provided maintenance services at City Hall Park and dismissing the argument that entanglement existed since the menorah created political divisiveness in Burlington: "We are not persuaded that such divisiveness alone constitutes excessive entanglement or establishes an independent violation of the Establishment Clause."[58] The second prong of the *Lemon* test "is the most sticky of the three prongs, as we view that the real meat of plaintiff's claim is that the placement of the menorah conveys the appearance of government endorsement of a particular religion, and thus has a primary effect of advancing religion." The court concluded: "In this case, we find at most an indirect, remote, or incidental benefit, and thus hold that the city has not violated the second prong of the *Lemon* test."[59]

What occurred over two decades was that the metaphoric wall of separation between church and state, a substantial barrier, was replaced with the metaphoric three-pronged test—not a barrier but a sharp instrument. While *prong* can easily be identified with a table fork, a pitchfork, or a digging fork, it can just as easily be identified as an instrument for battle, an instrument with which to pierce or stab. (The first example given in the *Oxford English Dictionary* of *prong* is "1492 *Ryman Poems* lv. 4 in *Archiv Stud. neu. Spr.* LXXXIX. 221 Dethe hathe feld me with his pronge.")[60] Since the *Lemon* test is a three-pronged instrument, it readily brings up the image of the *trident*, which the *OED* defines first as "1. An instrument or weapon with three prongs. a. *esp.* A three-pronged fish-spear or sceptre as the attribute of the sea-god Poseidon or Neptune, also figured as borne of Britannia." Then there is the "three-pronged spear used by the *retiarius* in ancient Roman gladiatorial combats."[61]

Unlike the high and impregnable wall, the prongs may not effectively ward off the assaults on the establishment clause. The three prongs are more effective as a defense against state intrusions into church affairs and vice versa than the "line" between church and state proposed by some justices; lines are for stepping over. Further, the three prongs would be more effective in keeping separate church and state matters than the metaphoric "door" suggested by Justice

Brennan's *Sherbert v. Verner* opinion: "The door of the Free Exercise Clause stands tightly closed against any governmental regulation of religious *beliefs* as such."[62] Doors do not assure substantial protection; they can be kept ajar, opened, broken down.

Other metaphors have been invoked in decisions involving church-state matters. Justice White, in 1980, referred to a "litmus-paper test."[63] Judge Cardamone of the U.S. court of appeals began his opinion in *Catholic H.S. Ass'n of Archdiocese of NY v. Culbert* (1985) by metaphorizing the metaphoric wall into a "parchment barrier": "The wall of the First Amendment delineates the permissible degree of this government's intrusion into the sphere reserved for religion. This parchment barrier must be constantly manned, the Founding Fathers believed, lest there be a union between church and state that will first degrade and evetually destroy both."[64] The parchment barrier, however, gave way to a different metaphor later in the opinion: "If we allow the camel to stick its nose into the constitutionally protected tent of religion, what will follow may not always be controlled. Thus, we must now turn to the question of whether the camel can be kept firmly tethered outside."[65]

In his dissenting opinion in *Everson*, Justice Rutledge, arguing that New Jersey's statute authorizing boards of education to provide payment for transportation of students to nonpublic schools was unconstitutional, drew on the "shield" metaphor: "Now as in Madison's day it is one of principle, to keep separate the separate spheres as the First Amendment drew them, to prevent the first experiment upon our liberties; and to keep the question from becoming entangled in corrosive precedents. We should not be less strict to keep strong and untarnished the one side of the shield of religious freedom than we have been of the other."[66] Other images were conveyed when Justice Clark, delivering the majority opinion in *Abington School Dist. v. Schempp*, arguing that school prayers were unconstitutional, declared: "It is no defense to urge that the religious practices here may be relatively minor encroachments on the First Amendment. The breach of neutrality that today is a trickling stream may all too soon become a raging torrent and, in the words of Madison, 'it is proper to take alarm at the first experiment on our liberties.'"[67]

Lines, doors, prongs, shields, entanglements, camels' noses—none of these convey the strength and sturdiness of the wall. When Justice Frankfurter argued in *McCollum* that "separation means separation, not something else" and that "Jefferson's metaphor in describing the relation between Church and State speaks of a 'wall of separation,' not a fine line easily overstepped," he concluded with still another metaphor: "We renew our conviction that 'we have staked the very existence of our country on the faith that complete separation between the state and religion is best for the state and best for religion.' If nowhere else, in the relation between Church and State, 'good fences make good neighbors.'"[68]

While Robert Frost did say, "Something there is that doesn't love a wall, / That wants it down," he also recognized that there are instances when walls are needed. He simply wanted to know, before he built the wall, what he was "walling in or walling out." The fields of religion and state are not orchards of apple trees and pine. Had Frost and his neighbor owned cows, Frost would have understood his neighbor's insistence that "good fences make good neighbors." The secular cows cannot be kept out of the garden or the ecclesiastical cows out of the wilderness simply by drawing "lines" and maintaining "blurred, indistinct, and variable barriers." While the wall of separation has on occasion been in disrepair, it is a valuable metaphor. Justice Stevens has suggested that we need to "resurrect the 'high and impregnable' wall between church and state constructed by the Framers of the First Amendment."[69]

5

The Metaphoric "Chilling Effect" and Related Tropes

These principles have particular significance when as in this case, the attack upon the statute on its face is for repugnancy to the First Amendment. In such case to force the plaintiff who has commenced a federal action to suffer the delay of state court proceedings might itself effect the impermissible chilling of the very constitutional right he seeks to protect.
—JUSTICE BRENNAN, *Zwickler v. Koota*[1]

Unlike the Court, I obtain no assistance for this conclusion from the ubiquitous and slippery "chilling effect" doctrine. . . . In these circumstances, to apply the amorphous chilling effect doctrine would serve only to chill the interests sought to be maintained by abstention.
—JUSTICE HARLAN, *Zwickler v. Koota*[2]

Particularly intractible in my mind is the relation of modern notions of "chilling effect" or "breathing space" for First Amendment freedoms and a comprehensive system of governmental licensing of speakers. . . . As First Amendment jurisprudence developed rapidly in the last two decades, venerable FCC policies remained in a stagnant backwash, a permanent "derelict in the stream of law."
—JUDGE BAZELON, *Citizens Committee to Save WEFM v. F.C.C.*[3]

The problems associated with determining the origins of the judicial tropes that have been established as principles and doctrines are exemplified in the variety of sources said to be the origins of the metaphoric marketplace of ideas and the wall of separation between church and state. John Milton's 1644 *Areopagitica* has been asserted by some to be the origin (incorrectly, I have argued) of the metaphoric marketplace; others place the origin in Justice Holmes's dissenting opinion in *Abrams*;[4] and for others, the origin of "marketplace of ideas" is to be found in Justice Brennan's 1965 concurring opinion in *Lamont v. Postmaster General*.[5]

Similarly, the controversial metaphoric wall of separation is usually traced to Thomas Jefferson's 1802 letter to the Danbury Baptist Association.[6] However, if one goes back to 1644, one finds Roger Williams speaking of the "gap in the hedge or wall of separation between the garden of the church and the wilderness of the world."[7] The first reference to the wall of separation in a Supreme Court decision appeared in the 1879 polygamy case *Reynolds v. United States*.[8] However, it was Justice Black's use of the metaphoric wall of separation in *Everson* in 1947 that was cited most often by the courts.[9] Determining the origins of these crucial metaphors becomes a matter of deciding what constitutes an "origin."

The origin of the "chilling effect" in judicial decision making can be traced to more than one source, depending on how one defines *origin*. In 1952, when the Supreme Court in *Wieman v. Updegraff* unanimously decided that the Oklahoma loyalty oath required of state employees, including teachers, was invalid, Justice Frankfurter wrote in his concurring opinion: "In view of the nature of the teacher's relation to the effective exercise of the rights which are safeguarded by the Bill of Rights and by the Fourteenth Amendment, inhibition of freedom of thought, and of action upon thought, in the case of teachers brings the safeguards of those amendments vividly into operation. Such unwarranted inhibition upon the free spirit of teachers affects not only those who, like the appellants, are immediately before the Court. It has an unmistakable tendency to chill that free play of the spirit which all teachers ought especially to cultivate and practice; it makes for caution and timidity in their associations by potential teachers."[10]

It was not till ten years later that the Court used the words *chilling effect* in *Gibson v. Florida Legis. Investigating Comm.* Gibson, the president of the Miami branch of the NAACP, had been ordered to appear before a Florida legislative investigating committee that had information that fourteen "Communists" had been associated with that branch. Gibson refused to produce the membership records demanded by the committee, and he was cited for contempt. When the case reached the Supreme Court, a majority decided for Gibson, Justice Goldberg recognizing the chilling effect that Florida's demand would have on First Amendment freedoms: "The strong associational interest in maintaining the privacy of membership lists of groups engaged in the constitutionally protected free trade in ideas and beliefs may not be substantially infringed upon such a slender showing as here made by the respondent. While, of course, all legitimate organizations are the beneficiaries of these protections, they are all the more essential here, where the challenged privacy is that of persons espousing beliefs already unpopular with their neighbors and the deterrent and 'chilling' effect on the free exercise of constitutionally enshrined rights of free speech, expression, and association is consequently the more immediate and substantial."[11]

While Frankfurter had referred to the "tendency to chill that free play of the spirit" and Goldberg had incorporated into the *Gibson* opinion the metaphoric "chilling effect," the "leading" and "seminal" case dealing with the chilling effect and deterrent effects of vague and overbroad statutes was, according to Frederick Schauer, *Dombrowski v. Pfister*.[12] In *Dombrowski* the Court decided for the appellants, a civil-rights organization and its leaders who had sought to restrain the state of Louisiana "from prosecuting or threatening to prosecute them under Louisiana's Subversive Activities and Communist Control Law and Communist Propaganda Control Law, which they alleged violated their rights of free expression under the First and Fourteenth amendments. Appellants contended that the statutes were excessively broad and susceptible of application in violation of those rights, and were being used by appellees in bad faith, not to secure valid convictions, but to deter appellants' civil rights efforts."[13] Justice Brennan, delivering the majority opinion, brought to bear the metaphoric "chilling effect":

> We held [in *Baggett v. Bullitt*] that the definition [of *subversive organization*], as well as the oath based thereon, denied due process because it was unduly vague, uncertain and broad. Where, as here, protected freedoms of expression and association are similarly involved, we see no controlling distinction in the fact that the definition is used to provide a standard of criminality rather than the contents of a test oath. This overly broad statute also creates a "danger zone" within which protected expression may be inhibited. . . . So long as the statute remains available to the State the threat of prosecutions of protected expression is a real and substantial one. Even the prospect of ultimate failure for such prosecutions by no means dispels their chilling effect on protected expression.[14]

Whatever the origin of the metaphor, whatever the "seminal" case, the "chilling effect" has been one of the most heavily relied-upon metaphors in judicial decision making. The metaphor has appeared in judicial opinions dealing with loyalty oaths and investigating committees; government surveillance of political meetings and censorship of library books; access to letters of recommendation and draft reclassification of students; obscenity, libel, and academic freedom.

Chill literally refers to temperature, "a bodily coldness with shivering," says *Webster's New World Dictionary*. The *OED* includes as one of its many entries under *chill*: "1. 'Cold; cold to the touch' (J.); now always unpleasantly, depressingly, or injuriously cold; that chills, tends to benumb, or causes to shiver."[15] Then, under the figurative uses of the word, the *OED* provides the following: "4. *fig.* a. A benumbing and depressing sensation or influence upon the feelings. To cast or throw a chill over: to damp the warmth or ardour of." Also: "4. *fig.* a. Said of circumstances or influences which repress warmth of feeling, enthusiasm, etc."[16]

The courts have used the figurative *chill* as a noun: "We find, however, that appellee has alleged and demonstrated more than a 'subjective chill.'"[17] The figurative *chill* has been widely used as a verb: "Faced with the possibility of such an inquisition, reporters and journalists would be reluctant to express their doubts. Indeed, they would be chilled in the very process of thought."[18] The figurative *chill* brings with it an image more threatening than a figurative "dampening effect" or a more literal "deterring effect." *Chill* brings with it numbing, coldness, shivering—all sensations that do not come from the more abstract *deter* and *inhibit*.

From one perspective, we are all chilled from participating in illegal acts simply because there are laws that prohibit those acts and the result is punishment for those who violate those laws. We are deterred from "breaking" the law, knowing that it would lead to punishment. The law that demands that I stop at a stop sign has an inhibiting effect on me; I have been persuaded that it is in my interest and the state's interest to stop at stop signs. The effect of the law is to curtail an "activity properly subject to government control."[19]

Frederick Schauer has referred to this type of deterrence as a "*benign* chilling effect—an effect caused by the intentional regulation of speech or other activity properly subject to governmental control."[20] The chilling effect referred to in so many judicial opinions is defined by Schauer as an "*invidious* chilling," an "invidious chilling of constitutionally protected activity. This can occur not only when activity shielded by the first amendment is implicated, but also when any behavior safeguarded by the Constitution is unduly discouraged."[21] "A chilling effect occurs," writes Schauer, "when individuals seeking to engage in activity protected by the first amendment are deterred from so doing by governmental regulation not specifically directed at that protected activity."[22]

Through the second half of the twentieth century, the metaphoric chilling effect was incorporated into over five hundred opinions coming from courts at various levels. What becomes evident is that the "chilled" person practices a self-censorship that in the end interferes with free communication. Along with the chilling effect comes a kind of prior

restraint; the self-censored ideas have not reached the citizenry because the speakers have been chilled into silence. The
suppression of these ideas through direct governmental prior
restraints would never be tolerated today.[23] But in the end,
whether through self-censorship caused by the "chilling" or
governmental prior restraint, the ideas remain uncommuni-
cated. If we are chilled into silence, if we practice self-censorship, the result is silence. This silence is no less silent than
what results from governmental prior restraints. An idea
unexpressed from fear of losing one's position or fear of
violating a vague statute remains just as unexpressed as the
idea silenced through prior restraint.

In 1964, when the Supreme Court decided the landmark
libel case *New York Times v. Sullivan*, Justice Brennan, delivering the opinion of a unanimous Court, while not specifically
citing the metaphoric chilling effect, emphasized the problem
of self-censorship:

> Erroneous statement is inevitable in free debate, and . . .
> it must be protected if the freedoms of expression are to
> have the "breathing space" that they "need . . . to sur-
> vive." . . . A rule compelling the critic of official conduct
> to guarantee the truth of all his factual assertions—and to
> do so on pain of libel judgments virtually unlimited in
> amount—leads to a comparable "self-censorship." Allow-
> ance of the defense of truth, with the burden of proving it
> on the defendant, does not mean that only false speech
> will be deterred. . . . Under such a rule, would-be critics
> of official conduct may be deterred from voicing their crit-
> icism, even though it is believed to be true and even
> though it is in fact true, because of doubt whether it can
> be proved in court or fear of the expense of having to do
> so. They tend to make only statements which "steer far
> wider of the unlawful zone." . . . The rule thus dampens
> the vigor and limits the variety of public debate. It is in-
> consistent with the First and Fourteenth Amendments.[24]

While Brennan spoke of self-censorship, "steer[ing] far
wider of the unlawful zone," and "dampen[ing] the vig-
or . . . of public debate," Justice Goldberg, in his concurring

opinion, referred directly to the chilling effect: "The opinion of the Court conclusively demonstrates the chilling effect of the Alabama libel laws on First Amendment freedoms in the area of race relations."[25]

By 1967, the metaphoric chilling effect had become a "doctrine" widely relied on in judicial arguments and decisions dealing with a variety of First Amendment controversies. When in *Walker v. City of Birmingham* (1967) the Supreme Court decided 5–4 against Martin Luther King and several other civil rights leaders who had proceeded to parade in Birmingham after an injunction had been issued enjoining them from parading without a permit, Justice Brennan dissented, stating his argument figuratively: "To give these freedoms [speech, assembly, and petition] the necessary 'breathing space to survive' . . ., the Court has modified traditional rules of standing and prematurity. . . . We have modeled both substantive rights and procedural remedies in the fact of varied conflicting interests to conform to our overriding duty to insulate all individuals from the 'chilling effect' upon exercise of First Amendment freedoms generated by vagueness, overbreadth and unbridled discretion to limit their exercise."[26]

When in 1967 the Supreme Court decided against the W. E. B. DuBois Clubs of America, which had refused to register as a "Communist-front organization," as demanded by the Subversive Activities Control Board, Justice Douglas dissented, emphasizing that such registration would have a chilling effect: "If an organization is classified a Communist front, serious consequences follow: employment of its members is restricted . . . ; application for or use of passports is made illegal . . . ; registration is required . . . ; use of the mails and of the radio and TV is curtailed . . . ; tax exemptions are denied. . . . At least some of these provisions are unconstitutional under our decisions as bills of attainder or as a denial of First and Fifth Amendment rights. Yet vindication would come only after long and protracted hearings and appeals. Meanwhile there would be a profound 'chilling effect' on the exercise of First Amendment rights within the principle of *Dombrowski v. Pfister*."[27] Two paragraphs later,

Douglas again incorporated the chilling effect into his argument: "Harassing them [members of the DuBois Clubs] by public hearings and by probing into their beliefs and attitudes, pillorying them for their minority views by exposing them to the hearings under this Act—these actions will have the same 'chilling effect' as the Court held the trial in *Dombrowski* would have had."[28]

In *Zwickler v. Koota* (1967), when Justice Brennan invoked the metaphoric chilling effect, Justice Harlan questioned the applicability of the metaphor in this case, referring to the metaphoric chilling effect as "the ubiquitous and slippery 'chilling effect' doctrine."[29]

During the Vietnam War, the chilling effect became integral to decisions related to student deferments and classifications. In 1967, the chilling effect became an important part of the argument presented by Judge Harold Medina in a case dealing with the reclassification of college students from II-S to I-A because of their participation in protest activities against the Vietnam War. In deciding for the students, who had conducted their protests at the local office of the draft board in Ann Arbor, Michigan, Judge Medina wrote: "The effect of the reclassification itself is immediately to curtail the exercise of First Amendment rights, for there can be no doubt that the threat of receiving a I-A classification upon voicing dissent from our national policies has an immediate impact on the behavior of appellants and others similarly situated. . . . Certainly the justiciability of a given case cannot rest upon a distinction between a statute void on its face and a statute which is being applied in an unconstitutional fashion, for the chilling effect of the illegal Government action is equally great."[30]

While Judge Medina used the chilling-effect doctrine in deciding for the students in *Wolff*, one year later Judge Thornberry, of the U.S. Court of Appeals for the Fifth Circuit, argued that the chilling-effect doctrine was not applicable where "a twenty two year old Negro from New Orleans" refused to be inducted after he had lost his student deferment as a result of dropping out of school. Judge Thornberry wrote: "It is true that in *Wolff* . . . the Second Circuit, intervened in behalf of the registrants before administrative remedies had been exhausted because first amendment rights of free speech and free assembly were at stake. The local board had reclassified the registrants in demonstrations protesting American involvement in Vietnam. . . . Since the reclassification by the local board undoubtedly had a chilling effect on the exercise of free speech, immediate judicial action was justified."[31] However, in this case "it is apparent that Dubernay was not reclassified as a penalty for exercising first amendment rights, and it is equally apparent that it would not have been a futile gesture for him to exhaust administrative remedies."[32]

In 1967, after Selective Service Director General Hershey sent a letter to all members of the Selective Service promulgating a policy that war protesters lose their draft deferments, fifteen college students and three national student organizations challenged the constitutionality of the "Hershey directive." The students sought a judgment voiding the directive and an injunction against its enforcement. While the U.S. Court of Appeals for the District of Columbia did hold "that the deferment policy announced in the Hershey directive is unauthorized and contrary to law," the court did not "grant the requested injunction to accompany" the declaratory judgment. In support of the students who had challenged the directive, Chief Judge Bazelon wrote, after making the chilling-effect metaphor an integral part of his opinion, "Accordingly, we think the deferment policy works a pronounced chilling effect on legal or protected conduct."[33] The court held that "given a complaining party whose First Amendment rights are chilled, a suit against that portion of the Hershey directive which purports to authorize denial of deferments for illegal activity not covered by the delinquency regulations presents a justiciable controversy."[34] *National Student Association v. Hershey* illustrates especially well the extensive reliance of a court on the "chill" and "chilling effect," the court incorporating the metaphor into its reasoning over thirty-five times.

While the courts did argue that reclassification of students for antiwar activities, Alabama's libel laws, and New York's loyalty oath all had a chilling effect, in 1971 the Supreme Court decided against a group of citizens who had argued that U.S. Army surveillance of their political meetings had a chilling effect. In the 1960s, the army conducted surveillance of civilian political meetings, collecting information about "public activities that were thought to have at least some potential for civil disorder."[35] As reported in the Court's opinion, "Some of the information came from Army Intelligence agents who attended meetings that were open to the public and who wrote field reports describing the meetings, giving such data as the name of the sponsoring organization, the identity of speakers, the approximate number of persons in attendance, and indication of whether any disorder occurred. And still other information was provided to the Army by civilian law enforcement agencies."[36]

In his attack on such surveillance, Justice Douglas observed in his dissent: "It is alleged that the Army maintained files on the membership, ideology, programs, and practices of virtually every activist political group in the country, including groups such as the Southern Christian Leadership Conference, Clergy and Laymen United Against the War in Vietnam, the American Civil Liberties Union, Women's Strike for Peace, and the National Association for the Advancement of Colored People. The Army uses undercover agents to infiltrate these civilian groups. The Army moves as a secret group among civilian audiences, using cameras and electronic ears for surveillance."[37]

The Court considered whether army surveillance of peaceful political meetings would have a chilling effect. Would people who might otherwise attend such meetings be inhibited from attending because of the presence of army surveillance? Would such surveillance constitute a violation of the First Amendment rights of speech and assembly? The majority concluded that the citizens had not demonstrated any serious chilling effect, while the four dissenters contended that such surveillance might indeed inhibit lawful behavior and First Amendment rights. In the majority opinion, Justice Burger argued that it was incumbent upon the citizens to demonstrate that they had sustained, or were immediately in danger of sustaining, a direct injury as a result of the government's actions. "The respondents do not meet this test," said Burger:

Their claim, simply stated, is that they disagree with the judgments made by the Executive Branch with respect to the type and amount of information the Army needs and that the very existence of the Army's data-gathering system produces a constitutionally impermissible chilling effect upon the exercise of their First Amendment rights. That alleged "chilling" effect may perhaps be seen as arising from respondents' very perception of the system as inappropriate to the Army's role under our form of government, or as arising from respondents' less generalized yet speculative apprehensiveness that the Army may at some future date misuse the information in some way that would cause direct harm to respondents. Allegations of a subjective "chill" are not an adequate substitute for a claim of specific present objective harm or a threat of specific future harm.[38]

Justice Douglas's disagreement with the majority's decision was expressed in a sharply worded dissent in which he argued, with heavy reliance on tropes, that such surveillance had an inhibiting effect:

Army surveillance, like Army regimentation, is at war with the principles of the First Amendment. Those who already walk submissively will say there is no cause for alarm. But submissiveness is not our heritage. . . . The Constitution was designed to keep government off the backs of the people. The Bill of Rights was added to keep the precincts of belief and expression, of the press, of political and social activities free from surveillance. The Bill of Rights was designed to keep agents of government and official eavesdroppers away from assemblies of people. The aim was to allow men to be free and independent and to assert their rights against government. There can be no influence more paralyzing of that objective than Army surveillance. When an intelligence officer looks over every nonconformist's shoulder in the library, or walks invisibly by his side in a picket line, or infiltrates his club, the America once extolled as the voice of liberty heard around the world no longer is cast in the image which Jefferson and Madison designed, but more in the Russian image.[39]

In his biography of Douglas, *Independent Journey*, James F. Simon observes that Douglas's dissenting opinion in *Laird v. Tatum* "was one of the most stirring pleas for a return to the protection of civil liberties that Justice Douglas ever wrote."[40] That Douglas's plea is so stirring and vital is to a large extent attributable to his heavy reliance on tropes.

How prophetic was Justice Douglas's concern when he alluded to the "intelligence officer look[ing] over every nonconformist's shoulder in the library." In the late 1980s, the FBI instituted its Library Awareness Program, a surveillance program that had as its purpose the identification, by librarians, of suspicious-looking library patrons who checked out scientific and technical books. The "chilling effect" of this program was recognized by Congressman Don Edwards, a former FBI agent, who indicated his displeasure with the program in a letter to John E. Otto, acting director of the FBI: "This goes too far. It makes librarians into FBI informants, and threatens to bring suspicion on innocent people. How do librarians know if someone is a 'hostile intelligence agent?' Because he has a Russian or other foreign accent? Because he is interested in books on technical or scientific subjects?" Then Edwards declared: "The chilling effect of FBI agents asking librarians to report on users far outweighs any possible counterintelligence benefit."[41] Librarians who criticized the FBI's Library Awareness Program were themselves placed under scrutiny.[42]

If one used Justice Burger's reasoning, the FBI's surveillance would not constitute an interference with the First Amendment rights of the citizens who hesitated to check out books from the library or the rights of the librarians who hesitated to criticize the FBI's program since they could not demonstrate any "immediate injury." As Burger put it in *Laird*, their "allegations of a subjective 'chill' are not an adequate substitute for a claim of specific present objective harm or a threat of specific harm." Justice Douglas recognized almost two decades earlier the seriousness and the chilling effect of such surveillance when he warned in his *Laird* dissent of the "intelligence officer look[ing] over every nonconformist's shoulder in the library."

About the time *Laird* was decided in 1971, the metaphoric chilling effect began to be widely relied upon by courts at various levels in dealing with censorship in school libraries and classrooms. In 1969, a high school teacher gave to each member of his English class a copy of the September 1969 *Atlantic Monthly* magazine in which there appeared an article discussing "dissent, protest, radicalism and revolt," especially as related to the Vietnam War. The article contained "a vulgar word for an incestuous son," as the court of appeals put it, and the teacher said he could not agree with the school committee's demand that he never use the word again in the classroom. The teacher was suspended and took the issue to court.

When the case reached the First Circuit Court of Appeals, Judge Aldrich, deciding for the teacher, pointed out that students who found the assignment personally distasteful could have had an alternative one. He asserted that the article was in no sense pornographic and that no less than five books in the school library contained the offensive word. As for the chilling effect, Judge Aldridge wrote: "We accept the conclusion of the court below that 'some measure of public regulation of classroom speech is inherent in every provision of public education.' But when we consider the facts at bar as we have elaborated them, we find it difficult not to think that its application to the present case demeans any proper concept of education. The general chilling effect of permitting such rigorous censorship is even more serious."[43]

The chilling-effect doctrine was invoked one year later in *Parducci v. Rutland*, in which a U.S. district court in Alabama decided for a high school English teacher who had been dismissed because she had assigned her eleventh-grade class to read, over the principal's objections, Kurt Vonnegut's story "Welcome to the Monkey House." Chief Judge Johnson stated: "The safeguards of the First Amendment will quickly be brought into play to protect the right of academic freedom because any unwarranted invasion of this right will tend to have a chilling effect on the exercise of the right by other teachers."[44]

The court was especially cognizant of the relationship between vague policies, or no policies, to guide teachers.

Judge Johnson pointed out that "the record shows that prior to plaintiff's dismissal, there was no written or announced policy at Jefferson Davis High School governing the selection and assignment of outside materials." In effect, the teacher was not given prior notice "that the conduct for which she was punished was prohibited." "Our laws in this country," said the court, "have long recognized that no person should be punished for conduct unless such conduct has been proscribed in clear and precise terms. . . . When the conduct being punished involves First Amendment rights, as is the case here, the standards for judging permissible vagueness will be even more strictly applied." The court emphasized that "in the case before the Court, we are concerned not merely with vague standards, but with the total absence of standards. When a teacher is forced to speculate as to what conduct is permissible and what conduct is proscribed, he is apt to be overly cautious and reserved in the classroom. Such a reluctance on the part of a teacher to investigate and experiment with new and different ideas is anathema to the entire concept of academic freedom."[45]

The relationship between lack of prior notice and the chilling effect was a factor two years later when a U.S. district court in Iowa decided for a ninth-grade drama teacher who had been dismissed from her coaching position because of the "drinking and profanity" she allowed in a student production to which the principal and superintendent had objected. That the teacher, Ms. Webb, was not given adequate prior notice that what she was teaching was proscribed was especially important in the court's decision. Speaking for the court, Judge Hanson wrote: "Although the defendants would be justified in proscribing all vulgarity in the classroom or on the stage, they did not give adequate notice to Miss Webb that they had done so; the circumstances led Miss Webb to believe that they had not done so. The termination of Miss Webb without giving her prior notice that the teaching method she employed was not allowed denied her due process of law, and cannot but have a chilling effect upon the academic freedom of Miss Webb and the other teachers of Lake Mills to innovate and to develop new and more effective teaching methods which are reasonably relevant to the subject matter they are assigned to teach."[46]

In 1978, after some parents in Minnesota complained about the use of the film *The Lottery* and an accompanying "trailer film" that discusses the story, the parents' objections focusing "on the alleged violence in the films and their purported impact on the religious and family values of students," the school board passed a resolution "to completely eliminate the film and the trailer from the District's curriculum. The board gave no reasons for its decision."[47] Several students challenged the school board's banning of the film and when in 1982 the case reached the Court of Appeals for the Eighth Circuit, the court decided for the students. Judge Heaney argued that the school board had "failed to clearly inform students and teachers what it was proscribing as the constitution requires." For support he turned to the now classic lines from *Keyishian*: "When one must guess what conduct or utterance may lose him his position, one necessarily will 'steer far wider of the unlawful zone.' . . . *The danger of that chilling effect upon the exercise of vital First Amendment rights must be guarded against by sensitive tools which clearly inform . . . what is being proscribed.*"[48] Judge Heaney italicized the chilling-effect sentence.

When the school board attempted to justify the banning of the films by taking the position that "the short story remains available to teachers and students in the library in printed form and a phonographic recording," Judge Heaney responded: "This fact is not decisive. Restraint on protected speech generally cannot be justified by the fact that there may be other times, places or circumstances for such expression. . . . The symbolic effect of removing the films from the curriculum is more significant than the resulting limitation of access to the story. The board has used its official power to perform an act clearly indicating that the ideas contained in the films are unacceptable and should not be discussed or considered. This message is not lost on students and teachers, and its chilling effect is obvious."[49]

In this 1982 opinion several references are made to the 1980 court of appeals decision in *Pico v. Board of Education*

where the court had held against a school board that had
banned several books from the Island Trees Union Free School
District in New York. The three judges wrote three separate
opinions, Judges Sifton and Newman deciding against the
school board, Judge Mansfield dissenting. In his concurring
opinion, Judge Newman was conscious of the chilling effect
resulting from the censorship:

> The removal of a book from a school library will often be
> the sort of clearly-defined, school-wide action that carries
> with it the potential for impermissible suppression of ideas.
> It is possible, of course, for removal to be a casual, insig-
> nificant decision, as when the school librarian replaces an
> obsolete book, or discards a rarely-used one to make shelf
> space available for other volumes. But the deliberate deci-
> sion, taken by leading school officials, that a book is to be
> removed from the school library because of its ideas can
> hardly be placed in the same category. They signal to the
> students and teachers an official message that the ideas
> presented in those books are unacceptable, are wrong,
> and should not be discussed or considered. The chilling
> effect of this message on those who would express the
> ideas is all too apparent.[50]

In 1982, the Supreme Court also decided, 5–4, against the
school board, Justices Brennan (announcing the judgment of
the Court) and Blackmun (concurring) relying on the meta-
phor-personification argument from *Keyishian* that "the First
Amendment . . . does not tolerate laws which cast a pall of
orthodoxy over the classroom," both citing from *Tinker* the
metaphoric "In our system, students may not be regarded as
closed-circuit recipients of only that which the State chooses
to communicate."[51]

While the chilling effect was being relied upon by the
various courts dealing with a variety of issues—libel, loyalty
oaths, student and teacher rights, censorship—the metaphor
was often accompanied with three other tropes: "overbreadth,"
"breathing space," and "steering far wider than the unlawful
zone." In fact, when the words *chilling effect* were introduced
in *Gibson* in 1962, the "breathing-space" personification ap-

peared in the same opinion. Delivering the majority opinion, Justice Goldberg wrote: "The First and Fourteenth Amendment rights of free speech and free association are fundamental and highly prized, and 'need breathing space to survive.' *NAACP v. Button.* . . . 'Freedoms such as these are protected not only against heavy-handed frontal attack, but also from being stifled by more subtle governmental interference.'"[52]

The "breathing-space" personification had been introduced into judicial discourse by Justice Brennan in 1962: "These [First Amendment] freedoms are delicate and vulnerable, as well as supremely precious in our society. The threat of sanctions may deter their exercise almost as potently as the actual application of sanctions. . . . Because First Amendment freedoms need breathing space to survive, government may regulate in the area only with narrow specificity."[53] Brennan led into the "breathing-space" personification by first invoking the metaphoric "overbreadth" doctrine: "It makes no difference that the instant case was not a criminal prosecution and not based on a refusal to comply with a licensing requirement. The objectionable quality of vagueness and overbreadth does not depend upon absence of fair notice to a criminally accused or upon unchanneled delegation of legislative powers, but upon the danger of tolerating, in the area of First Amendment freedoms, the existence of a penal statute susceptible of sweeping and improper application."[54]

The combination of these three tropes appeared in Justice Marshall's dissenting opinion in *Arnett v. Kennedy* (1974), along with several others: "The majority misunderstands the overbreadth principle which concerns the potential deterrent effect on constitutionally protected speech of a statute that is overbroad or vague on its face. The focus of the doctrine is not on the individual actor before the court but on others who may forgo protected activity rather than run afoul of the statute's proscriptions. Hence, the Court has reversed convictions where the subject speech could have been punished under a more narrowly drawn statute because the statute as drawn purported to cover, and might deter others from engaging in, protected speech."[55]

Marshall then quoted from *Keyishian*, in which the Court had relied on the "breathing-space" personification and the metaphoric "chilling effect" and "steer far wider." Justice Marshall relied on still another trope, the "sword of Damocles":

> By the uncertainty of its scope, the standard here creates the very danger of a chilling effect that concerned the Court in *Keyishian*. Employees are likely to limit their behavior to that which is unquestionably safe, for "the threat of dismissal from public employment is . . . a potent means of inhibiting speech." *Pickering*, 391 U.S., at 574. The dismissal standard hangs over their heads like a sword of Damocles, threatening them with dismissal for any speech that might impair the "efficiency of the service." That this Court will ultimately vindicate an employee if his speech is constitutionally protected is of little consequence — for the value of a sword of Damocles is that it hangs — not that it drops. For every employee who risks his job by testing the limits of the statute, many more will choose the cautious path and not speak at all.[56]

The influence of these three tropes — "chilling effect," "overbreadth," and "breathing space" — on judicial argument is especially evident in *Gasparinetti v. Kerr* (1977), a case dealing with police-department regulations placing restrictions on the speech of police officers. The Court of Appeals for the Third Circuit placed all three tropes together in two separate parts of the opinion. Early in the opinion, Judge Garth, drawing on three Supreme Court decisions, wrote:

> "A clear and precise enactment may nevertheless be 'overbroad' if in its reach it prohibits constitutionally protected conduct." *Grayned v. City of Rockford*. . . . "Because the First Amendment freedoms need breathing space to survive, government may regulate in the area only with narrow specificity." *NAACP v. Button*. . . . Since there is a great danger that the exercise of first amendment rights will be chilled by penalties on speech, see *Keyishian v. Board of Regents*. . . , the regulation must be in "terms susceptible of objective measurement," *Cramp v. Board of Public Instruction*. . . .

> When faced with an overbreadth challenge a court must decide, first, if there is a legitimate and substantial state interest in regulating a class of speech, and, if so, whether that interest is being "pursued by means that broadly stifle fundamental personal liberties when the end can be more narrowly achieved."[57]

Later in the opinion, referring to the difficulty a police officer would have in making a fine distinction between finding a department policy "unwise" and finding the policy "stupid," interpretation of the policy indicating that the former was a violation of the regulation but the latter not, the court again turned to the three tropes in developing its argument: "We do not think that a police officer should be required to make such a subtle distinction when it involves his first amendment rights. It is precisely this kind of broad, overinclusive restriction on speech which deprives first amendment freedoms of the breathing space those liberties need to survive . . . since the person regulated can never be certain that he will not be penalized for speech which is indeed protected. That avoidance of this chilling effect is at the heart of the overbreadth doctrine."[58]

Justice O'Connor, delivering the opinion of the Court in *Philadelphia Newspapers, Inc. v. Hepps*, incorporated the "chilling-effect" and the "breathing-space" tropes into her opinion. An important element in her argument was that "freedoms of expression require 'breathing space.'"[59] Later, Justice O'Connor drew on the chilling-effect doctrine to support her position:

> The need to encourage debate on public issues that concerned the Court in the governmental-restriction cases is of concern in a similar manner in this case involving a private suit for damages: placement by state law of the burden of proving truth upon media defendants who publish speech of public concern deters such speech because of the fear that liability will unjustifiably result. . . . Because such a "chilling" effect would be antithetical to the First Amendment's protection of true speech on matters of public concern, we believe that a private-figure plaintiff

must bear the burden of showing that the speech at issue
is false before recovering damages for defamation from a
media defendant.[60]

The "breathing-space" personification appeared several
times in Chief Justice Rehnquist's opinion in *Hustler Magazine
v. Falwell* where the Court decided for the magazine, Falwell
claiming "emotional distress" resulting from a parody. Chief
Justice Rehnquist said: "But even though falsehoods have
little value in and of themselves, they are 'nevertheless inevitable in a free debate, ' . . . and a rule that would impose
strict liability on a publisher for false factual assertions would
have an undoubted 'chilling' effect on speech relating to
public figures that does have constitutional value. 'Freedoms
of expression require "breathing space." ' . . . This breathing
space is provided by a constitutional rule that allows public
figures to recover for libel or defamation only when they can
prove *both* that the statement was false and that the statement
was made with requisite level of culpability."[61] Later in the
opinion, Rehnquist relied on the personification to conclude
his argument:

> We conclude that public figures and public officials may
> not recover for the tort of intentional infliction of emotion-
> al distress by reason of publications such as the one here
> at issue without showing in addition that the publication
> contains a false statement of fact which was made with
> "actual malice," i.e., with knowledge that the statement
> was false or with reckless disregard as to whether or not it
> was true. This is not merely a "blind application" of the
> *New York Times* standard, . . . it reflects our considered
> judgment that such a standard is necessary to give ade-
> quate "breathing space" to the freedoms protected by the
> First Amendment.[62]

All of these tropes are not recognized equally as figurative expressions. The "overbreadth" metaphor has become a
dead metaphor. More often than not, the person using the
metaphor and the reader or listener does not recognize that a
term is being used nonliterally. *Breadth* originally referred to

the width of an object. The *OED* gives as the first definition "Measure or distance from side to side of a surface; width, extent across." The second definition: "A piece (of cloth, etc.) of the full breadth, without reference to its length; a width." Definition 4: "*fig.* Largeness (of mind, sentiment, or view), liberality catholicity; also, wide or broad display of a quality." According to the *OED*, it was not until the nineteenth century that *breadth* appeared as a metaphor.[63] Today one is more likely to see *breadth* in reference to the nonmaterial (knowledge, concerns, freedoms, etc.) than objects; the metaphoric use of the term has become more widespread than the literal.

Just how much impact and power does the overbreadth doctrine have? More than one justice has declared that the overbreadth doctrine's application is "strong medicine." In *Broadrick v. Oklahoma* (1972), Justice White not only recognized that the "First Amendment needs breathing space"[64] but also expressed concern about "facial overbreadth," and at one point referred to the medicinal qualities of "overbreadth": "Application of the overbreadth doctrine in this manner is, manifestly, strong medicine."[65] As Justice White sees it, the application of the overbreadth doctrine is not only "strong medicine" but "manifestly, strong medicine." The problem with this wording is that *manifest* means "clearly revealed to the eye, mind, or judgment; open to view or comprehension; obvious."[66] *Manifestly*, the *OED* tells us, is "evidently, unmistakably."[67] Something that is manifest is apparent to the senses, is evident.[68] The difficulty is that obviously, plainly, apparent to my senses—manifestly—the application of the overbreadth doctrine is not a "medicine." White's *manifestly* demetaphorizes "strong medicine"; but the sentence makes sense only if the language is seen as nonliteral.

Almost two decades later, in 1990, Justice White, in *Osborne v. Ohio*, stated: "The overbreadth doctrine, as we have recognized, is indeed 'strong medicine.'"[69] Justice O'Connor also saw medicinal qualities in the overbreadth doctrine when she delivered the opinion of the Court in *Airport Comm'rs v. Jews for Jesus* (1972): "A statute may be invalidated on its face, however, only if the overbreadth is 'substantial.' . . . The requirement that the overbreadth be substantial arose from our recognition that application of the overbreadth doctrine is, 'manifestly, strong medicine.'"[70]

While the "overbreadth" metaphor has become a dead metaphor, the judiciary's use of "chilling effect" does make one more conscious that language is not being used literally. *Chill* is too readily identified with the physical, and one can hardly avoid the nonphysical sense when it appears in court opinions dealing with First Amendment freedoms. As indicated earlier, the metaphoric *chill* brings with it coldness, shivering, sensations that make it more effective in conveying danger and fear than the more abstract *deter* or *inhibit*. "Chilling effect" creates a different reality than "inhibiting effect"; injury, danger, and physical threat accompany the former but not the latter.

"Breathing space," even more than "chilling effect," is clearly recognizable as a trope, a personification that carries with it images of life, vitality, inhaling and exhaling; to be breathing is to be alive. When Justices Goldberg, Brennan, Rehnquist, O'Connor, and others declare that the First Amendment freedoms "need breathing space to survive," the personification of the freedoms, attributing to the abstractions the ability to breathe, to live or die, brings forth a reality that a literal expression of the idea would not. With "breathing space to survive" comes a sense of more urgency, much more a sense of life and death, than does a literal assertion that "if we want to maintain our First Amendment freedoms, we must allow people to express themselves as freely as possible." Further, another trope such as "in order to enjoy our First Amendment freedoms, we must give them plenty of room to expand" would not carry the urgency and sense of survival that the "breathing-space" personification does.

Through the use of these tropes, the courts have determined to a significant extent how we conceptualize our First Amendment freedoms. When a metaphor or a personification has been repeated during a two-decade period over five hundred times (as in the case of "chilling effect") and over three hundred times ("breathing space") in published opinions, this tropological language cannot be ignored as mere embellishment and ornament. People in power are imposing tropes that affect our perceptions. The sheer repetition of these tropes illustrates their influence on judicial decision making. Such an extensive reliance on the figurative "chilling effect" and "breathing space" is not to be viewed as unusual, for as Judge Richard Posner has observed, "Science, not to mention everyday thought, is influenced by metaphors. Why shouldn't law be?"[71]

6

The Metaphoric
"Captive Audience"

After a tiring vacation or an unproductive business trip, you go to the airport to catch your plane home. You stand in line at the ticket counter to check in your luggage, and you are approached by a member of the International Society of Krishna Consciousness who hands you a religious tract and suggests a contribution. Are you a "captive audience"? Having checked in your luggage, you wearily walk down the airport corridor toward the departure area. You are confronted with a political message, at one of the advertising areas, entitled *SWAPO Rape of Namibia*: "Do you Know—1. SWAPO (South West Africa People's Organization) is a Soviet-bloc terrorist group? 2. SWAPO is trying to take over Namibia by violence? 3. SWAPO is financed by the United Nations? 4. U.S. taxpayers finance the United Nations." Sketches labeled "Military Equipment Supplied by Soviet Bloc" and "SWAPO Terrorism" appear in the display. As you walk down the corridor, are you a "captive audience" to a political message you would just as soon not be exposed to at this time and place?

Finally you reach the boarding area, waiting to board the plane in twenty minutes. Sitting in this boarding area thinking about getting home with as little hassle as possible, you are approached by a member of the Jews for Jesus movement who is distributing religious literature of the organization. Are you a "captive audience" in this boarding area?

You are not literally a captive in any of these instances. Literally, a person is a captive when forcibly confined, restrained, or subjugated as a prisoner, the word *captive*, derived from *capere*, meaning "to seize." Captivity is often identified with violence and war. The *OED's* first definition of *captive* is "Taken prisoner of war, or by force; kept in confinement or bondage."[1] While you may not be literally a captive audience at the various locations in the airport, you may, according to the courts, be metaphorically in captivity in some areas of the airport. The metaphoric "captive audience" has played an important role in First Amendment decisions related to expression in a variety of locations: airports, buses, schools, homes.

In the airport cases, the degree of captivity appears to determine to a large extent whether the proselytizers will get First Amendment protection. The U.S. Court of Appeals for the District of Columbia, in deciding that the anti-SWAPO ad could not be banned from the airport corridors, contended that "a person in the airports' concourses or walkways who considers an advertisement—commercial or noncommercial—to be objectable enjoys the freedom simply to walk away that a passenger on a bus does not."[2] The reference to being a captive on a bus is based on a 1974 Supreme Court decision, *Lehman v. City of Shaker Heights*, in which the Court decided that the city's refusal to make available advertising space for a candidate who wanted to place his ads in city buses did not violate the candidate's free-speech or equal-protection rights.[3] The Court concluded that the bus riders were a captive audience, and in his concurring opinion, Justice Douglas wrote: "In my view the right of the commuters to be free from forced intrusions on their privacy precludes the city from transforming its vehicles of public transportation into forums for the dissemination of ideas upon this captive audience."[4]

Justice Brennan, with three other justices, dissented in *Lehman*, rejecting the city's arguments. After observing that "commercial and public service advertisements are routinely accepted for display, while political messages are absolutely forbidden,"[5] Brennan wrote:

> The city contends that its ban against political advertising
> is bottomed upon its solicitous regard for "captive riders"
> of the rapid transit system, who are "forced to endure the

advertising thrust upon [them]." . . . Since its rapid transit system is primarily a mode of transportation, the city
argues that it may prohibit political advertising in order to
shield its transit passengers from sometimes controversial
or unsettling speech. Whatever merit the city's argument
might have in other contexts, it has a hollow ring in the
present case, where the city has voluntarily opened its
rapid transit system as a forum for communication. In
that circumstance, the occasional appearance of provocative speech should be expected.[6]

Brennan argued further that the passengers were not
forced to read the messages:

Moreover, even if it were possible to draw a manageable
line between controversial and noncontroversial messages, the city's practice of censorship for the benefit of
"captive audiences" still would not be justified. This is not
a case where an unwilling or unsuspecting rapid transit
rider is powerless to avoid messages he deems unsettling. . . . Transit passengers are not forced or compelled
to read any of the messages, nor are they "incapable of de-
clining to receive [them]." . . . Should passengers chance
to glance at advertisements they find offensive, they can
"effectively avoid further bombardment of their sensibilities simply by averting their eyes."[7]

In 1981, the Ninth Circuit Court of Appeals decided that
the ordinance requiring advance registration by those desiring to exercise First Amendment rights at the Portland International Airport was unconstitutional.[8] In deciding for Jews
for Jesus, the court held that "persons desiring to exercise
their free speech rights may not be required to give advance
notice and to identify themselves and their sponsors to Port
authorities."[9] However, Judge Smith dissented, arguing that
people who use airports are "captives": "The people who use
airports are of necessity funnelled through narrow portals.
They must travel in relatively fixed channels from the exit gate
to the luggage carrousel; from the ticket counter to the departure gate. These people are in a sense captives. They do not

have the freedom to choose alternate routes, as do users of the city streets, nor the freedom to deviate from the route, once chosen, to avoid annoyance or disturbance. I think it is the duty of the airport board to make travel as convenient as possible for these captives."[10]

The U.S. district court in Dallas, Texas, deciding for the International Society of Krishna Consciousness (ISKON), which had challenged the constitutionality of an ordinance passed by the cities of Dallas, Forth Worth, and Grapevine regulating the solicitation of charitable contributions at the Dallas/Fort Worth Airport, concluded that "at least part of the airport terminal buildings are public forums, and therefore the portion of the resolution and ordinances that prohibits solicitation within the terminal buildings is facially unconstitutional as overbroad."[11] In considering the captive-audience question, court declared: "Some parts of the inside terminals are probably private (for example, the areas restricted to flight personnel); other areas may or may not be public forums (for example, the American Airlines main departure lounge or the Braniff individual departure seating areas); but clearly there are portions of the terminal (for example, the public corridors and entrance halls to the airport terminal buildings) that are public forums. In those areas the public is not a captive audience (as they may be in the departure lounge areas), nor is access otherwise restricted for safety or security reasons (as it presumably is in the flight personnel areas)."[12]

A U.S. district court in New York, in *Intern. Soc. for Krishna Consciousness v. Lee* (1989), agreed with ISKCON "that the airports' character, pattern of activity and nature of purpose make the terminals appropriate places for the exercise of First Amendment activity and place them squarely within the public forum family. Given that finding, no argument is presented here — nor can one be made in earnest — that defendant's blanket prohibition on leafletting and solicitation is narrowly tailored to further a compelling state interest."[13] The court rejected the Port Authority's captive-audience argument: "Defendant further argues that the presence of captive audiences distinguishes the airports from the traditional public fora of streets and parks. . . . With this contention, we do not agree. Captive audiences group outside city concert halls, movie theaters, and outdoor concession stands to the same extent as they form at airport ticket counters, baggage conveyor belts, and security checkpoints."[14]

The court further rejected the Port Authority's argument that pedestrian congestion and security concerns were unique to the terminal facilities: "Indeed, if concerns over the movement of traffic were sufficient justification for the suppression of First Amendment activity, then the clogged and narrow arteries of downtown Manhattan might, as easily, be denied public forum status. Like the presence of captive audiences, the Port Authority's legitimate concerns over congestion and security are more appropriately the subject of time, place and manner restrictions."[15]

Where one judge sees the passenger waiting in line at the ticket counter as a captive, another judge sees the same passenger as not much different from the person waiting in a movie-theater line. Where one judge sees the passenger walking from the ticket counter to the boarding gate as a captive, another judge does not.

Since the middle of the twentieth century, the "captive audience" has appeared so often in court opinions dealing with a variety of First Amendment issues that it has become a crucial, durable trope appearing in the premises used by judges in arguments to justify their decisions. And ever since the middle of the twentieth century, courts have been disagreeing on what constitutes "captivity" and who is a "captive audience." In 1951, the District of Columbia Court of Appeals decided against the Public Utilities Commission, which had permitted the installation of loudspeakers in some District of Columbia buses and streetcars, loudspeakers over which music, announcements, time signals, and six minutes of advertising per hour were broadcast. The court declared: "Transit passengers commonly have to hear the broadcasts whether they want to or not. . . . WWDC-FM, the transmitting station, advertised in 1949 that Transit Radio was 'delivering a guaranteed audience.' Formerly they were free to read, talk, meditate or relax. The broadcasts have replaced freedom of attention with forced listening."[16]

The court dealt with the captive audience and "forced listening":

No occasion had arisen until now to give effect to freedom from forced listening as a constitutional right. Short of imprisonment, the only way to compel a man's attention for many minutes is to bombard him with sound that he cannot ignore in a place he must be. The law of nuisance protects him at home. At home or at work, the constitutional question has not arisen because the government has taken no part in forcing people to listen. Until radio was developed and someone realized that the passengers of a monopoly are a captive audience, there was no profitable way of forcing people to listen while they travel between home and work or on necessary errands.[17]

The Public Utilities Commission appealed, and the following year the Supreme Court concluded that the commission's order permitting the radio broadcasting on the buses and streetcars was constitutional.[18] Arguing that there was no violation of the First Amendment, the Court asserted that the programs did not interfere "substantially with the conversation of passengers or with rights of communication constitutionally protected in public places" and that "there is no substantial claim that the programs have been used for objectionable propaganda."[19] The Court also rejected the lower court's position that the radio programs were an invasion of the constitutional right of privacy of the passengers:

This claim is that no matter how much Capital Transit may wish to use radio in its vehicles as part of its service to its passengers and as a source of income, no matter how much the great majority of its passengers may desire radio in those vehicles, and however positively the Commission, on substantial evidence, may conclude that such use of radio does not interfere with the convenience, comfort and safety of the service but tends to improve it, yet if one passenger objects to the programs as an invasion of his constitutional right of privacy, the use of radio on the vehicles must be discontinued. This position wrongly assumes that the Fifth Amendment secures to each passenger on a public vehicle regulated by the Federal Government a right of privacy substantially equal to the privacy to which he is entitled in his own home.[20]

Justice Frankfurter found the transit system's broadcasting practice so objectionable that he took no part in the consideration or decision of this case. At the end of his two-paragraph explanation, Frankfurter wrote: "My feelings are so strongly engaged as a victim of the practice in controversy that I had better not participate in judicial judgment upon it."[21]

Justice Douglas, dissenting, argued that the transit riders were indeed a captive audience: "The streetcar audience is a captive audience. It is there as a matter of necessity, not of choice. One who is in a public vehicle may not of course complain of the noise of the crowd and the babble of tongues. One who enters any public place sacrifices some of his privacy. My protest is against the invasion of his privacy over and beyond the risks of travel."[22]

In 1984, the Chicago Transit Authority (CTA) refused to accept the Planned Parenthood Association's advertising for display on CTA's buses, trains, and facilities. The Planned Parenthood Association charged that this was a violation of its First Amendment rights. In deciding for the Planned Parenthood Association, a U.S. district court in Illinois noted that "CTA had displayed cards and signs . . . advertising and communicating with the public as to" political candidates, draft registration, AIDS, religious organizations, gun registration, and other products, causes, and groups.[23] Speaking to the issue of the audience's captivity, the court said:

> What of the "captive audience" doctrine in this case? As
> *Erznoznik* teaches . . . , it must be shown the medium is
> "so obtrusive as to make it impossible for an unwilling in-
> dividual to avoid exposure to it." Although transit facili-
> ties are more cramped and restricted than public streets,
> CTA has certainly not shown its medium of advertising
> makes it *impossible* for an unwilling individual to avert his
> eyes (contrast, for example, the passengers' inability to es-
> cape messages delivered by loudspeakers on transit vehi-

cles dealt with in *Public Utilities Commission v. Pollak* . . .).
CTA cannot justify its content-based regulation on the basis of the "captive audience" doctrine. It is of course not
impossible for CTA riders to avert their eyes from the
printed message PPA [Planned Parenthood Association]
seeks to deliver.[24]

Just as the judiciary has not always agreed whether one is
in captivity at the airport terminal (or certain locations at the
airport) or on the bus, so have they disagreed about the extent
of one's captivity in the home. In 1969, the captive audience
was a consideration in the Supreme Court decision in *Rowan v.
Post Office Dept.* where the Court decided for the Post Office,
which had been given the power by Congress to prohibit
mailers of sexually provocative and sexually arousing advertisements from sending such ads to people who had requested that such mailings not be delivered to them. The
postmaster would order the mailers to delete the names of
those people who had so requested from their lists. Chief
Justice Burger, delivering the opinion of the Court, said: "In
today's complex society we are inescapably captive audiences
for many purposes, but a sufficient measure of individual
autonomy must survive to permit every household to exercise
control over unwanted mail."[25]

The Chief Justice argued that no one has a right to force
even good ideas on an unwilling recipient: "We therefore
categorically reject the argument that a vendor has a right
under our Constitution or otherwise to send unwanted material into the home of another. If this prohibition operates to
impede the flow of even valid ideas, the answer is that no one
has a right to press even 'good' ideas on an unwilling recipient. That we are often 'captive' outside the sanctuary of the
home, are subject to objectionable speech and other sounds
does not mean we must be captive everywhere."[26]

While in *Rowen* the Court argued that a householder's
captivity in his or her own home gave Congress the power to
prohibit mailers of sexually provocative advertisements from
sending such ads to people who had requested that such
mailings not be delivered to them, in *Consolidated Edison Co. v.*

Public Service Comm'n. (1980) the Court did not see the householders as captive when receiving pro-nuclear-power propaganda included in their utility billings. In 1976, the Consolidated Edison Company of New York had placed into its billing
envelopes written material entitled "Independence Is Still a
Goal, and Nuclear Power Is Needed to Win the Battle." The
Public Service Commission ruled that utilities could not use
bill inserts to discuss "political matters, including the desir-
ability of future development of nuclear power. . . . The Commission concluded that Consolidated Edison customers who
receive bills containing inserts are a captive audience of
diverse views who should not be subjected to the utility's
beliefs. Accordingly the Commission barred utility companies from including bill inserts that express 'their opinions or
viewpoints on controversial issues of public policy.' "[27]

Justice Powell, delivering the majority opinion, rejected
the Commission's argument that the prohibition was needed
"to avoid forcing Consolidated Edison's views on a captive
audience." Powell declared:

> Even if a short exposure to Consolidated Edison's views
> may offend the sensibilities of some consumers, the abili-
> ty of government 'to shut off discourse solely to protect
> others from hearing it [is] dependent upon a showing that
> substantial privacy interests are being invaded in an es-
> sentially intolerable manner. . . . Where a single speaker
> communicates to many listeners, the First Amendment
> does not permit the government to prohibit speech as in-
> trusive unless the "captive" audience cannot avoid objec-
> tionable speech. . . . The customer of Consolidated
> Edison may escape exposure to objectionable material
> simply by transferring the bill insert from envelope to
> wastebasket.[28]

While the wastebasket was available in 1980 to those
receiving the pro-nuclear-power materials along with their
billings, the wastebasket was apparently not available in 1969
to householders who received sexually provocative advertisements.

What of unsolicited advertisements for contraceptives? Is the householder in captivity when receiving such ads in the mail? Title 39 U.S.C. §3001(e)(2) states that "any unsolicited advertisements of matter which is designed, adapted, or intended for preventing conception is nonmailable matter, shall not be carried or delivered by mail, and shall be disposed of as the Postal Service directs." When Youngs Drug Products Corporation proposed to mail unsolicited advertisements promoting its products, along with material discussing venereal disease and family planning, it was told by the Post Office that such mailings would violate the U.S. Code. Justice Marshall, delivering the opinion of the Court in *Bolger v. Youngs Drug Products Corp.* (1983), declared §3001(e)(2) unconstitutional as applied to the mailings. In deciding against the Post Office, the Court said: "We have never held that the Government itself can shut off the flow of mailings to protect those recipients who might potentially be offended. The First Amendment 'does not permit the government to prohibit speech as intrusive unless the "captive" audience cannot avoid objectionable speech.' *Consolidated Edison*. . . . Recipients of objectionable mailings, however, may 'effectively avoid further bombardment of their sensibilities simply by averting their eyes.' . . . Consequently, the 'short, though regular, journey from mail box to trash can . . . is an acceptable burden, at least so far as the Constitution is concerned.'"[29]

While in *Consolidated Edison* Justice Powell suggested that the objectionable mailings could be transferred from "envelope to wastebasket," Justice Marshall suggested in *Bolger* that the recipient could transfer the objectionable ads "from mail box to trash can," both contending that the "captive audience" in the home could easily avoid the objectionable materials, the captivity minimized because exposure to the ads could be remedied by the recipient.

While *Bolger* and *Consolidated Edison* tell us that we can avoid offensive advertisements mailed to us by discarding them in the wastebasket or trash can, *F.C.C. v. Pacifica Foundation* (1978) tells us that our ability to turn off the radio is not enough.

On October 30, 1973, a New York FM radio station broadcast George Carlin's recorded monologue "Filthy Words" after it had advised the radio audience that the recording included "sensitive language which might be regarded as offensive to some." After a listener's complaint about the broadcast of the Carlin recording, the FCC declared that Pacifica (which owned the radio station) "could have been the subject of administrative sanctions" as a result of broadcasting materials containing "indecent" language. When the issue reached District of Columbia Court of Appeals, Judge Tamm wrote: "The Commission also attempts to justify its Order by claiming that, due to the intrusive nature of broadcasting, a captive audience is present. This argument is persuasive when the degree of captivity makes it impractical for the unwilling viewer or auditor to avoid exposure. However, as the Supreme Court noted in *Lehman v. City of Shaker Heights* . . . , '[t]he radio can be turned off.'"[30]

However, that was not enough for the majority of the Supreme Court that one year later reversed, Justice Stevens arguing for the plurality:

> The broadcast media have established a uniquely pervasive presence in the lives of all Americans. Patently offensive, indecent material presented over the airwaves confronts the citizen, not only in public, but also in the privacy of the home, where the individual's right to be left alone plainly outweighs the First Amendment rights of an intruder. *Rowen v. Post Office Dept.* . . . Because the broadcast audience is constantly tuning in and out, prior warnings cannot completely protect the listener or viewer from unexpected program content. To say that one may avoid further offense by turning off the radio when he hears indecent language is like saying that the remedy for an assault is to run away after the first blow.[31]

Justice Powell argued in his concurring opinion that the FCC "was entitled to give this factor [the audience's captivity] appropriate weight in the circumstances of the instant case":

> Broadcasting—unlike most other forms of communication—comes directly into the home, the one place where people ordinarily have the right not to be assaulted by un-

invited and offensive sights and sounds. . . . Although
the First Amendment may require unwilling adults to absorb the first blow of offensive but protected speech when
they are in public before they turn away . . . , a different
order of values obtains at home. "That we are often 'captives' outside the sanctuary of the home and subject to
objectionable speech and other sounds does not mean we
must be captives everywhere." . . . The Commission also
was entitled to give this factor appropriate weight in the
circumstances of the instant case.[32]

In his dissenting opinion Justice Brennan argued that the
listener at home was not in such a state of captivity that he
could not turn off the radio: "Even if an individual who
voluntarily opens his home to radio communications retains
privacy interests of sufficient moment to justify a ban on
protected speech if those interests are 'invaded in an essen-
tially intolerable manner,' *Cohen v. California* . . . , the very
fact that those interests are threatened only by a radio broadcast precludes any intolerable invasion of privacy; for unlike
other intrusive modes of communication, such as sound trucks,
'[t]he radio can be turned off,' *Lehman v. Shaker Heights* . . .
and with minimum of effort. As Chief Judge Bazelon aptly
observed below, 'having elected to receive public air waves,
the scanner who stumbles onto an offensive program is in the
same position as the unsuspecting passers-by in *Cohen* and
Erznoznik . . . ; he can avert his attention by changing channels or turning off the set.'"[33] Brennan suggested that the
listener who "inadvertently tunes into a program he finds
offensive . . . can simply extend the arm and switch stations
or flick the 'off' button."[34]

While Brennan spoke of the "individual who voluntarily
opens his home to radio communications" and "the scanner
who stumbles onto an offensive program" and "inadvertently
tunes into a program he finds offensive," Justices Stevens and
Powell used figurative language creating an ominous threat to
the "captive audience." First, Stevens portrayed Pacifica's radio broadcast of offensive speech as an "intruder" that carries
with it the connotations of forced entry, of trespass and

encroachment; *intruders*, especially in reference to a home, creates images of something physical, a criminal, to be protected against. In his next sentence Stevens continues the threatening image by asserting that "prior warnings cannot completely protect the listener or viewer from unexpected program content," this content, of course, being the "intruder" against whom the listener at home needed protection. Stevens follows this with an analogical argument that also relies on the language of violence: "To say that one may avoid further offense by turning off the radio when he hears indecent language is like saying that the remedy for an assault is to run away after the first blow." Aside from the questionable analogical argument, the sentence identifies, through analogy, nonviolent radio indecent speech with the physical and violent "assault" and "first blow."

Justice Powell takes up the "assault" image by contending that the "one place where people ordinarily have the right not to be assaulted by uninvited and offensive signs and sounds" is one's home. And while Stevens had used the assault–first blow literally in an analogical argument, Powell uses the same violent language not to state an analogy but to present a figurative "first blow": "Although the First Amendment may require unwilling adults to absorb the first blow of offensive but protected speech when they are in public. . . ." Powell has personified offensive speech, giving it the power to land a "first blow" on unwilling adults. Having identified offensive speech with the physical, threatening, and dangerous "intruder," "assault," and "first blow," the Court could more easily come to the conclusion that Pacifica's broadcasting of the George Carlin recording was not protected by the First Amendment. After all, an *assault* is "an onset or rush upon any one with hostile intent; an attack with blows or weapons."[35]

Justices Stevens, Powell, and Brennan all cited *Cohen v. California* (1971) where the Court had given First Amendment protection to Paul Cohen, who had worn on the back of his jacket the message "Fuck the Draft" while he walked down the corridors of the Los Angeles County Courthouse. In response to the state's argument that Cohen's offensive message was thrust upon a captive audience, Justice Harlan, delivering the opinion of the Court, after pointing out that this was not an obscenity or a fighting-words case, devoted a significant portion of his opinion to the captive-audience issue:

> Finally, in arguments before this Court much has been made of the claim that Cohen's distasteful mode of expression was thrust upon unwilling or unsuspecting viewers, and that the State might therefore legitimately act as it did in order to protect the sensitive from otherwise unavoidable exposure to appellant's crude form of protest. Of course, the mere presumed presence of unwitting listeners or viewers does not serve automatically to justify curtailing all speech capable of giving offense. . . . While this Court has recognized that government may properly act in many situations to prohibit intrusion into the privacy of the home of unwelcome views and ideas which cannot be totally banned from the public dialogue, *e.g., Rown v. Post Office Dept.* . . . , we have at the same time consistently stressed that "we are often 'captives' outside the sanctuary of the home and subject to objectionable speech." . . . The ability of government, consonant with the Constitution, to shut off discourse solely to protect others from hearing it is, in other words, dependent upon a showing that substantial privacy interests are being invaded in an essentially intolerable manner. Any broader view of this authority would effectively empower a majority to silence dissidents simply as a matter of personal predilections.
>
> In this regard, persons confronted with Cohen's jacket were in a quite different posture than, say, those subjected to the raucous emissions of sound trucks blaring outside their residences. Those in the Los Angeles courthouse could effectively avoid further bombardment of their sensibilities simply by averting their eyes. And, while it may be that one has a more substantial claim to a recognizable privacy interest when walking through a courthouse corridor than, for example, strolling through Central Park, surely it is nothing like the interest in being free from unwanted expression in the confines of one's own home. . . . Given the subtlety and complexity of the factors involved if Cohen's "speech" was otherwise entitled to constitutional protection, we do not think the fact

that some unwilling "listeners" in a public building may
have been briefly exposed to it can serve to justify this
breach of the peace conviction where, as here, there was
no evidence that persons powerless to avoid appellant's
conduct did in fact object to it, and where that portion of
the statute upon which Cohen's conviction rests evinces
no concern, either on its face or as construed by the California courts, with the special plight of the captive auditor, but, instead, indiscriminately sweeps within its
prohibitions all "offensive conduct" that disturbs "any
neighborhood or person."[36]

If those persons offended by Cohen's message could avert
their eyes to avoid "further bombardment of their sensibilities," what of those people in Skokie, Illinois, who were
offended by having Nazis parading in their town? In deciding
in 1978 that the village of Skokie could not prohibit through
the town's permit system the march by the Nazis in front of
the village hall, the Seventh Circuit Court of Appeals argued:
"This case does not involve intrusion into people's homes.
There *need* be no captive audience, as Village residents may, if
they wish, simply avoid the Village Hall for thirty minutes on
a Sunday afternoon. . . . Absent such intrusion or captivity,
there is no justifiable substantial privacy interest to save
[Ordinance] 995 from constitutional infirmity, when it attempts, by fiat, to declare the entire Village, at all times, a
privacy zone that may be sanitized from the offensiveness of
Nazi Ideology and symbols."[37]
Are you a captive audience as you walk down the sidewalk
and look up to see in a Seattle apartment window an American flag placed upside down, over which is taped a peace
symbol? You are not, said the Supreme Court in *Spence v.
Washington,* the Court deciding for Spence, who had placed
the upside-down flag with the peace symbol in his apartment
window. The Court took into consideration the captive-audience factor along with the interests the state may have in
banning such a display: "The first interest at issue is prevention of the breach of the peace. In our view, the Washington
Supreme Court correctly rejected this notion. It is totally
without support in the record. We are also unable to affirm

the judgment below on the ground that the State may have desired to protect the sensibilities of passersby. 'It is firmly settled that under our Constitution the public expression of ideas may not be prohibited merely because the ideas are themselves offensive to some of their hearers.' *Street v. N.Y.* . . . Moreover, appellant did not impose his ideas upon a captive audience. Anyone who might have been offended could easily have avoided the display."[38]

Are you a captive audience as you drive down the street and are confronted with nudity shown on the screen at a drive-in theatre? In 1975, the Supreme Court relied on *Rowan, Cohen, Lehman,* and *Spence* in a case involving a drive-in-theater owner in Jacksonville, Florida, who had been convicted of violating an ordinance that prohibited the showing of films containing nudity when the screen could be seen by the public from a public street or place. In declaring the ordinance unconstitutional, Justice Powell concluded that passersby were not a captive audience: "When the government, acting as censor, undertakes selectively to shield the public from some kinds of speech on the ground that they are more offensive than others, the First Amendment strictly limits its power. . . . Such selective restrictions have been upheld only when the speaker intrudes on the privacy of the home . . . , or the degree of captivity makes it impractical for the unwilling viewer or auditor to avoid exposure."[39]

After quoting from Justice Harlan's *Cohen* opinion, Justice Powell continued: "The plain, if at times disquieting, truth is that in our pluralistic society, constantly proliferating new and ingenious forms of expression, 'we are inescapably captive audiences for many purposes.' *Rowan v. Post Office Dept.* . . . Much that we encounter offends our esthetic, if not our political and moral, sensibilities. Nevertheless, the Constitution does not permit government to decide which types of otherwise protected speech are sufficiently offensive to require protection for the unwilling listener or viewer. Rather, absent the narrow circumstances described above, the burden normally falls upon the viewer to 'avoid further bombardment of [his] sensibilities simply by averting [his] eyes.' *Cohen v. California.* . . . See also *Spence v. Washington.*"[40]

One anomaly that stands out is that as the courts have relied on the metaphoric "captive-audience" doctrine, they have also relied on the metaphoric "marketplace of ideas." Apparently there are people in the free marketplace who are in captivity. This captivity-in-the-marketplace anomaly is especially evident in the cases involving the rights of students. On the one hand, students are often seen as captive audiences when they are in school; yet the school and the classrooms repeatedly are designated by the courts as marketplaces of ideas. One of the most influential paragraphs cited by courts dealing with the First Amendment rights of students comes from the Supreme Court's 1967 *Keyishian* opinion in which Justice Brennan declared: "Our nation is deeply committed to safeguarding academic freedom, which is of transcendent value to all of us and not merely to the teachers concerned. That freedom is therefore a special concern of the First Amendment, which does not tolerate laws that cast a pall of orthodoxy over the classroom. 'The vigilant protection of the constitutional freedoms is nowhere more vital than in the community of American schools.' *Shelton v. Tucker.* . . . The classroom is peculiarly the 'marketplace of ideas.'"[41]

When in 1971 the Second Circuit Court of Appeals found parts of the Stamford, Connecticut, Board of Education's policy on distribution of printed matter on school grounds deficient and unenforceable, the court asserted that "a public school is undoubtedly a 'marketplace of ideas.'"[42] In 1982, a U.S. district court in Maine, deciding that the book *365 Days* had unlawfully been banned from the Woodland High School library in Baileyville, Maine, stated: "Public schools are major marketplaces of ideas, and first amendment rights must be accorded all 'persons' in the market for ideas, including secondary school students . . . seeking redress of state action banning a book from the 'warehouse of ideas.'"[43]

Court after court has portrayed the school as a marketplace of ideas, but at the same time court after court has defined students as a captive audience. However, apparently all students are not captive in all parts of the school during the school day. The courts have not been in agreement about where and when a student is in captivity.

In 1983, an economics professor at Midland College in Midland, Texas, was disciplined by the dean and vice president of the college after they had received a formal complaint from a student that Professor Martin was continually using profane language in class, profanities such as *hell*, *damn*, and *bullshit*. Professor Martin was warned that if he continued to use such language, he would be subject to suspension or termination. "Heedless of the administrators' concerns, Martin continued to curse in class, using words including 'bullshit,' 'hell,' 'damn,' 'God damn,' and 'sucks.' Two students filed written complaints concerning Martin's speech in the classroom on June 19, 1984, which included the following statements: 'the attitude of the class sucks,' '[the attitude] is a bunch of bullshit,' 'you may think economics is a bunch of bullshit,' and 'if you don't like the way I teach this God damn course there is the door.'"[44] The dean, having been informed of this "outburst," initiated action to terminate Martin, and the termination was approved by the college's board of trustees.

Professor Martin instituted a lawsuit alleging "deprivation of his first amendment right of free speech, abridgement of an alleged right of academic freedom, and denials of due process and equal protection."[45] Among other things, Martin argued that cussing out his students was an expression of his frustration with their progress and was used to "motivate" them. In deciding against Martin, the Fifth Circuit Court of Appeals emphasized that Martin's students were a captive audience. Therefore, said the court, "we hold that the students in Martin's classroom, who paid to be taught and not vilified in indecent terms, are subject to the holding of *Pacifica*, which like *Cohen*, recognizes that surroundings and context are essential, case-by-case determinants of the constitutional protection accorded indecent language. Martin's language is unprotected under the reasoning of these cases because, taken in context, it constituted a deliberate, superfluous attack on a 'captive audience' without an academic purpose or justification."[46]

Although the Fifth Circuit Court of Appeals saw the college students as a captive audience, the Supreme Court, ten years earlier, decided in *Healy v. James* that Central Connecticut State College had violated the First Amendment rights of students who had been rebuffed by college officials when the students wanted to organize a local chapter of the Students for a Democratic Society as a campus organization with official recognition, and in so deciding the Court declared that "the college classroom with its surrounding environs is peculiarly the 'marketplace of ideas,' and we break no new constitutional ground in reaffirming this Nation's dedication to safeguarding academic freedom."[47]

Although the Supreme Court asserts that "the college classroom and its surrounding environs is peculiarly the 'marketplace of ideas,'" lower courts have defined the students in this marketplace as captive persons. In 1970, the First Circuit Court of Appeals relied on the "captive-audience" metaphor in deciding against an art instructor at the University of Massachusetts whose paintings had been put on display on the walls of a corridor in the Student Union and then taken down because of the controversial nature of the paintings. After considering the instructor's constitutional interest, the court said: "We turn to the question whether defendants have demonstrated a sufficient counter-interest to justify their action. The corridor was a passageway, regularly used by the public, including children. Several of the paintings were nudes, male or female, displaying the genitalia in what was described as 'clinical detail.' A skeleton was fleshed out only in this particular. One painting bore the title, 'I am the only virgin in my school.'" The college officials, said the court, "were entitled to consider the primary use to which the corridor was put. . . . On the basis of the complaints received, and even without such, defendants were warranted in finding the exhibit inappropriate to that use. Where there was, in effect, a captive audience, defendants had a right to afford protection against 'assault upon individual privacy.'"[48]

Student captivity was an important element in a district court decision against a high school biology teacher who had used his classroom as a "springboard for expounding his ideas concerning the superintendent, the school board and the school system," had told his tenth-grade biology class of his personal dealings with prostitution in Japan, and discussed masturbation "in a mixed class, to the extent that individual students were asked if they had ever masturbated and that if they said they hadn't, they were lying."[49] Recognizing the teacher's right to speak on these matters outside the classroom, the court declared that "it is clear that this case does *not* concern First Amendment utterances or statements made by a teacher *outside* the classroom. It is imperative to note here that were that the case Mr. Moore in all probability would be entitled to relief."[50] The tenth-grade biology students "have the right and freedom not to listen and as a captive audience should be able to expect protection from improper classroom activities. Plaintiff has the right to criticize his employers and the school administration but is limited in the exercise of that right to the extent that its exercise may not invade the classroom occupied by fifteen year olds and must be balanced against the need for meaningful school administration."[51]

At the same time that the court saw the students as a captive audience, it saw the classroom as a marketplace of ideas. Relying on the tropes from *Keyishian*, the court said: "While the classroom may be '[t]he marketplace of ideas [with] [t]he nation's future depend[ing] upon leaders trained through wide exposure to that robust exchange of ideas which discovers truth out of a multitude of tongues, [rather] than through any kind of authoritative selection,' straight criticism by a teacher of an educational system is quite a different matter than the presentation of ideas with commentary reflecting two sides of an issue, leaving a preference as to that issue left up to the individual student's discretion."[52]

In effect, what we have here is a captive audience in a marketplace of ideas where two sides are not being presented. The weakness of the applicability of the commercial "marketplace" metaphor becomes apparent, for (1) in the free marketplace there is no captivity, and (2) in the free marketplace there is no requirement that "two sides" be presented or made available.

The captivity of the student is not limited to the classroom. In 1983, Matthew Fraser, a student at Bethel High School in Bethel, Washington, delivered a half-minute nominating speech in support of a fellow student running for a student-government office. The speech was delivered to approximately six hundred high school students attending an assembly that was part of a school-sponsored educational program in self-government. Students who did not attend the assembly were required to report to the study hall. Fraser's nominating speech led to a three-day suspension and the school authorities' withdrawal of permission for him to deliver a graduation speech. Fraser's nominating speech was as follows:

> I know a man who is firm—he's firm in his pants, he's firm in his shirt, his character is firm—but most of all, his belief in you, the students of Bethel is firm.
> Jeff Kuhlman is a man who takes his point and pounds it in. If necessary, he'll take an issue and nail it to the wall. He doesn't attack things in spurts—he drives hard, pushing and pushing until finally—he succeeds.
> Jeff is a man who will go to the very end—even the climax, for each and every one of you.
> So vote for Jeff for A.S.B. vice-president—he'll never come between you and the best our high school can be.[53]

School authorities suspended Fraser for violating the school's disruptive-conduct rule, which prohibited the use of "obscene, profane language or gestures." Fraser, a member of the Honor Society who had won statewide honors as a debater, took his case to the U.S. district court, which decided for Fraser, concluding that Fraser's rights under the First and Fourteenth Amendments had been violated by subjecting him to a three-day suspension and removing his name from the list of candidates for graduation speaker.[54] The school board appealed to the court of appeals, which also decided for Fraser.[55]

When the case reached the Supreme Court, Chief Justice Burger, for the majority, decided against Fraser, arguing that previous decisions "recognize the obvious concern on the parts of parents, and school authorities acting *in loco parentis* to protect children—especially in a captive audience—from exposure to sexually explicit, indecent or lewd speech."[56] In effect, the Court said that students were in captivity at a school assembly they were not required to attend, an assembly that was part of a school-sponsored educational program in self-government at an institution the courts have again and again declared a marketplace of ideas.

Are students captive in the school library? In 1979, a U.S. district court in New Hampshire had to decide whether the school board's removal of *Ms.* magazine from the Nashua High School library constituted a violation of the First Amendment rights of students, teachers, and parents. In ordering the school board to replace all issues of *Ms.* magazine and to resubscribe to the magazine, the court declared: "The court also finds that the actions of the Board taken at their meeting of March 27, 1979 wherein all issues of *Ms.* were reviewed and two were returned to the library shelves is pretextual and self-serving. . . . Here as in *Right to Read* . . . , the publication was banned by the Board without reading it, the female Board members were 'sheltered' from the alleged improper material, and no claim is advanced or supported that the publication is obsolete or worn out or that adequate shelf space is unavailable. Those cases which deal with 'captive audiences' . . . or whether a magazine containing an allegedly 'filthy' poem should be promoted rather than suppressed . . . are apposite."[57] As the court saw it, in the context of the school library, students are not a captive audience.

Are students in captivity when they are exposed to an article about contraception appearing in the school newspaper? In 1977, a U.S. district court in Virginia decided for high school students who sued school officials who had prohibited the publication in the school newspaper of an article entitled "Sexually Active Students Fail to Use Contraception." In deciding for the students, the court rejected the school board's contention that the Hayfield Secondary School students were a captive audience. The court stated:

The defendants [school board] have asserted . . . that the subscription tie-in with the yearbook, the distribution in home rooms, the official status of the newspaper, and peer pressure, coupled with mandatory attendance all combined to compel the student body's exposure to the

contents of *The Farm News*. The court is not persuaded
that these circumstances establish the kind of captive audience that concerned the *Lehman* court. No substantive
distinction can be drawn between the relative lack of
choice in exposure to the communication in this case and
that in *Tinker*. If anything, the students of Hayfield are
less captive because they must act affirmatively to pick up
the newspaper. In *Tinker* the non-protesting students were
required to avert their eyes to avoid the message.[58]

The school board appealed, and the Fourth Circuit Court of
Appeals cited with approval the district court's argument that
"the students are not a captive audience merely because of
their compulsory attendance at the school."[59]

Are students a captive audience when they might be
exposed to an underground newspaper distributed at their
high school? In 1979, while giving constitutional protection
to high school students who had written and distributed *off*
school grounds an underground newspaper, *Hard Times*, which
contained some indecent language, the Second Circuit Court
of Appeals at the same time recognized the power of school
officials to regulate on-campus distribution of the underground newspaper. In his concurring opinion, Judge Newman saw the students as captives: "The First Amendment
does not prevent a school's reasonable efforts toward the
maintenance of campus standards of civility and decency.
With its captive audience of children, many of whom, along
with their parents, legitimately expect reasonable regulations, a school need not capitulate to a student's preference for
vulgar expression. A school's authority to condemn indecent
language is not inconsistent with a student's right to express
his views. In short, the First Amendment gives a high school
student the classroom right to wear Tinker's armband, but not
Cohen's jacket."[60] Other courts have given constitutional protection to students who distributed their underground newspapers on school grounds, even though those newspapers
contained "earthy" language.[61]

While the Supreme Court has given protection to a student distributing an underground newspaper containing of-

fensive materials on a college campus,[62] it has not decided a high school underground-newspaper case, and one can only speculate whether the metaphoric "captive audience" would be a determining factor for the Court in deciding the fate of a high school underground newspaper containing earthy, indecent, and vulgar language. While Chief Justice Burger did argue in *Fraser* that school officials had the right to protect students from Fraser's indecent language in his nominating speech because the students were a captive audience, it may be that that degree of captivity is not present where students are exposed to the earthy language appearing in underground newspapers, which can be ignored or rejected by the students. After all, what has become clear is that once students enter that schoolhouse gate, they are not all automatically in captivity at all times in all places on the school campus.

In *Tinker* (1969), Justice Fortas, delivering the opinion of the Court, declared that "in our system, state-operated schools may not be enclaves of totalitarianism. School officials do not possess absolute authority over their students. . . . In our system, students may not be regarded as closed-circuit recipients of only that which the State chooses to communicate. They may not be confined to the expression of those sentiments that are officially approved."[63] While the schools may not, as some justices have argued, be "enclaves of totalitarianism" and students may not "be regarded as closed-circuit recipients," several justices have said that the function of schools is to "inculcate," as Chief Justice Burger put it, "fundamental values."[64]

The strongest defense of "inculcation" in education has come from Justice Rehnquist, who proposed in his dissenting opinion in *Island Trees v. Pico* (1982): "Public schools fulfill the vital role of teaching students the basic skills necessary to function in our society, and of 'inculcating fundamental values necessary to the maintenance of a democratic system.' . . . The idea that such students have a right to access, in the school, to information other than that thought by their educators to be necessary is contrary to the very nature of an inculcative education."[65]

Rehnquist's view of "inculcative education" was expressed in definite terms: "Elementary and secondary schools are inculcative by nature. The libraries of such schools serve as supplements to this inculcative role. Unlike university or public libraries, elementary and secondary school libraries are not designed for free-wheeling inquiry; they are tailored, as the public school curriculum is tailored, to the teaching of basic skills and ideas."[66]

When four years later the Court decided against Fraser, Chief Justice Burger asserted: "The role and purpose of the American school system was well described by two historians, saying 'public education must prepare pupils for citizenship in the Republic. . . . It must inculcate the habits and manners of civility as values in themselves conducive to happiness and as indispensable to the practice of self-government in the community and the nation.' Beard and Beard, New Basic History of the United States 228 (1968)."[67]

There is an anomaly in the Court's asserting that students are not "closed-circuit recipients" and then telling us that the schools have an inculcative function. *Inculcation*, unlike *education*, implies that students are closed-circuit recipients. The word *inculcate* is derived from the Latin *inculcare*, which means literally "to stamp in with the heel, tread in, cram in, press in, impress upon (the mind)."[68] It is not uncoincidental that the first uses of the word *inculcate* dealt with religious matters related to faith and not inquiry, to doctrine and not diversity, to orthodoxy and not freedom.

In contrast, *educate* means literally "to lead out, to elicit, to draw out," the word *educate* being derived from *e-ducare*. To *educe*, unlike *inculcate*, means to arrive at something through reasoning. Inculcating students runs counter to the Court's position in *Tinker* that students are not "closed-circuit recipients of only that which the State chooses to communicate."

If the school libraries are not, as Justice Rehnquist argues metaphorically, "designed for free-wheeling inquiry," then defining the schools as "marketplaces of ideas" is a misapplication of the metaphoric "marketplace." We are confronted with a kind of doublethink: a free market in which there is no free-wheeling inquiry; captives in the free market; students who are not closed-circuit recipients being inculcated. The inconsistency in the metaphors reveals a confusion about the relevance of the marketplace to our educational system and what constitutes a captive audience.

While students are in captivity when attending a school assembly at which attendance is not required (*Fraser*), they are not in captivity when they are in the school library (*Salvail*). While we are not in captivity when confronted with Cohen's "Fuck the Draft" message in the Los Angeles County Courthouse corridor (*Cohen*), we are in captivity when we receive in our mailboxes sexually provocative advertisements (*Rowan*). While we are not in captivity when we see Spence's upside-down American flag with a peace symbol taped onto it (*Spence*), we are in captivity when we listen to our radios in our homes (*Pacifica*). While we are not in captivity when we drive by a drive-in theater that has nudity on the screen visible from the street (*Erznoznik*), we are in captivity at the betting window at the racetrack.[69]

In 1978, the majority of the Supreme Court had argued in *Pacifica* that radio listeners were captives and that even prior warnings were not enough, for such "prior warnings cannot completely protect the listener . . . from unexpected program content. To say that one may avoid further offense by turning off the radio when he hears indecent language is like saying that the remedy for an assault is to run away after the first blow."[70] Almost a half century earlier, Justice Brandeis, in *Packer Corporation v. Utah*, affirming a conviction for displaying a billboard advertising cigarettes in Utah, argued that the radio could be turned off: "The young people as well as the adults have the message of the billboard thrust upon them by all the arts and devices that skill can produce. In the case of newspapers and magazines, there must be some seeking by the one who is to see and read the advertisement. The radio can be turned off, but not so the billboard or street car placard."[71]

Over the decades, the metaphoric "captive audience" has not served us well, raising more questions than it answers. In the end, whether one is a captive audience listening in the home, walking through the airport, studying in the school library, placing a bet at the racetrack, opening one's mail, or sitting in a college classroom may, like obscenity and a number of other things in life, lie in the eye of the beholder.

7

"Shedding" Rights at the "Schoolhouse Gate" and Other Judicial Metonymies

While the trope most heavily relied on by the courts has been the metaphor, other tropes have played an important role in judicial decision making. Just as the metaphors "marketplace of ideas," "wall of separation," "captive audience," and "chilling effect" have become integral to judicial reasoning, so have several metonymies and personifications. Just as the passages so often cited from court opinions are the metaphoric passages, so with passages expressed through metonymy, synecdoche, and personification. These latter nonliteral uses of language have appeared almost as regularly in judicial opinions as the metaphor.

The importance and role of metonymy, especially in political discourse, has been recognized by several scholars. Murray Edelman has recognized the functions of both metaphor and metonymy: "It is through metaphor, metonymy, and syntax that linguistic references evoke mythic cognitive structures in people's minds. This is hardly surprising, for we naturally define ambiguous situations by focusing on one part of them or by comparing them with familiar things."[1] When identifying metonymy as one of his "four master tropes," Kenneth Burke states: "The basic 'strategy' in metonymy is this: to convey some incorporeal or intangible state in terms of the corporeal or tangible, e.g., to speak of 'the heart' rather than 'the emotions.' If you trail language back far enough, of course, you will find that all our terms for 'spiritual' states were metonymic in origin."[2] Distinguishing between metaphor and metonymy, Lakoff and Johnson point out that "metaphor and metonymy are different kinds of processes. Metaphor is principally a way of conceiving of one thing in terms of another, and its primary function is understanding. Metonymy, on the other hand, has primarily a referential function, that is, it allows us to use one entity to *stand for* another. But metonymy is not merely a referential device. It also serves the function of providing understanding."[3]

J. David Sapir makes the following distinctions between metaphor, metonymy, and synecdoche:

> Metaphor states an equivalence between terms taken from separate semantic domains: George the Lion might be an expression applied to a football player, for instance. Metonymy replaces or juxtaposes contiguous terms that occupy a distinct and separate place within what is considered a single semantic or perceptual domain. Homer will often be used instead of the *Iliad* ("You will read in Homer. . . ."), where agent replaces act; or the phrase "deep in his cups," where "cups" as container stands for the sherry or wine that is contained. Synecdoche, like metonymy, draws its terms from a single domain; however, one term always includes or is included by the other as a kind for type, part for whole: France for a specific Frenchman, sail for ship.[4]

While the metaphor and metonymy differ, say Lakoff and Johnson, "like metaphors, metonymic concepts structure not just our language but our thoughts, attitudes, and actions. And, like metaphoric concepts, metonymic concepts are grounded in our experience. In fact, the grounding of metonymic concepts is in general more obvious than is the case with metaphoric concepts since it usually involves direct physical or causal connection."[5]

While these twentieth-century scholars have observed the role and influence of metonymy, especially in structuring our attitudes and actions, rhetoricians of previous centuries had already discussed metonymy and its influence on meaning. For example, the eighteenth-century rhetorician Joseph Priestley devoted Lecture XXVII in his *Course of Lectures on Oratory and Criticism* to metonymy. Early in his lecture, Priestley writes of the sources of metonymies, and the sources he identifies are not much different from those discussed by twentieth-century scholars. Priestley wrote in 1777:

> It is almost endless to enumerate all the relations of things which afford a foundation for this figure of speech [metonymy]. Some of the principal of them are those of *cause and effect*, in all its varieties; *the subject and its attributes*, or circumstances; the *agent and the instrument*; *general and particular, abstract and concrete terms*: and *the whole and its parts*, which alone is referred to *synecdoche*. For example, we put the effect for the cause when we say *day arose*, instead of saying the *sun arose*; . . . a particular for a general term, when we say *a Maecenas* for a patron of *learning*, and *a Nero* for a *tyrant*.[6]

As to the advantages of using the metonymy, Priestley recognizes that through metonymy one can convey an idea with more impact than through the use of "plainer terms" and literal language:

> When a person is called *a Maecenas*, ideas of honour and esteem are more readily transferred to him, than if he were called in plainer terms *a promoter of learning*, and *a patron of learned men*. Every pleasing idea of this kind hath been so long and so intimately connected with the name of that favourite of Augustus, that we thereby convey more definite and stronger ideas than we could by any other, though longer form of expression. With the same advantage is a tyrant called *a Nero*, a poet a *second Homer*, and a philosopher a *second Sir Isaac Newton*. There is a kind of *accumulation of meaning* in these expressions, by means of long, extensive, and repated associations of ideas.[7]

One of the most cited and most influential metonymies appearing in court decisions dealing with the First Amendment rights of students and teachers comes from the Supreme Court's 1969 *Tinker* opinion in which Justice Fortas, delivering the opinion of the Court, wrote: "First Amendment rights, applied in light of the special characteristics of the school environment, are available to teachers and students. It can hardly be argued that either students or teachers shed their constitutional rights to freedom of speech or expression at the schoolhouse gate."[8] The metonymic "shed their constitutional rights to freedom of speech or expression at the schoolhouse gate" was immediately cited by the lower courts. *Tinker* was decided on February 24, 1969; within three months, the lower courts began incorporating the *Tinker* metonymy into their opinions.

Two weeks before *Tinker* was decided, University of Tennessee officials announced that a contract for the appearance of Dr. Timothy Leary on campus would not be issued, just as a contract for the appearance of Dick Gregory had been denied a few months earlier by college authorities. The students and faculty who sought temporary and permanent injunctive relief and a declaratory judgment in U.S. district court that the student-invited-speaker policy of the University was unconstitutional, alleged "present and future injury in the nature of violation of their First and Fourteenth Amendment rights because of the refusal of the defendants to allow Gregory and Leary to speak."[9]

While injunctive relief was denied, the district court granted declaratory relief, the court concluding that the university student-invited-speaker regulations were a violation of the First Amendment, since the regulations were too broad and too vague. In support of its April 18, 1969, decision the court cited *Tinker*, taking from *Tinker* the metonymic "It can hardly be argued that either students or teachers shed their constitutional rights to freedom of speech or expression at the schoolhouse gate."[10]

In May, a U.S. district court in Michigan, deciding for a high school student who had been expelled from school because while at school he had in his possession publications allegedly obscene, concluded in *Vought v. Van Buren Public Schools* that the expelled student had not been given a hearing and was thus denied due process.[11] In deciding for the student, the court declared: "The Supreme Court, on February 24 of this year, stated that 'First Amendment rights, applied in light of the special characteristics of the school environment, are available to teachers and students' and that they do not 'shed their constitutional rights to freedom of speech or expression at the schoolhouse gate.'"[12]

In August, the Eighth Circuit Court of Appeals decided against two Central Missouri State College students who had been suspended from college as a result of their involvement at a mass demonstration, their "destructive interference with the rights of others," and their "actual or potentially disruptive conduct." In so deciding, the court relied heavily on *Tinker*, quoting the schoolhouse-gate passage and devoting an entire page to several passages from *Tinker*, especially those sentences dealing with potentially disruptive conduct and material interference with school activities.[13]

In October, a district court in Minnesota decided for a high school senior who had been prevented by school officials from attending high school because of his long hair, and in so deciding, the court declared:

> Stripped of its peripheral aspects, the court regards this case as solely a "long hair" case. Neither the United States Supreme Court nor the Court of Appeals for the Eighth Circuit has had the opportunity to pass upon the issue presented by this case. The only pronouncement, outside the denial of certiorari in *Ferrel* . . . , and though specifically stated not to be a hair style case, is *Tinker* . . . , a First Amendment case, where the Court stated: "It can hardly be argued that either students or teachers shed their constitutional rights to freedom of speech or expression at the schoolhouse gate. This has been the unmistakable holding of this Court for almost 50 years." So plaintiff here does not lose his constitutional rights, even though not based on the First Amendment, on entering the school's domain.[14]

By 1985, the *Tinker* metonymy had become a "principle" when the Maine Supreme Judicial Court decided against a teacher, student, and speaker who claimed their constitutional rights had been violated when the school board canceled a proposed "Tolerance Day" program at the high school because the scheduling of a homosexual speaker as part of the Tolerance Day program led to threats of picketing and bomb and sabotage threats against the school. The Maine court said: "When the Board of Directors of S.A.D. 59 [School Administrative District 59] cancelled the proposed Tolerance Day symposium, it acted within its broad power to manage the curriculum of the Madison schools. Although we whole-heartedly endorse the statement of the United States Supreme Court that '[i]t can hardly be argued that either students or teachers shed their constitutional rights to freedom of speech or expression at the schoolhouse gate, ' . . . that principle does not require a court to overturn the decision of the Board in this case."[15]

This principle was, in part, what gave John Tinker, age fifteen, Christopher Eckhardt, sixteen, and Mary Beth Tinker, thirteen, constitutional protection on February 24, 1969. These junior and senior high school students had worn black arm-bands to school to express their objections to American involvement in the Vietnam War, especially the bombings carried out by the American forces. The students were told by school officials not to return to school unless they agreed not to wear the armbands. Following their suspensions in December 1965, the students took their case to the U.S. district court, which decided against them,[16] as did the evenly divided Eighth Circuit Court of Appeals.[17]

When the case reached the Supreme Court, Justice Fortas provided an argument tropologically phrased, an argument that had a widespread influence. When Fortas wrote of students and teachers not "shedding" their rights at the "schoolhouse gate," his words determined the extent to which the argument and opinion was to be subsequently cited. Fortas could just as well have said that "student and teachers do not give up their rights to speech and expression when they go to school" or that "when students and teachers arrive at school, they maintain their rights of speech and expression." Such language, however, would not have had the impact or influence of his metonymies.

In asserting that teachers and students do not "shed" their constitutional rights to freedom of speech and expression "at the schoolhouse gate" Fortas expressed the argument in two nonliteral uses of language, perhaps three. First, constitutional rights, being abstractions, cannot literally be shed; second, Fortas obviously does not intend that we take "schoolhouse gate" literally, for very few schools today have gates and are seldom referred to as "schoolhouses."

The verb *shed* literally means "1. to pour out; give off; emit. 2. to cause to flow in a stream or fall in drops; let flow or drop; as, she shed tears. 3. to send forth or spread about; radiate; diffuse; impart; as, he sheds confidence wherever he goes. 4. to cause to flow off without penetration; throw off; repel: as, oilskin sheds water. 5. to cast off or lose (a natural growth or covering, as leaves, skin, hair, etc.)"[18] Fortas has taken the fifth literal definition, "to cast off or lose," which is literally applied to "leaves, skin, hair" and used it metonymically. To "shed" one's rights creates a different image than to "give up" or to "lose" one's rights. Shedding brings with it a visual dimension that "give up" or "lose" do not.

Another facet of Fortas's figurative sentence is his use of *schoolhouse*. In fact, in the context of this case it is especially figurative since the schools attended by the students involved in *Tinker* were junior and senior high schools, not elementary schools. The definition of *schoolhouse* provided by *Webster's Third New International Dictionary* is "a building used as a school and especially an elementary school (little red schoolhouse)." There is something nostalgic about *schoolhouse*, especially when combined with *gate*. Few schools, particularly junior and senior high schools, have gates anymore, especially at entrances. Fortas's metonymies allow us to visualize a process and structure which would be missing if he had simply declared that students and teachers don't give up their constitutional rights when they go to school. Clearly, Fortas provided a metonymic premise upon which judicial arguments of many subsequent opinions have been based.

In delivering the opinion of the Court in *Tinker*, Fortas relied on several other tropes to support the Court's decision. For example, he argued that "in our system, state-operated schools may not be enclaves of totalitarianism" and that "in our system, students may not be regarded as closed-circuit recipients of only that which the State chooses to communicate."[19] Several lines later, Fortas drew on Justice Brennan's figurative language in *Keyishian*: "The classroom is peculiarly the 'marketplace of ideas.' The Nation's future depends upon leaders trained through wide exposure to that robust exchange of ideas which discovers truth 'out of a multitude of tongues [rather] than through any kind of authoritative selection.'"[20]

The metonymic "multitude of tongues" had been introduced into judicial decision making in 1943 by Judge Learned Hand, who wrote in *United States v. Associated Press*:

> Neither exclusively, nor even primarily, are the interests of the newspaper industry conclusive; for that industry serves one of the most vital of all general interests: the dissemination of news from as many different sources, and with as many different facets and colors as is possible. That interest is closely akin to, if indeed it is not the same as, the interest protected by the First Amendment; it presupposes that right conclusions are more likely to be gathered out of a multitude of tongues, than through any kind of authoritative selection. To many this is, and always will be, folly; but we have staked upon it our all.[21]

Judge Hand's metonymy immediately had its impact. When the Associated Press appealed to the Supreme Court, it was decided that the antitrust laws applied to the mass media, and in his concurring opinion Justice Frankfurter said that he found himself "entirely in agreement with Judge Learned Hand" and then proceeded to cite the above passage with the metonymic "multitude of tongues."[22]

That so many courts subsequently referred to the "multitude of tongues" is partly explained by the fact that almost always Hand's passage is cited through Justice Brennan's influential *Keyishian* opinion.[23] The "multitude of tongues" metonymy subsequently appeared in judicial opinions dealing with newspapers and monopoly, the rights of students and teachers, library censorship, libel, and radio and F.C.C. regulations. Ten years after Judge Hand introduced the metonymy, the Supreme Court, deciding for a New Orleans newspaper publishing company that had been charged with violating the Sherman Act, emphasized the importance of the daily newspaper in a free society and quoted at length from Judge Hand's opinion, including the "multitude of tongues" passage.[24]

In the landmark *New York Times v. Sullivan* case, Justice Brennan, delivering the opinion of the Court, wrote: "We consider this case against the background of a profound national commitment to the principle that debate on public issues should be uninhibited, robust, and wide-open, and that it may well include vehement, caustic, and sometimes unpleasantly sharp attacks on government and public officials."[25] Brennan prefaced this assertion with quotes from several Supreme Court opinions and Judge Hand's "multitude of tongues."[26]

In 1967, when the District of Columbia Court of Appeals held that the fairness doctrine was constitutional and that the FCC requirement that the radio station furnish reply time to a person who had been personally attacked, the court emphasized the "public interest" involved in this case: "A broadcast station, not being a common carrier, and having both the duty and the right of determining whether a controversial program is in the public interest, must, after having exercised that determination by broadcasting a particular program, in the public interest afford equal opportunity for the broadcast of the other side of that controversial issue. This burden exists equally well when the initial broadcast consists of a personal attack upon a person or organization."[27] The court supported its position partly by relying on Judge Hand's "multitude of tongues" passage.[28]

In protecting the First Amendment rights of an Arizona State University professor who had been dismissed from his teaching position because he had "failed to exercise appropriate restraint or to exercise critical self-discipline and judgment in using, extending and transmitting knowledge" and had "failed to meet his obligations to promote conditions of free inquiry and to further public understanding of academic freedom,"[29] a U.S. district court in Arizona declared in 1972: "Insofar as the plaintiff's words upset the Legislature or faculty because of the contents of his views, and particularly the depth of his social criticism, this is not the kind of detriment for which plaintiff can constitutionally be penalized."[30] The court brought Hand's metonymy to bear as it appeared in Brennan's *Keyishian* opinion.

When a district court decided in *Right to Read Defense Committee v. School Committee* (1978) that school officials could not ban *Male and Female Under 18*, an anthology of writings by adolescents, from the Chelsea, Massachusetts, high school library, Judge Tauro relied twice on the metaphoric "marketplace of ideas" and the metaphoric "students may not be regarded as closed-circuit recipients," his own "the First Amendment is not merely a mantle which students and faculty must doff when they take their place in the classroom," and "the most effective antidote to the poison of mindless orthodoxy is ready access to a broad sweep of ideas and philosophies"; he also warned against "santizing" the school library of views divergent from successive school committees. In addition to these tropes (and others), Judge Tauro wrote of the "warehouse of ideas" just before citing Hand's metonymy through *Keyishian*:

> The fundamental notion underlying the First Amendment
> is that citizens, free to speak and hear, will be able to
> form judgments concerning matters affecting their lives,
> independent of any governmental suasion or propaganda.
> Consistent with that noble purpose, a school should be a
> readily accessible warehouse of ideas. "The Nation's future
> depends upon leaders trained through wide exposure to
> that robust exchange of ideas which discovers truth 'out
> of a multitude of tongues, [rather] than through any kind
> of authoritative selection."[31]

In 1981, when the Third Circuit Court of Appeals concluded that a school superintendent had not violated the First Amendment rights of students and their parents when he canceled a student drama production entitled *Pippin* because its sexual content was inappropriate, Judge Rosenn wrote a concurring opinion in which he explained: "Although I agree with the majority that school authorities enjoy broad discretion in the making of decisions in curricular matters, I write separately to emphasize that their discretion is not unfettered and that courts have a duty to vindicate the complementary constitutional rights of students to express and hear more than one point."[32] After citing several landmark Supreme Court decisions related to the rights of students and teachers, Judge Rosenn invoked Hand's "multitude of tongues," again through *Keyishian*: "These and other judicial decisions which were willing to intrude into the operation of school systems emphasize the essential role played by education in the intellectual and moral development of our youth, and the concomitant need to expose our youngsters 'to that robust exchange of ideas which discovers truth "out of a multitude of tongues, [rather] than through any kind of authoritative selection.'"[33]

When a district court in California decided in 1989 for the American Arab Anti-Discrimination Committee, which had challenged the McCarran-Walter Act's provisions related to the deportation of aliens, Judge Wilson concluded: "Applying established First Amendment principles, we find that the McCarran-Walter provisions are substantially overbroad in violation of the First Amendment."[34] To support its decision, the court relied on the metaphoric "marketplace of ideas" and Judge Hand's metonymic "multitude of tongues": "The maintenance of the 'uninhibited marketplace of ideas,' crucial for our democracy's prosperity . . . , requires that each idea be afforded the same protection whether espoused by a citizen or an alien within this country. . . . As Judge Hand stated, the First Amendment 'presupposes that right conclusions are more likely to be gathered out of a multitude of tongues, than through any kind of authoritative selection. To many this is, and always will be folly; but we have staked upon it our all.'"[35]

The metonymic "tongue" has had a long history. After providing the literal definition of *tongue*, the *OED* lists scores of examples of *tongue* as a figure of speech. The literal definition is "An organ, possessed by man and by most vertebrates, occupying the floor of the mouth, and attached at its base to the hyoid bone; often protusible and freely moveable. . . ."[36] The *OED* traces the figurative use of *tongue* back to the ninth century, noting that "in many contexts it is impossible to separate the sense of the organ from that of its work or use."[37]

As one might expect from one whose works are permeated with tropes, Shakespeare has placed the metonymic "tongue" in several of his plays. *As You Like It*: "This our life . . . findes tongues in trees, bookes in the running brookes."[38] *Taming of the Shrew*: "I will charme him first to keepe his tongue."[39] *Macbeth*: "Why doe we hold our tongues?"[40] *The Merchant of Venice*: "Who are you? tell me for more certainty, / Albeit He sweare that I do know your tongue."[41] *Julius Caesar*:

> Show you sweet Caesar's wounds, poor, poor dumb
>   mouths.
> And bid them speak for me: but were I Brutus,
> And Brutus Antony, there were an Antony
> Would ruffle up your spirits, and put a tongue
> In every wound of Caesar, that should move
> The stones of Rome to rise and mutiny.[42]

While Hand asserts that the First Amendment "presupposes that right conclusions are more likely to be gathered out of a multitude of tongues," one must be cognizant that *multitude* simply means a great number of people or things; *multitude* means many, not necessarily different. The "multitude of tongues" could just as easily be of one voice; a "multitude of tongues" could just as easily be a means for conformity as for diversity. It was a multitude of tongues that greeted Adolf Hitler at Nazi rallies, a multitude of tongues that shouted "Sieg Heil!" There is nothing inherent in "multitude of tongues" to suggest exchanging ideas or achieving a diversity of ideas. This First Amendment presupposition, while reflective of democratic ideals, must be carefully watched.

One should also be cognizant that where Judge Hand said "right conclusions are more likely to be gathered out of a multitude of tongues," Justice Brennan spoke of "discover[ing] truth 'out of a multitude of tongues.'" While Hand's "multitude of tongues" would more likely lead to a "gathering" of "right conclusions," Brennan's "tongues" would lead to the "discovery" of "truth." To "gather" is different from to "discover," and "right conclusions" are different from "truth." Hence, it is of some importance whether a court cites Hand's metonymy as it appeared in his 1943 opinion or as it appeared in Brennan's 1967 *Keyishian* opinion.

Other metonymies, while not as widely cited, have had their influence on judicial decision making. When the Supreme Court held in 1989 that Gregory Johnson's flag burning at the Republican Convention in 1984 was protected by the First Amendment, Chief Justice Rehnquist dissented, asserting at the outset of his dissenting opinion: "In holding this Texas statute unconstitutional, the Court ignores Justice Holmes' familiar aphorism that 'a page of history is worth a volume of logic.'"[43] Rehnquist then proceeds to quote from Ralph Waldo Emerson's "Concord Hymn": "By the rude bridge that arched the flood / Their flag to April's breeze unfurled, / Here once the embattled farmers stood / And fired the shot heard round the world." This poetry is followed in the next paragraph with the first stanza of the "Star Spangled Banner." This in turn is followed with sixty lines from John Greenleaf Whittier's poem "Barbara Frietchie." All this poetry in Rehnquist's opinion is part of that "page of history" that is "worth more than a volume of logic."

Holmes had introduced the metonymic aphorism in a 1921 Supreme Court opinion dealing with wills and taxation: "But that matter [on indirect and direct taxes] also is disposed of by Knowlton v. Moore, not by an attempt to make some scientific distinction, which would be at least difficult, but on an interpretation of language by its traditional use, — on the practical and historical ground that this kind of tax always has been regarded as the antithesis of a direct tax, — 'has ever been treated as a duty or excise, because of the particular occasion which gives rise to its levy.' . . . Upon this point a page of history is worth a volume of logic."[44]

Toward the end of his dissenting opinion, Rehnquist admonishes the majority: "The Court concludes its opinion with a regrettably patronizing civics lecture, presumably addressed to the Members of both Houses of Congress, the members of the 48 state legislatures that enacted prohibitions against flag burning, and the troops fighting under that flag in Vietnam who objected to its being burned: 'The way to preserve the flag's special role is not to punish those who feel differently about these matters. It is to persuade them that they are wrong.'"[45] The Court, of course, does not conclude its opinion with a literal "civics lecture." Rehnquist has used *lecture* in a figurative sense; the *OED*, after listing the literal definitions of *lecture*, provides the figurative use: *"fig.* A 'lesson', an instructive counsel or example."[46]

The Chief Justice concludes his dissenting opinion with the metonymic clichés of men who "must fight and perhaps die for the flag": "The Court decides that the American flag is just another symbol, about which not only must opinions pro and con be tolerated, but for which the most minimal public respect may not be enjoined. The government may conscript men into the Armed Forces where they must fight and perhaps die for the flag, but the government may not prohibit the public burning of the banner under which they fight. I would uphold the Texas statute as applied in this case."[47] Aside from the question of whether men in the armed forces die for the literal flag, Rehnquist's "troops fighting under the flag in Vietnam" and "burning of the banner under which they fight" are metaphorical. Troops at one time did fight "under the flag" at battles where the flag was carried into combat while men fought "under it." Today, the flag may be flying at the headquarters company, but it is no longer carried into battle, especially not in Vietnam where in guerrilla warfare holding the banner high as men moved into the jungle combat would have been disastrous. One difficulty with the metonymic "dying for the flag" and the metaphoric "fighting under the banner" is that they have become clichés used by too many people in too many political speeches and letters to the editor, sentimentalizing and glorifying war. While Rehnquist at the outset of his opinion cites Holmes's aphorism "a page of history is worth a volume of logic," his poetic history and argument based on overused metonymy and metaphor undercuts the validity of Holmes's metonymic aphorism.

In 1943, Justice Jackson provided in the landmark *West Virginia State Bd. of Education v. Barnette* one of the most widely cited metaphors in judicial decision making and a less-known metonymy. In deciding for the students of the Jehovah's Witness faith who had refused to salute the flag and had been expelled from school, Justice Jackson, delivering the opinion of the Court, wrote: "If there is any fixed star in our constitutional constellation, it is that no official, high or petty, can prescribe what shall be orthodox in politics, nationalism, religion, or other matters of opinion or force citizens to confess by word or act their faith therein."[48] Jackson's "fixed star in our constitutional constellation" became one of the most quoted metaphors in judicial opinions dealing with First Amendment freedoms.

Emphasizing the need for school boards to perform their functions "within the limits of the Bill of Rights," Jackson introduced a less-recognized metonymy: "Such Boards are numerous and their territorial jurisdiction often small. But small and local authority may feel less sense of responsibility to the Constitution, and agencies of publicity may be less vigilant in calling it to account. . . . There are village tyrants as well as village Hampdens, but none who acts under color of the law is beyond the reach of the Constitution."[49]

The "village Hampdens" Jackson refers to is a metonymy based on the seventeenth-century English stateman John Hampden, who opposed Charles I and was "a symbol of opposition to royal tyranny. In the Short Parliament and again in the Long he sat for Buckinghamshire, and only Pym among his fellow-members has won greater celebrity as a parliamentarian champion. Inevitably he was one of the Five Members whom the King tried to arrest in 1642. When the fighting began Hampden raised troops in Buckinghamshire and secured the county for Parliament. He showed himself to be a man of decisive action advocating in 1643 a Parliamentarian attack on the King's headquarters at Oxford, and it was in the course of Rupert's counter-attack against this that he was mortally wounded in a skirmish at Chalgrove Field."[50] Considering that few readers of Jackson's opinion would know the identity of John Hampden, Jackson's choice of the metonymic Hampden over another better-known defender of freedom remains a mystery. Unless one recognizes Hampden, the metonymy remains ineffective.

Jackson's metaphoric "color of the law" is then followed with the personification "reach of the Constitution." The figurative "color of the law" appeared in the OED under "figurative senses" of the word *coloure*: "Outward appearance, show, aspect, semblance of (something): generally . . . , that which serves to conceal or cloak the truth, or to give a show of justice to what is in itself unjustifiable. Often in *Colour of Law, Colour of Reason.*" The *OED* provides a seventeenth-century example: "To defend them, without any colour of Law or justice" and a nineteenth-century example: "The general heads of breaches of privilege . . . are these three: 1st Evasion, 2nd Force, 3rd Colour of Law."[51] Tracing the background of "colour of law," J. E. S. Simon says of this metaphor:

> Sometimes a party put in a plea designed to make what was really a point of fact appear to be a point of law, so as to transfer the decision from the jury to the judge: this was called *colour*. The expression was in due course applied to the title [that] was in question. "If the defendant," wrote Blackstone, "in assise or action of trespass, be desirous to refer the validity of his title specially, and at the same time *give colour* to the plaintiff, bad indeed in point of law, but of which the jury are not competent judges." Blackstone, *Commentaries* 308.[52]

A metonymic variation on "one man's meat is another's poison" appeared in the Supreme Court's 1971 opinion in *Cohen v. California* where the Court gave constitutional protection to Cohen's "Fuck the Draft" placed on the back of his jacket he wore in the Los Angeles County Courthouse corridor. Justice Harlan, delivering the opinion of the Court, metaphorically and metonymically argued: "Surely the State has no right to cleanse public debate to the point where it is grammatically palatable to the most squeamish among us. Yet no readily ascertainable general principle exists for stopping short of that result were we to affirm the judgment below. For, while the particular four-letter word being litigated here is perhaps more distasteful than most others of its genre, it is nevertheless often true that one man's vulgarity is another's lyric."[53] First, one cannot literally "cleanse" debate; second, cleansing debate to the point of making it "palatable" personifies debate (consistent with the "distasteful" four-letter word);

and third, "one man's vulgarity is another's lyric" is metonymy, as is "one man's meat is another's poison."

In several of his opinions arguing for First Amendment protection for obscene works, Justice Douglas introduced metonymic variations on this theme of what is acceptable to one person may be offensive to another. In his 1966 *Ginzburg* dissent Douglas wrote: "Some like Chopin, others like 'rock and roll.' . . . Man was not made in a fixed mould. . . . Each of us is a very temporary transient with likes and dislikes that cover the spectrum."[54] In his 1973 *Miller* dissent, Justice Douglas declared: "The Court is at large because we deal with tastes and standards of literature. What shocks me may be sustenance for my neighbor. What causes one person to boil up in rage over one pamphlet or movie may reflect only his neurosis, not shared by others."[55]

In an innovative version of Cohen's jacket and Tinker's armband, Judge Newman of the Second Circuit Court of Appeals, deciding for high school students who had been suspended for publishing an allegedly "morally offensive, indecent, and obscene" publication, wrote: "The First Amendment gives a high school student the classroom right to wear Tinker's armband, but not Cohen's jacket."[56]

Judge Newman's metonymic "wear Tinker's armband, but not Cohen's jacket" made an impression on Chief Justice Burger, who, deciding against Fraser, the high school student who had used sexual innuendos and vulgar language in a speech before a high school assembly, wrote: "It does not follow . . . that simply because the use of an offensive form of expression may not be prohibited to adults making what the speaker considers a political point [a reference to *Cohen*], that same latitude must be permitted to children in a public school. In *New Jersey v. T.L.O* . . . , we reaffirmed that the constitutional rights of students in public school are not automatically coextensive with the rights of adults in other settings. As cogently expressed by Judge Newman, 'the First Amendment gives a high school student the classroom right to wear Tinker's armband, but not Cohen's jacket.' "[57]

In 1974, the Supreme Court was confronted with the question whether "a city which operates a public rapid transit system and sells advertising space for car cards on its vehicles is required by the First and Fourteenth Amendments to accept paid political advertising on behalf of a candidate for public office."[58] In deciding against the candidate, the Court not only relied on the metaphoric "captive audience" but also turned to the metonymic "Hyde Park" in reaching its decision. Justice Blackmun, stating the judgment of the Court, wrote: "The managerial decision to limit car card space to innocuous and less controversial commercial and service oriented advertising does not rise to the dignity of a First Amendment violation. Were we to hold to the contrary, display cases in public hospitals, libraries, office buildings, military compounds, and other public facilities immediately would become Hyde Parks open to every would-be pamphleteer and politician. This the Constitution does not require."[59] The difficulty with Blackmun's use of the metonymic "Hyde Parks" is that "display cases" are a form of silent, usually unobtrusive, communication. Such "display cases" do not involve the sometimes raucous, confrontational, belligerent give-and-take communicative setting of Hyde Park. Blackmun's "Hyde Park" metonymic argument is misplaced.

Arguing that Connecticut's statute prohibiting the use of "any drug, medicinal article or instrument for the purpose of preventing conception" was unconstitutional, Justice Douglas declared in his dissenting opinion in *Poe v. Ullman* (1961): "The regulation as applied in this case touches the relationship between man and wife. It reaches into the intimacies of the marriage relationship. If we imagine a regime of full enforcement of the law in the manner of an Anthony Comstock, we would reach the point where search warrants issued and officers appeared in bedrooms to find out what went on."[60] At this point in his opinion, Douglas inserts a footnote pointing out that Anthony Comstock (1844–1915) was "the Congregationalist who inspired the foundation of the New York Society for the Suppression of Vice in 1873 and the Watch and Ward Society of Boston in 1876 and who inspired George Bernard Shaw to use the opprobrious word 'comstockery' in *Mrs. Warren's Profession*."[61] In suggesting that Comstock was responsible for the passage of the Connecticut law involved in *Poe*, Douglas's metonymic use of Comstock is especially appropriate.

While the Connecticut statute would prohibit the use of contraceptives not only in the "bedroom" but also outside this "innermost sanctum of the home," Douglas opted for the metonymic "bedroom" to emphasize the invasion of privacy, especially the privacy we associate with the bedroom. The bedroom appears again in Douglas's next paragraph when he quotes from "a noted theologian who conceives of the use of a contraceptive as a 'sin' [but who] nonetheless admits that a 'use' statute such as this enters a forbidden domain. '. . . . As it stands, the statute is, of course, unenforceable without police invasion of the bedroom, and is therefore indefensible as a piece of legal draughtmanship."[62] All of this figurative language is then followed in the next paragraph with Douglas's assertion: "This notion of privacy is not drawn from the blue. It emanates from the totality of the constitutional scheme under which we live."[63]

What is important to note here is not Douglas's metaphoric cliché "drawn from the blue" but his contention that the notion of privacy "emanates from the totality of the constitutional scheme under which we live." This latter metaphor is especially noteworthy, since "emanates" is directly related to Douglas's "penumbra" that played such an important role five years later in *Griswold v. Connecticut* where the Court reversed the convictions of violating statutes making it illegal to prescribe birth-control devices or material for married couples.

However, when Douglas asserted in *Griswold* that "the First Amendment has a penumbra where privacy is protected from governmental intrusion" and that "specific guarantees in the Bill of Rights have penumbras," we are taken into the metaphoric world, not the metonymic. Literally, *penumbra* refers to a kind of shadow, an almost complete dark shadow, *pen* meaning "almost," and *umbra* meaning the "darkest part of a shadow."

In 1989, the Supreme Court justices expressed their differences about who was being "Orwellian" in *County of Allegheny v. American Civil Liberties U.* where the Court concluded that "the display of the creche in the County Courthouse has this unconstitutional effect [of promoting or endorsing religious beliefs]" and "the display of the menorah in front of the City-County Building, however, does not have this effect, given its 'particular physical setting.'"[64] Justice Kennedy (with whom the Chief Justice, Justice White, and Justice Scalia joined, concurring in part and dissenting in part) accused the Court of lending "its assistance to an Orwellian rewriting of history":

> The approach adopted by the majority contradicts important values embodied in the [Establishment] Clause. Obsessive, implacable resistence to all but the most carefully scripted and secularized forms of accommodation requires this Court to act as a censor, issuing national decrees as to what is orthodox and what is not. What is orthodox, in this context, means what is secular; the only Christmas the State can acknowledge is one in which references to religion have been held to a minimum. The Court thus lends its assistance to an Orwellian rewriting of history as many understand it. I can conceive of no judicial function more antithetical to the First Amendment.[65]

Justice Blackmun, stating the judgment of the Court, responded in a section supported by a majority:

> Although Justice Kennedy repeatedly accuses the Court of harboring a "latent hostility" or "callous indifference" toward religion . . . , nothing could be further from the truth, and the accusations could be said to be as offensive as they are absurd. Justice Kennedy apparently has misperceived a respect for religious pluralism, a respect commanded by the Constitution, as hostility or indifference to religion. No misperception could be more antithetical to the values embodied in the Establishment Clause.[66]

Blackmun then asserts, even more forcefully: "Justice Kennedy's accusations are shot from a weapon triggered by the following proposition: If government may celebrate the secular aspects of Christmas, then it must be allowed to celebrate the religious aspects as well because, otherwise, the government would be discriminating against citizens who celebrate Christmas as a religious, and not just a secular, holiday. . . . This proposition, however, is flawed at its foundation."[67]

In Blackmun's next paragraph the question is raised about who is being "Orwellian": "It follows directly from the Constitution's proscription against government affiliation with religious beliefs or institutions that there is no orthodoxy on religious matters in the secular state. Although Justice Kennedy accuses the Court of 'an Orwellian rewriting of history,' *ibid*, perhaps it is Justice Kennedy himself who has slipped into a form of Orwellian newspeak when he equates the constitutional command of secular government with a prescribed orthodoxy."[68]

Having accused the Court of "an Orwellian rewriting of history," Kennedy associates the justices with the "memory hole," "doublethink," and the destruction of words that was part of George Orwell's *1984*. The identification of the Court with the totalitarian world of *1984* is apparently too much for Blackmun, who must retort that it is Kennedy "who has slipped into a form of Orwellian newspeak." The Justices appear to have regressed into *tu quoque* argument. The difficulty begins when Kennedy refers to the Court's reasoning as Orwellian immediately after he interprets the Court's position as meaning "what is orthodox, in this context, means what is secular; the only Christmas the State can acknowledge is one in which references to religion have been held to a minimum."

It is one thing to disagree with the Court's interpretation; it is something else to refer to it as Orwellian. As Blackmun recognized, "A secular state, it must be remembered, is not the same as an atheistic or antireligious state. A secular state establishes neither atheism nor religion as its official creed."[69]

What the Court argued to support its decision on creche and menorah was hardly an Orwellian rewriting of history, for in *1984* Winston Smith *knowingly* distorted the facts: "The *Times* of the nineteenth of December had published the official forecasts of the output of various classes of consumption goods in the fourth quarter of 1983, which was also the sixth quarter of the Ninth Three-Year Plan. Today's issue contained a statement of the actual report, from which it appeared that the forecasts were in every instance grossly wrong. Winston's job was to rectify the original figures by making them agree with the later ones.'"[70] This deliberate misrepresentation of the facts was then followed with the deliberate destruction of documents: "As soon as Winston had dealt with each of the messages, he clipped his speak-written corrections to the appropriate copy of the *Times* and pushed them into the pneumatic tube. Then, with a movement which was as nearly as possible unconscious, he crumpled up the original message and any notes that he himself had made, and dropped them into the memory hole to be destroyed by the flames."[71] This was, in part, the rewriting of history in Orwell's *1984*. Justice Kennedy's accusation that this is what the Court was doing is surely an unfortunate misapplication of the metonymic "Orwellian."

So seldom does one find a judge discussing metonymy that it is a surprise to read Judge Richard Posner's observations about a metonymy appearing in Justice Holmes's dissenting opinion in the influential *Lochner v. New York*.[72] When in 1905 the Supreme Court struck down a New York statute that limited the number of hours laborers could work in bakeries and confectionery establishments, Justice Holmes dissented and introduced a metonymy that Judge Posner sees as especially significant. Holmes had written: "The liberty of the citizen to do as he likes so long as he does not interfere with the liberty of others to do the same, which has been a shibboleth for some well-known writers, is interfered with by school laws, by the Post Office, by every state or municipal institution which takes his money for purposes thought desirable, whether he likes it or not. The Fourteenth Amendment does not enact Mr. Herbert Spencer's Social Statics."[73] Spencer's *Social Statics*, published in 1850, dealt with property, the imperfection of humans, the immorality of government, and related subjects; in 1864, an American edition of this work was published.

The metonymic "Mr. Herbert Spencer's Social Statics," Judge Posner argues, has affected the persuasiveness of Holmes's opinion:

How much weaker the sentence would have been if for
"Mr. Herbert Spencer's Social Statics" Holmes had written
"laissez-faire," or even if for "enacts" he had written
"adopts"! The absurdity of the idea that the Constitution
would enact a book with a weird title, written by an En-
glishman, lends emotional force to the sentence and—my
essential point—operates as a substitute for proof.
Holmes has made Spencer's book the metaphor (broadly
defined; technically the figure of speech employed is not a
metaphor, but metonymy) for the philosophy of laissez-
faire. And metaphors [and metonymies], because of their
concreteness, vividness, and, when they are good, unexpectedness, are more memorable than their literal equivalents. This is one reason why the dissent in *Lochner* not
only contributed to the shift of opinion that culminated
many years later in the repudiation of "Lochnerism" but
also became the symbol of opposition to the judicial philosophy reflected in the majority opinion.[74]

After examining Holmes's *Lochner* language and argument, Posner concludes: "It is not, in short, a good judicial
opinion. It is merely the greatest judicial opinion of the last
hundred years. To judge it by 'scientific' standards is to miss
the point. It is a rhetorical masterpiece, and evidently rhetoric
counts in law; otherwise, the dissent in *Lochner* would be
forgotten."[75] While one may not agree that Holmes's *Lochner*
opinion is "the greatest judicial opinion of the last hundred
years," one must concur with Judge Posner that "rhetoric
counts in law."

Like metaphors, "metonymic concepts structure not just
our language but our thoughts, attitudes, and actions."[76] Just
as the metaphoric "marketplace of ideas" and "wall of separation" between church and state have affected our perceptions
and the judiciary's decisions, so have the metonymic "multitude of tongues" and "shedding" one's rights at the "schoolhouse gate" been influential in our conceptualization of abstractions. Like some of the judicial metaphors, the judicial
metonymies have become "principles" and "standards" invoked in legal argument.

8

Personifying Justice, the Constitution, and Judicial Opinions

Justice is a blindfold woman with a scale in one hand and a sword in the other; "our Constitution is color-blind"; "the law knows no heresy"; and judicial decisions have "progeny." Like metaphor and metonymy, personification has played an important role in judicial argument and decision making.

In his *Lectures on Rhetoric and Belles Lettres*, Hugh Blair, the eighteenth-century professor of rhetoric in Edinburgh, discussed the various tropes, including personification, "when we introduce inanimate objects acting like those that have life."[1] Writing of the appropriate and inappropriate uses of personification, Blair said:

> Cicero, for instance, speaking of the cases where killing another is lawful in self-defense, uses the following words: "Aliquando nobis gladius ad occidendum hominem ab ipsis porrigitur legibus." (Orat. pro Milone). . . .
> The laws are personified, as reaching forth their hand to give us a sword for putting one to death. Such short personifications as these may be admitted, even into moral treatises, or works of cool reasoning; and, provided they be easy and not strained, and that we are not cloyed with too frequent returns to them, they have a good effect on style, and render it both strong and lively.[2]

Richard Whately, the nineteenth-century English rhetorician, devoted a chapter in his *Elements of Rhetoric* to "Energy" and the tropes, including personification. The term *energy*, he

167

explains, corresponds "with what Dr. Campbell [the Scottish rhetorician George Campbell] calls Vivacity; so as to comprehend every thing that may conduce to stimulate attention, — to impress strongly on the mind the Arguments adduced, — to excite the Imagination, and to arouse Feelings."[3] In his discussion of "personifying metaphors," Whately wrote: "Of metaphors, those generally conduce most to that Energy and Vivacity of style we are speaking of, which illustrate an *intellectual* by a *sensible* object; the latter being always the most early familiar to the mind, and generally giving the most distinct impression to it. Thus we speak of *'unbridled* rage,' *'deep-rooted* prejudice.' , . . . But the highest degree of Energy (and to which Aristotle chiefly restricts the term) is produced by such Metaphors as attribute *life* and *action* to things inanimate."[4]

Whately then turns his attention to the role of gender in personification, pointing out that when we speak of "virtue" or "our Country" as a female, "they are, by that very circumstance, personified": "Our language possesses one remarkable advantage, with a view to this kind of Energy, in the constitution of its *genders*. All nouns in English, which express objects that are really neuter, are considered as strictly of the neuter gender; the Greek and Latin, though possessing the advantage . . . of having a neuter gender, yet lose the benefit of it, fixing the masculine or feminine genders upon many nouns denoting things inanimate; whereas in English, when we speak of any object in the masculine or feminine gender, that form of expression at once confers personality upon it."[5]

That personification is an apt trope to be used in judicial reasoning is suggested when Blair states that personification "may be admitted" in "moral treatises or works of cool reasoning," provided it is not "strained." That personification is an effective trope is suggested by Whately when he asserts that "the highest degree of Energy . . . is produced by such Metaphors as attribute life and action to things inanimate." More recently, Bertrand Bronson asks: "Is there any other resource at the disposal of the poet so perfectly calculated to unite the general with the particular, the abstract with the concrete?"

Answering his question, Bronson states that personification "opens views of the widest conceptual horizons, and at the same time brings them into close and familiar neighborhood. It lends strangeness to the conventional; it brings the dead to life. As of everything else in the domain of human expression, Shakespeare is the greatest, most inexhaustible master of it, as every page of his work stands ready to testify: 'Liberty plucks Justice by the nose,' 'Time hath . . . a wallet at his back in which he puts alms for oblivion.'"[6]

Through the personifications appearing in judicial opinions, the "dead" are brought to "life," the unfamiliar becomes familiar, the abstract is humanized. As Lakoff and Johnson have explained, personification "allows us to comprehend a wide variety of experiences with nonhuman entities in terms of human motivations, characteristics, and activities."[7]

As with the more influential metaphors and metonymies appearing in judicial argument, some personifications introduced in a judicial opinion are subsequently cited by other courts in arriving at decisions. In 1953, the Supreme Court decided in *Avery v. Georgia* that the conviction and sentencing of death of a "Negro who was convicted of rape" had to be reversed because of racial discrimination in the selection of the jury. Justice Frankfurter stated in his concurring opinion: "The stark resulting phenomenon here was that somehow or other, despite the fact that over 5% of the slips were yellow [white and yellow slips placed in jury box, yellow slips with names of blacks], no Negro got onto the panel of 60 jurors from which Avery's jury was selected. The mind of justice, not merely its eyes, would have to be blind to attribute such an occurrence to mere fortuity."[8]

In another context, the Frankfurter personification was incorporated into *State v. Altrui* where the Supreme Court of Connecticut upheld an assault conviction: "In view of the principle that waiver of the privilege against self-incrimination is not lightly to be inferred it is not at all clear that Solevo [a key witness] was not justified in claiming the privilege in this case. It is a fair inference that Kelsey [an acquaintance of Solevo] attempted to tamper with a key state witness. Though justice may be blind, it is not stupid. The mind of justice, not merely its eyes, would have to be blind to attribute such an occurrence to mere fortuity."[9]

The reference to blindness is to the "lady of Justice," Themis, who is blindfolded, with a scale in one hand and a sword in the other, the former conveying balanced judgment, the latter authority and protection. Frankfurter's personification animates in two ways. First, Justice is given a mind; second, Justice is given blinded eyes. Judge Parskey of the Connecticut Supreme Court further personifies Justice by claiming that she is not "stupid."

Frankfurter's reference to Justice's eyes as "its eyes" is a bit jarring, for having humanized Justice with eyes, Frankfurter dehumanizes her with "it." While justice has historically been personified as a person holding a scale and a sword, the personification is a "she." Benjamin Cardozo suggested: "Justice is not to be taken by storm. She is to be wooed by slow advances." Lord Atkin stated in a 1936 opinion: "Justice is not a cloistered virtue; she must be allowed to suffer the scrutiny and respectfull, even though outspoken, comments of ordinary men." Others have portrayed Justice as female. Alexander Pope: "Poetic Justice, with her lifted scale, / Where in nice balance truth with gold she weighs, / And solid pudding against empty praise." Samuel Butler: "For Justice, tho' she's painted blind, / Is to the weaker side inclin'd." Swinburne: "He called upon justice by her other name of mercy; / he claimed for all alike the equity of compassion."[10]

However, while Justice is a "she," historically the judge administering justice has been a "he." While the statue of Justice outside the courthouse is a she, the judge inside the courthouse has been a he. In her 1982 *Judicature* essay, Susan Carbon points out: "Until this century, the number of women judges in America was so small that one could literally count them all on a single hand." By 1950, "At least 29 states had had one or more women judges, and 11 women had served on the federal judiciary. It was not until 1979, however, that every state could report that its bench had included at least one woman judge."[11] Joan Dempsey Klein, past president of the National Association of Women Judges, reported in 1981: "While we are still in the process of gathering accurate data, it is safe to say women judges constitute about 5 percent of the appellate and general trial courts and 7 percent of the specialized family courts.

Even with the recent appointments made by President Carter, women comprise only some 5.4 percent of the federal judiciary."[12] *Human Rights* reported in 1983: "According to a study by *The Washington Post*, all but four of the first 72 judges appointed by President Reagan to federal trial and appellate courts were white males. Three women were appointed federal trial judges and one black federal judge was elevated to a circuit court of appeals. President Carter, by contrast, appointed 260 federal judges—including 41 women and 37 blacks."[13] It would have been enlightening for Themis if she had temporarily taken off her blindfold, for while she heard that the Constitution was color-blind, she could not see that the judicial system was not gender-blind.

It was in 1896 that the personification "our Constitution is color-blind" was introduced into judicial discourse. Justice Harlan dissented in the landmark case *Plessy v. Ferguson* where the majority of the Court supported the separate-but-equal doctrine and decided to keep railway facilities racially segregated: "Our Constitution is color-blind, and neither knows nor tolerates classes among citizens. In respect of civil rights, all citizens are equal before the law. The humblest is the peer of the most powerful."[14] Not only did Harlan attribute eyesight to the Constitution, but he also personified the document into knowing and tolerating. Justice Harlan's personification of the Constitution had significant influence as his "our Constitution is colorblind" has appeared in scores of judicial opinions since 1896.

However, as noted by Justices Brennan and Marshall in *University of California Regents v. Bakke*, the personification has not always been accepted. Justice Brennan observed that "no decision of this Court has ever adopted the proposition that the Constitution must be colorblind."[15] Pointing out that Harlan's personification has at times been rejected by the Court, Brennan said: "The assertion of human equality is closely associated with the proposition that differences in color or creed, birth or status, are neither significant nor relevant to the way in which persons should be treated. None-theless, the position that such factors must be 'constitutionally an irrelevance . . . , summed up by the shorthand phrase '[O]ur Constitution is colorblind,' *Plessy v. Ferguson* . . . , has never been adopted by this Court as the proper meaning of the Equal Protection Clause. Indeed, we have expressly re-jected this proposition on a number of occasions."[16]

Justice Marshall, also writing a separate opinion in *Bakke*, referred to Harlan's *Plessy* personification:

> Most importantly, had the Court been willing in 1896, in
> *Plessy v. Ferguson*, to hold that the Equal Protection Clause
> forbids differences in treatment based on race, we would
> not be faced with this dilemma in 1978. We must remem-
> ber, however, that the principle that the "Constitution is
> colorblind" appeared only in the opinion of the lone dis-
> senter. . . . The majority of the Court rejected the princi-
> ple of color blindness, and for the next 60 years, from
> *Plessy* to *Brown v. Board of Education*, ours was a Nation
> where, *by law*, an individual could be given "special"
> treatment based on the color of his skin.[17]

The color-blind personification, along with other tropes, played an important role in a 1978 district court decision upholding the constitutionality of the 10 percent minority-business-enterprise requirement of the Public Works Employ-ment Act. Judge Pettine extended the color-blind personifica-tion to the point that it became crucial to his argument:

> The Thirteenth Amendment "[b]y its own unaided
> force and effect . . . abolished slavery, and established
> universal freedom . . ." and "clothes congress with power
> to pass all laws necessary and proper for abolishing all
> badges and incidents of slavery in the United States. . . ."
> . . . .
> There will be a day when the burdens of prior dis-
> crimination have been eased and then erased. The vision
> of the Thirteenth and the Fourteenth Amendments of a
> society free of racial inequality, color-blind, in which dif-

ferences among persons arise from merit alone, will be realized.

That time is not yet come. The power of Congress to
legislate to eradicate the vestiges of slavery, its badges and
incidents, remains in force today as it did over 100 years
ago. . . . "The Constitutional imperative to eliminate the
badges of slavery has not dimmed in the 114 years since
President Lincoln issued the Emancipation Proclamation."
. . . .

The federal court has special responsibility in safeguarding the strictures of the Civil War Amendments and
the Fifth Amendment. In the long-run, it must protect the
vision of a color-blind society free of legal divisions based
on the color of one's skin and the origin of one's family.
But it would be wishful thinking to believe that a color-
blind society can be created in a short time.
. . . .

It is now but 28 years since *Brown v. Board of Education*
overruled *Plessy v. Ferguson*. It is too early, far too early, to
argue that the legislature may not use race-sensitive classifications to remedy past discrimination. For this Court
to hold otherwise would be to shut our eyes, like Justice
Bradley [Supreme Court Justice who held that Fourteenth
Amendment did not protect blacks against racial discrimination practiced by private individuals], to the pervasive
racial inequality remaining to be undone.[18]

The image of sight runs throughout Judge Pettine's opinion: "the vision of the Thirteenth and the Fourteenth Amendments," "a color-blind society," "the Constitutional imperative
to eliminate the badges of slavery has not dimmed," "the
federal court must protect the vision of a color-blind society,"
"it would be wishful thinking to believe that a color-blind
society can be created in a short time," "for this Court to hold
otherwise would be to shut our eyes." In reference to *Plessy*,
Judge Pettine wrote: "Soon the Court would turn a blind eye
to the state reimposition of white supremacy and, in effect,
give its constitutional imprimatur."[19] Since this is a case
dealing with the color of one's skin, the emphasis on the
extended personification is consistent with the issue being
decided. The judge has argued that it is proper for Congress

to pass laws to abolish all the visual "badges . . . of slavery in the United States." Further, it is proper for the court to help remedy the pervasive racial inequality existing in a society not yet color-blind. The personification becomes integral to the judge's argument and decision.

In 1961, Justice Douglas, concurring in *Garner v. Louisiana* where the Supreme Court gave constitutional protection to sit-ins at segregated lunch counters in private establishments, drew on Justice Harlan's *Plessy* personification: "Those who license enterprises for public use should not have under our Constitution the power to license it for the use of only one race. For there is the overriding constitutional requirement that all state power be exercised so as not to deny equal protection to any group. As the First Mr. Justice Harlan stated in dissent in *Plessy v. Ferguson* . . . , '. . . in view of the Constitution, in the eye of the law, there is in this country no superior, dominant, ruling class of citizens. There is no caste here. Our Constitution is colorblind."[20]

But is the Constitution completely color-blind? In 1961, a U.S. district court in New York decided that black students had been denied the equal protection guaranteed by the Fourteenth Amendment as a result of continued racially seg-regated schools in New Rochelle, New York. Judge Kaufman noted that "the Board argues that it would be violative of the law to accord Negroes special privileges not allowed to other minority groups. It points to the fact that several other ele-mentary schools in New Rochelle have student compositions which are primarily of one religious or national-origin group, and argues that if permissive zoning privileges were afforded to the Lincoln pupils, the same privileges would have to be given to these other minorities."[21] At this point in his opinion, Judge Kaufman responded to the school board's argument: "But, the Constitution is not this color-blind. The *Brown* decision dealt only with Negroes; it was based on factual findings which may not be applicable to other minority groups."[22]

Five years later, the Fifth Circuit Court of Appeals, decid-ing to enjoin Alabama school officials from discriminating on the basis of color or race in the operation of the school system, stated: "The defendants err in their contention that the HEW and the courts cannot take race into consideration in establishing standards for desegregation. '[T]he Constitution is not this colorblind.' "[23] Attributing this latter personification to Judge Kaufman, the court went on to explain:

> The Constitution is both colorblind and color conscious. To avoid conflict with the equal protection clause, a classification that denies a benefit, causes harm, or imposes a burden must not be based on race. In that sense, the Constitution is color blind. But the Constitution is color conscious to prevent discrimination being perpetuated and to undo the effects of past discrimination. The criterion is the relevancy of color to a legitimate governmental purpose. . . . If the Constitution were absolutely colorblind, consideration of race in the census and in adoption proceedings would be unconstitutional.[24]

A U.S. district court in Georgia, concluding that there was no racial discrimination in a jury-selection process as contended by a black person who had been convicted of rape, declared, "Justice . . . must be colorblind": "Regardless of the selection system employed, it must be struck down if it contains an element of racial discrimination. . . . Justice, to be meaningful, must be colorblind. With these elementary principles in mind, we feel that petitioner's [prisoner's] contentions can not hold water."[25] The difficulty with the court's personification here is that since Justice is already blindfolded, why must she also be color-blind? There is a difference between saying "The Constitution is color-blind" and "Justice must be color-blind." Further, the metaphoric cliché "cannot hold water" adds little to the persuasiveness of the opinion.

Before attributing color-blindness to the inanimate, one would do well to be aware of what *color-blind* literally means: "Unable to see certain colours; unable to discriminate between individual colours, or shades of colour (the strict meaning ought to be 'blind to clour' as a whole; but this rarely exists, except in the case of the totally blind), the term is applied with much laxity to any constitutional inability to discriminate between colours, the common type being inability to distinguish the red and the green rays of the spectrum from each other."[26] Hence, a color-blind Constitution is not blind to all colors; it is "unable to see certain colours." I suspect that it is not the latter that is meant by those who speak of the Constitution as colorblind.

Whether the Constitution is totally color-blind, partially color-blind, or can see no colors, it surely must be animate to possess any of these qualities. When in 1920 Justice Holmes delivered the opinion of the Court in *Missouri v. Holland*, he wrote of the "begetters" and the creation of an "organism": "When we are dealing with words that also are a constituent act, like the Constitution of the United States, we must realize that they have called into life a being the development of which could not have been forseen completely by the most gifted of its begetters. It was enough for them to realize or to hope that they had created an organism; it has taken a century and has cost their successors much sweat and blood to prove that they created a nation. The case before us must be considered in the light of our whole experience and not merely in that of what was said a hundred years ago."[27] Holmes's language indicates a "living Constitution."

Justice Brennan, in *Hazelwood School Dist. v. Kuhlmeier* (1988), rejecting the majority's "excuses" offered to support its position that school authorities had not violated high school students' First Amendment rights when the principal deleted two pages of articles from an issue of the school newspaper, concluded his dissenting opinion with a paragraph that relied on several tropes, including the personification "our Constitution is a living reality":

> The Court opens its analysis in this case by purporting to reaffirm *Tinker*'s time-tested proposition that public school students "do not shed their constitutional rights to freedom of speech or expression at the schoolhouse gate." . . . That is an ironic introduction to an opinion that denudes high school students of much of the First Amendment protection that *Tinker* itself prescribed. Instead of "teach[ing] children to respect the diversity of ideas that is fundamental to the American system," . . . and "that our Constitution is a living reality, not parchment pre-

served under glass," . . . the Court today "teach[es] youth
to discount important principles of our government as
mere platitudes." . . . The young men and women of Hazelwood East expected a civics lesson, but not the one the
Court teaches them today.[28]

By deciding against the students, the Court's decision,
according to Brennan, not only led to a "shedding" of rights
but a "denuding" of high school students of First Amendment
protection provided by *Tinker*. Brennan's "nudity" trope suggests a question about what influence Fortas's metonymy
would have had if he had said in *Tinker* that "students and
teachers cannot be denuded at the schoolhouse gate of their
freedoms of speech or expression" or that "students and
teachers, entering the schoolhouse gate, cannot constitutionally be denuded of their freedoms of speech or expression." The nudity trope may have been too suggestive, too
sexual. *Roget's Thesaurus* provides the following under *nudity*:
"nakedness, bareness; the nude, the altogether or the buff
[both informal], the raw [slang]; state of nature, birthday suit
[informal]; not a stitch, not a stitch to one's name; décolleté,
décolletage, toplessness, nudism, gymnosophist, stripper,
stripteaser, ecdysiast."[29]

"That our Constitution is a living reality, not parchment
preserved under glass" is taken from Judge Irving Goldberg's
1972 *Shanley* opinion in which he wrote: "One of the great
concerns of our time is that our young people, disillusioned
by our political processes, are disengaging from political
participation. It is most important that our young become
convinced that our Constitution is a living reality, not parchment preserved under glass."[30]

The courts have personified not only justice and the
Constitution but also the law. One influential personification
of law appeared in an 1872 Supreme Court opinion written by
Justice Samuel Miller: "The law knows no heresy, and is
committed to the support of no dogma, the establishment of
no sect."[31] Delivering the opinion of the Court, Justice Miller
argued that it was not the government's place to have the
courts define the correctness of conflicting religious views, in

this case a controversy between pro- and antislavery factions of a Presbyterian church in Louisville, Kentucky. Justice Miller wrote: "In this country the full and free right to entertain any religious belief, to practice any religious principle, and to teach any religious doctrine which does not violate the laws of morality and property, and which does not infringe personal rights, is conceded by all. The law knows no heresy."[32]

Justice Miller's personification was subsequently cited again and again by courts deciding cases involving the religion clauses of the First Amendment. In 1944, the Supreme Court decided for Guy W. Ballard (alias Saint Germain, Jesus, George Washington, and Godfre Ray King), who had been convicted for using, and conspiring to use, the mails to defraud by soliciting funds and members for the "I Am" movement. Justice Douglas, delivering the opinion of the Court, wrote: "On whichever basis that court rested its action, we do not agree that the truth or verity of respondents' religious doctrines or beliefs should have been submitted to the jury. Whatever this particular indictment might require, the First Amendment precludes such a course, as the United States seems to concede. 'The law knows no heresy, and is committed to the support of no dogma, the establishment of no sect.' "[33]

"The law knows no heresy" appeared in a different context in 1968 when the Supreme Court declared unconstitutional Arkansas's "antievolution" statute prohibiting "the teaching in its public schools and universities of the theory that man evolved from other species of life." Justice Fortas, delivering the opinion of the Court, declared: "The antecedents of today's decision are many and unmistakable. They are rooted in the foundation soil of our Nation. They are fundamental to freedom."[34] One of those antecedents "rooted in the foundation soil of our Nation" was *Watson v. Jones*, and the passage Fortas cited from *Watson* was the personification: "As early as 1872, this Court said: 'The law knows no heresy, and is committed to the support of no dogma, the establishment of no sect.' . . . This has been the interpretation of the great First Amendment which this Court has applied in the many and subtle problems which the ferment of our national life has presented for decision within the Amendment's broad command."³⁵

In *Presbyterian Church v. Hull Church* (1969) the question presented to the Supreme Court was "whether the restraints of the First Amendment, as applied to the States through the Fourteenth Amendment, permit a civil court to award church property on the basis of the interpretation and significance the civil court assigns to aspects of church doctrine."³⁶ Justice Brennan, delivering the opinion of the Court, emphasized the similarities between *Watson* and this case and argued that the *Watson* Court had pointed out "that it was wholly inconsistent with the American concept of the relationship between church and state to permit civil courts to determine ecclesiastical questions. In language which has a clear constitutional ring, the Court said, 'In this country the full and free right to entertain any religious beliefs, to practice any religion principle, and to teach any religious doctrine which does not violate the law of morality and property, and which does not infringe personal rights, is conceded to all. The law knows no heresy.'"³⁷

Seven years later, Justice Brennan again delivered the opinion of the Court in a religious dispute involving a defrocked bishop and again cited the *Watson* personification, along with his own "in language which has a clear constitutional ring." After citing a passage from *Watson*, Brennan wrote: "In language having 'a clear constitutional ring,' . . . *Watson* reasoned: 'The law knows no heresy.'"³⁸

The *Watson* personification also found its way into the reasoning of the lower courts. In 1988, the U.S. District Court for the District of Puerto Rico declared: "Embedded in the First Amendment is the proposition that 'the law knows no heresy.'"³⁹

In a 1987 case, the District of Columbia Court of Appeals concluded that a law that granted the "Christian Science Board of Directors of the First Church of Christ, Scientist (First Church) an extended copyright on all editions of Science and Health with Key to the Scriptures (Science and Health) the central theological text of the Christian Science faith," was a violation of the establishment clause. In so deciding, the court said: "Government is . . . barred from assuming a position in the debate [over religious truth] by attempting to establish religious truth by fiat. In matters of religion, truth, including purity of doctrinal statement, is left for the citizenry to determine by persuasion, not for resolution by exertion of governmental authority." To support this position, the court declared in a note that "this commitment was given forceful expression by the [Supreme] Court: 'The law knows no heresy.'"[40]

Having instilled life into justice, the Constitution, and law, courts have also personified their decisions. Decisions "beget" decisions; decisions have "progeny." The English word *progeny* is derived from *progignere* which means "to beget." Literally, progeny are children, descendents, offspring. In *Shanley v. Northeast Ind. School Dist.* the Fifth Circuit Court of Appeals, deciding against school officials who had suspended several high school seniors for distributing near the school an underground newspaper, argued tropologically:

> This case is anomalous in several respects, a sort of judicial believe-it-or-not. Essentially, the school board has submitted a constitutional fossil, exhumed and respired to stalk the First Amendment once again long after its substance had been laid to rest. Counsel for the school board insists vigorously that education is constitutionally embraced solely by the Tenth Amendment, leaving education entirely without the protective perimeters of the rest of the Constitution. We find this a rather quaint approach to the constitutional setting of education in light of *West Virginia State Board of Education v. Barnette* . . . ; *Tinker v. Des Moines Independent Community School Dist.* . . . [several other decisions cited]. Even the educational progeny of *Plessy v. Ferguson* . . . held that the manner in which a state operated its public school system *must* be subject to constitutional review.[41]

Through the use of several tropes, the court has attacked the school board's actions against the students: "This case is . . . a sort of judicial believe-it-or-not"; the board has "submitted a constitutional fossil, exhumed and respired to stalk the First Amendment"; "constitutionally embraced"; "the protective perimeters of the rest of the Constitution"; "a rather quaint approach"; "the educational progeny of *Plessy v. Ferguson.*" The "progeny" personification is accompanied with several metaphors and the irony "quaint approach," *quaint* being used ironically since the literal definition of *quaint* is "agreeably curious, especially in an old fashioned way."[42]

The same court relied on still other tropes in supporting its decision; Judge Goldberg referred to the marketplace of ideas: "While a school is certainly a market-place for ideas, it is just as certainly not a market place. The educational process is thwarted by the milling, mooing, and haranguing, along with the aggressiveness that often accompanies a constitutionally protected exchange of ideas on the street corner."[43] The court concluded its opinion with an extended metaphor:

> *Tinker's* dam to school board absolutism does not leave
> dry the fields of school discipline. This court has gone a
> considerable distance with the school boards to uphold its
> disciplinary fiats where reasonable. . . . *Tinker* simply irri-
> gates, rather than floods, the fields of school discipline. It
> sets canals and channels through which school discipline
> might flow with the least possible damage to the nation's
> priceless topsoil of the First Amendment. Perhaps it
> would be well if those entrusted to administer the teach-
> ing of American history and government to our students
> began their efforts by practicing the document on which
> that history and government are based. Our eighteen-
> year-olds can now vote, serve on juries, and be drafted;
> yet the board fears the "awakening" of their intellects
> without reasoned concern for its effect upon school disci-
> pline. The First Amendment cannot tolerate such intol-
> erance.[44]

One problem with this water-control extended metaphor is that while earlier in the court's opinion the *Plessy* decision was personified as having progeny, the *Tinker* decision is depersonalized into a structure, a dam. Further, the extended metaphor brings too much attention to itself, what with "irrigates," "floods," "fields of school discipline," "canals and channels," and "topsoil of the First Amendment." And then it is jarring to have the First Amendment, having just been identified with inanimate soil, personified as not "tolerat[ing] such intolerance," the latter being not only a personification, but also a polyptoton (scheme, not a trope), which is the "repetition of the same word or root with different grammatical functions or forms."[45]

The "progeny" personification appeared in Justice Brennan's *Bakke* opinion. Referring to the separate-but-equal doctrine, he wrote: "Not until 1954 — only 24 years ago — was this odious doctrine interred by our decision in *Brown v. Board of Education* . . . , and its progeny, which proclaimed that separate schools and public facilities of all sorts are inherently unequal and forbidden under our Constitution."[46] Not only has *Brown* been personified, but so too has separate but equal, an "odious doctrine" that was "interred" by *Brown*.

In a dissenting opinion relying heavily on several tropes, Justice Blackmun argued in *Webster v. Reproductive Health Services* that a Missouri abortion statute was unconstitutional and in so arguing declared: "As discussed at perhaps too great length above, the plurality makes no serious attempt to carry 'the heavy burden of persuading . . . that changes in society or in the law dictate' the abandonment of *Roe* and it numerous progeny."[47] Blackmun concluded his dissenting opinion with warnings expressed in figurative language: "For today, at least, the law of abortion stands undisturbed. For today, the women of this Nation still retain the liberty to control their destinies. But the signs are evident and very ominous, and a chill wind blows."[48]

In the area of First Amendment rights as applied to students and teachers, it has been *Tinker* and its progeny that have been especially recognized by the courts. In 1977, the Second Circuit Court of Appeals decided for school officials who had prohibited high school students from taking a survey of the sexual attitudes of students at Stuyvesant High School in New York City with the intent of publishing the results of the survey in a student publication. The court declared: "Although this case involves a situation where the potential disruption is psychological rather than physical, *Tinker* and its progeny hold that the burden is on the school officials to demonstrate that there was reasonable cause to believe that distribution of the questionnaire would have caused a significant psychological harm to some of the Stuyvesant students."[49]

One year later, when the Second Circuit Court of Appeals decided for several Granville, New York, high school students who had been suspended from school for their publication and distribution off campus of an allegedly "morally offensive, indecent, and obscene" tabloid, the court distinguished between the facts of that case and "*Tinker* and its progeny": "The case before us . . . arises in a factual context distinct from that envisioned in *Tinker* and its progeny. While prior cases involved expression within the school itself, all but an insignificant amount of relevant activity in this case was deliberately designed to take place beyond the schoolhouse gate."[50]

In 1980, a U.S. district court in Georgia decided against school officials who had on various occasions censored the high school newspaper because it contained material officials deemed inaccurate, in poor taste, and possibly libelous. After asserting that "a logical starting point when discussing student First Amendment rights is the landmark case of *Tinker*," the court said: "The *Tinker* standard of material and substantial disruption has been applied by numerous courts, including those in this circuit, in cases involving student publications. . . . In *Shanley* . . . the Fifth Circuit Court of Appeals summarized the decisional implications of *Tinker* and its progeny as follows."[51]

Several other important Supreme Court decisions have had their progeny. Chief Justice Burger, dissenting in *Gertz v. Robert Welch, Inc.*, wrote: "The doctrines of the law of defamation have had a gradual evolution primarily in the state courts. In *New York Times v. Sullivan* . . . and its progeny this Court entered the field."[52] Justice O'Connor, dissenting in an establishment-clause case, argued: "To survive the *Lemon* test a statute must have both a secular legislative purpose and a principal or primary effect that neither advances nor inhibits religion. Under *Lemon* and its progeny, direct state aid to parochial schools that has the purpose or effect of furthering the religious mission of the schools is unconstitutional."[53] "*Dombrowski* and its progeny'" has been relied on by various courts in arriving at decisions: "The District Court, while noting that 'it would seem desirable and preferable that . . . litigation attacking municipal ordinances and state statutes, particularly statutes with purely local application, be instituted in state courts,' nevertheless held that it was compelled to reach the merits under the teaching of *Dombrowski* and its progeny."[54] While this court was "compelled" under "the teaching of *Dombrowski* and its progeny," another court declared: "*Dombrowski* and its progeny require that certain criteria must be satisfied before plaintiffs are entitled to relief."[55] That these progeny could "compel" and "require" emphasizes the power and influence of the offspring.

Judicial tests, like justice, the Constitution, law, and decisions, are also personified. Justice Douglas, concurring in *Brandenburg v. Ohio*, declared: "Out of the 'clear and present danger' test came other offspring."[56] While we are on the subject of progeny and offspring, we must note Justice Brennan's "pregnant" personification in the flag-burning case *Texas v. Johnson*: "Pregnant with expressive content, the flag as readily signifies this Nation as does the combination of letters found in 'America.'"[57]

One of the most memorable and persuasive opinions in the area of freedom of speech is Justice Brandeis's concurring opinion in *Whitney v. California*, and one of the most memorable passages so often quoted from his opinion relies on figurative language, including personification: "They [those who won our independence] recognized the risks to which all human institutions are subject. But they knew that order cannot be secured merely through fear of punishment for its infraction; that it is hazardous to discourage thought, hope and imagination; that fear breeds repression; that repression breeds hate; that hate menaces stable government; that the path of safety lies in the opportunity to discuss freely supposed grievances and proposed remedies."[58]

The passage "that fear breeds repression; that repression breeds hate; that hate menaces stable government" derives its force and influence not only through the nonliteral use of *breeds* but also through Brandeis's use of *anadiplosis*, a scheme in which the speaker repeats the last word of a phrase or clause at the beginning of the following phrase or clause. Further, the rhythmic antithesis "supposed grievances and proposed remedies" provides Brandeis's message with a sense of completeness.

The impact of the personifications of justice, the Constitution, law, and judicial opinions on our perceptions of these rather abstract entities cannot be underestimated. For a century there has been an ongoing controversy whether we have a "living" Constitution. If the Constitution is a "living reality, not parchment preserved under glass," or as Justice Holmes put it, "The provisions of the Constitution are not mathematical formulas . . . ; they are organic, living institutions transplanted from English soil," or Justice Frankfurter—"The Constitution . . . is an organism, not merely a literary composition"—if it is a "living" Constitution we are "expounding," then our perception of the document is different from what is created from a "static" and "mechanistic" Constitution.

Which trope is accepted, which trope prevails, cannot help but influence the reasoning and decision making of the courts. Recognizing that the First Amendment requires "breathing space" to survive leads us to see this abstraction as something more than inanimate. Through personification, the inanimate, abstract First Amendment becomes a living being that brings the perceptions of suffocation, survival, life and death. Through personification, the "parchment under glass," whether the First Amendment or the Constitution, takes on human qualities that need to be tended more carefully, for we then deal with something mortal.

9

Metaphorizing Speech into "Fire" Leading to a "Conflagration"

In his now classic 1941 work *Free Speech in the United States* Zechariah Chafee, Jr., began chapter 1 with the following observations: "Never in the history of our country, since the Alien and Sedition Laws of 1798, has the meaning of free speech been the subject of such sharp controversy as during the years since 1917. Over nineteen hundred prosecutions and other judicial proceedings during the war, involving speeches, newspaper articles, pamphlets, and books, were followed after the armistice by a widespread legislative consideration of bills punishing the advocacy of extreme radicalism."[1] In 1919, the Supreme Court upheld the convictions of Eugene Debs, Jacob Frohwerk, Charles Schenck, Elizabeth Baer, Jacob Abrams, and others who had been sentenced to up to twenty years in prison for their utterances against U.S. participation in World War I, against compulsory conscription, against Wall Street, against capitalism.[2] Within a decade, the Court also upheld the convictions of Socialists, Communists, and Anarchists such as Benjamin Gitlow and Anita Whitney.[3]

In two landmark decisions coming out of this period, *Schenck v. United States* and *Gitlow v. New York*, the "fire" metaphor played an important role in the Court's arguments leading to its decisions. The Court's use of the "fire" metaphor and analogue had the effect of identifying Schenck's and Gitlow's speech with the dread, perils, and destructiveness associated with fire. Schenck had been convicted of violating the Espionage Act of 1917 as a result of his preparation and distribution of a circular that compared conscription to slavery and "intimated that conscription was despotism in its worst form and a monstrous wrong against humanity in the interest of Wall Street's chosen few. [The circular] said 'Do not submit to intimidation,' but in form at least confined itself to peaceful measures such as a petition for the repeal of the act."[4] After describing and discussing the content of Schenck's anticonscription, anticapitalist circular, Justice Holmes, upholding Schenck's conviction, enunciated his "clear and present danger" test along with his "falsely shouting fire in a theatre and causing a panic" analogue. Holmes wrote for a unanimous Court: "The character of every act depends upon the circumstances in which it is done. . . . The most stringent protection of free speech would not protect a man in falsely shouting fire in a theatre and causing a panic. . . . The question in every case is whether the words are used in such circumstances and are of such a nature as to create a clear and present danger. It is a question of proximity and degree."[5]

Holmes did not use as his analogue a person standing on a street corner and shouting personal insults or distributing religious pamphlets so offensive to others that a breach of the peace may occur. He did not use a situation involving "persuasive" discourse. By using the "falsely shouting fire" analogue, Holmes succeeded in attributing to Schenck's speech the dangers, immediacy, and seriousness implied in "falsely shouting fire in a theatre and causing a panic."

But the analogue is not applicable to Schenck's distribution of anticonscription circulars. One may agree that the First Amendment does not protect the person who falsely shouts fire in a theatre and causes a panic and at the same time argue that the analogue is irrelevant to Schenck's denunciations of the war and compulsory conscription. We know through experience what will happen if a person falsely shouts fire in a theatre and causes a panic: Some people are going to get hurt or killed. The causal connection between the speech and the danger is clear. In Schenck's case, however, there was no evidence that any person had refused or was thinking about refusing to enter military service as a result of reading Schenck's anticonscription circular. Nor was there evidence that the circular had affected the morale of members of the armed forces.

Since two of the three charges against Schenck dealt with conspiracy to violate the Espionage Act, no evidence of actual obstruction of the recruiting service was needed, according to Holmes. This element of conspiracy makes the analogue even less relevant, for "falsely shouting fire" contains nothing remotely related to conspiracy. Yet the impression of a nexus between the two becomes difficult to avoid since Holmes said, in effect, that just as a person cannot expect First Amendment protection for falsely shouting fire in a theatre and causing a panic, neither can Schenck expect constitutional protection for his political expression.

While it can readily be ascertained whether it is true that someone falsely shouted fire in a theatre, whether there actually was a fire, whether there was a panic, determining the truth or falsity of Schenck's anticonscription, anticapitalist opinions claiming that conscription was "despotic" and that such conscription was defended by "cunning politicians" and the "mercenary capitalistic press" is quite different. The analogue blurs the important distinction between proving the falsity of what is shouted by a person in a theatre and the falsity of the opinions expressed in Schenck's circular.

This failure to distinguish between statements of fact and statements of opinion was a "procedure" used by Federalist judges in the prosecutions of Jeffersonian Republicans who had been charged with violating the Sedition Act of 1798, which prohibited the printing and publishing of "any false, scandalous and malicious writing or writings against the government of the United States, or the President of the United States, with intent to defame the said government, or either house of said Congress, or the said President, or to bring them, or either of them, into contempt or disrepute; or to excite against them, or either of them, the hatred of the good people of the United States." One of those prosecuted was Congressman Matthew Lyon, who was indicted for "(1) publishing an article in which he vigorously attacked the Adams administration, asserting that under President Adams 'every consideration of the public welfare was swallowed up in a continual grasp for power, in an unbounded thirst for ridiculous pomp, foolish adulation, and selfish avarice'; (2) publishing a letter from Joel Barlow, then in France, in which Barlow stated that congress should commit President Adams to the mad house, but, instead treated him 'with more servility than ever George III experienced from either House of Parliament.' "[6] Lyons was convicted and sent to jail. As James Smith has indicated, "Instead of the government's having to prove that the words of the accused were false, scandalous, and malicious, the defendant had to prove that they were true."[7] The more the defendant attempted to prove the "truth" of the statements, the more this demonstrated to the court the bad intent of the defendant. What makes all of this relevant to *Schenck* is that the courts, as Smith points out, refused "to distinguish between a false statement of facts and erroneous opinions."[8] In 1919, Holmes's "falsely shouting fire in a theatre" analogue dealt with speech capable of being factually verified, while Schenck's speech was perhaps an "erroneous opinion."

Further, the analogue is inapplicable since Holmes combines two elements, falsely shouting fire *and* causing a panic. In the case of Schenck, there is no evidence that his "false" opinions led to anything but indifference on the part of young men subject to conscription. There was nothing comparable to the "panic" side of the analogue. The presentation of "falsely shouting fire in a theatre and causing a panic" in the context of *Schenck* is misleading both in the first part of the analogue related to the "falsity" and in the second part, "*and* causing a panic." Schenck's speech was not "false"; nor did it have a comparable "panic" effect.

Clearly, the imminence and degree of the danger emanating from Schenck's distribution of anticonscription circulars had little to do with the imminence and degree of danger coming from the act of falsely shouting fire in a theatre and causing a panic. But once one accepts the analogue as appropriate, once the analogue has the effect of creating "a strong pull on our fancy," to use Monroe Beardsley's words, "then we find that our thinking is directed not by the force of argument at hand, but by the interest of the image in our mind." Once one is committed to the analogue as appropriate, the decision to decide against Schenck appears reasonable.

One week after the Supreme Court decided against Schenck, it also decided against Jacob Frohwerk, who had been convicted of violating the 1917 Espionage Act, Holmes again using the fire symbol to justify restrictions on speech. Frohwerk had published in the *Missouri Staats Zeitung* several articles questioning the constitutionality of compulsory conscription to send American troops to France and claiming that "we went to war to protect the loans of Wall Street."[9] Holmes delivered the opinion of a unanimous Court, inserting into his opinion a reference to fire; this time the metaphor was "kindle a flame": "We must take the case on the record as it is, and on that record it is impossible to say that it might not have been found that the circulation of the paper was in quarters where a little breath would be enough to kindle a flame and that the fact was known and relied upon by those who sent the paper out."[10]

As in *Schenck*, there was no evidence that Frohwerk's words had any effect on the war effort, that anybody had been persuaded by his articles. As in *Schenck*, Holmes's argument included the fire image. In *Frohwerk*, "a little breath would be enough to kindle a flame." Not only was there the potential for fire, but the metaphor also tells us that it would not have taken much to "kindle the flame," just a "breath" — those articles in the *Missouri Staats Zeitung*!

The fire metaphor was used by the Court in another landmark freedom-of-speech case from this period, *Gitlow v. New York*.[11] The metaphor was much more extended than that in *Frohwerk*. In 1920, Benjamin Gitlow and three others were convicted for violating New York's Criminal Anarchy statute and sentenced to prison. Gitlow had distributed several thousand copies of a "Left Wing Manifesto" that in the words of the Court, "advocates and urges in a fervent language mass action which shall progressively foment industrial disturbances and through political mass strikes and revolutionary mass action overthrow and destroy organized parliamentary government."[12] In 1925, the Supreme Court decided against Gitlow, even though the Court admitted that "there is no evidence of any effect resulting from the publication and circulation of the Manifesto."[13] The "Manifesto" may have had no effect, but the Court declared that "utterances inciting to overthrow of organized government by unlawful means" "by their very nature, involve danger to the public peace and to the security of the State. They threaten breaches of the peace and ultimate revolution. And the immediate danger is none the less real and substantial, because the effect of a given utterance cannot be accurately foreseen."[14]

It was at this point in the opinion that the Court used the fire metaphor, which, once accepted as a legitimate metaphorical argument, meant that there was no way that the majority of the Court could give Gitlow's speech First Amendment protection. Justice Sanford, delivering the opinion of the Court, wrote:

> A single revolutionary spark may kindle a fire that, smouldering for a time, may burst into a sweeping and destructive conflagration. It cannot be said that the State is acting arbitrarily and unreasonably when, in the exercise of its judgment as to the measures necessary to protect the public peace and safety, it seeks to extinguish the spark without waiting until it has enkindled the flame or blazed into the conflagration. It cannot reasonably be required to defer the adoption of measures for its own peace and safety until the revolutionary utterances lead to actual disturbances of the public peace or imminent and immediate danger of its own destruction; but it may, in the exercise of its judgment, suppress the threatened danger in its incipiency.[15]

Once Gitlow's speech was associated with "a single revolutionary spark," "kindl[ing] a fire" that "may burst into a sweeping and destructive conflagration," the decision to uphold Gitlow's conviction was inevitable. The danger was compounded since the spark was identified with "enkindled," kindling being easily lit; a spark placed into kindling will quickly lead to flames. Also, the danger was significantly increased with the possibility that the fire "may burst into a

sweeping and destructive conflagration," *conflagration* meaning "a big, destructive fire."[16]

But the majority seemed to want it both ways. It wanted to
convey the seriousness and imminence of the danger through
the phrases "kindle the fire" and "enkindled the flame," yet it
appeared to minimize the seriousness and imminence when
it spoke of "a fire smouldering for a time." While a smoldering
fire can be dangerous, it is usually smelly and smoky; in fact,
the word *smolder* is derived from the German word for "smell."
Dictionary definitions of *smolder* always include references to
either smell or smoke, or both.[17] A smoldering fire is detect-
able, hardly a serious and imminent danger to an alert government.

In the sentence immediately preceding the "revolutionary
spark" statement, the Court used a metaphor that was a
reflection of a metaphor used in the brief presented to the
Court by the state of New York: "It is apparent, from an
examination of the manifesto, that the intent was to incite the
readers to use unlawful means to bring about the conquest
and destruction of the existing government, and to do this
forthwith. It is clear that the manifesto contemplated action
immediately or in the near future. The imminence of the
danger that unlawful action will result from advocacy of the
doctrine of criminal anarchy cannot be measured mathematically. 'Imminent' does not necessarily mean the next
moment."[18]

While the New York brief asserted that "the imminence of
the danger . . . cannot be measured mathematically," Justice
Sanford used another metaphor to convey the idea that a strict
definition or precision of the danger was not necessary.
Writing for the majority, Sanford, referring to "utterances
inciting to the overthrow of organized government by unlawful means," said: "Such utterances by their very nature, involve danger to the public peace and to the security of the
State. They threaten breaches of the public peace and ultimate
revolution. And the immediate danger is none the less real
and substantial because the effect of a given utterance cannot
be accurately foreseen. The State cannot reasonably be required to measure the danger from every such utterance in

the nice balance of a jeweler's scale."[19] Both the state of New York and the Supreme Court argued that the precision of mathematics or the jeweler's scale was not needed to "measure" the imminence of the danger or the danger itself, both metaphors relieving the state and the Court of the obligation to establish very carefully the danger and its imminence. These metaphorical arguments made it much easier to decide against Gitlow, for it was enough to conclude that the danger from his speech was "potential," was going to become serious in the "near future."

In addition to the metaphorical "the imminence of the danger . . . cannot be measured mathematically," the New York brief introduced the danger of snakes: "It cannot be that the Government is powerless to act until the plotters have perfected their plans and are ready to strike the fatal blow. If the Government were bound to delay its action until the arrival of the time for the striking of the blow, it might then be too late, and the Government might perish because of its failure to take seasonable protective measures. The time to kill a snake is when it is young."[20] Once Gitlow has metaphorized into a snake, it was but one small step to justifying his "eradication."

But the difficulty with the "snake" metaphor is that all snakes are not dangerous; some snakes are useful. Just as it may not be advisable to kill all young snakes, so it may be inadvisable to kill all "revolutionary" ideas. To kill both at an early stage of development would in many instances cause more harm than good. Some young snakes mature into useful reptiles helping to maintain a balance in nature. Likewise, some young revolutionary ideas eventually develop into acceptable and beneficial social and political policies.

But the snake conjures in the minds of most readers creatures that ought to be killed: Snakes slither; snakes are hard to handle; snakes blend into the terrain; snakes are poisonous. The metaphor is particularly inappropriate since one widespread fear of snakes is based on the fact that they are often difficult to detect, for they do blend in with the terrain and they do strike swiftly. On the other hand, Gitlow did not surreptiously blend into the terrain. He openly published and distributed the "Left Wing Manifesto," a thirty-four-page document described by Zechariah Chafee, Jr., in the following terms: "After twenty pages of somniferous type telling the recent history of the world, it reaches its first incendiary passage: 'Strikes are developing which verge on revolutionary action, and in which the suggestion of proletarian dictatorship is apparent, the strike-workers trying to usurp functions of municipal government as in Seattle, and Winnipeg. The mass struggle of the proletariat is coming into being.'"[21] On the effects of Gitlow's "Manifesto," Chafee wrote: "Any agitator who read these thirty-four pages to a mob would not stir them to violence, except possibly against himself. This Manifesto would disperse them faster than the Riot Act."[22]

The New York brief presented to the Supreme Court contained still another ominous analogue, comparing Gitlow's speech to "poisons": "The disseminating or making public of bad sentiments, destructive of the ends of society, is the crime which society corrects. A man may be allowed to keep poisons in his closet, but not publicly vend them as cordials."[23] Once Gitlow's "bad sentiments" were identified with "poisons" that are developed, produced, and distributed for the sole purpose of killing, the conclusion was clear: Such poisonous speech could not be given First Amendment protection.

Justices Holmes and Brandeis dissented in *Gitlow*, arguing that "there was no present danger of an attempt to overthrow the Government by force on the part of the admittedly small minority who shared the defendant's views."[24] Holmes's tropes, unlike the majority's, minimized the dangers of Gitlow's "Manifesto": "It is said that this manifesto was more than a theory, that it was an incitement. Every idea is an incitement. It offers itself for belief and if believed it is acted on unless some other belief outweighs it or some failure of energy stifles the movement at its birth. The only difference between the expression of an opinion and an incitement in the narrower sense is the speaker's enthusiasm for the result. Eloquence may set fire to reason. But whatever may be thought of the redundant discourse before us it had no chance of starting a present conflagration."[25]

The birth metaphor carries with it the sense of development over a period of time: conception, gradual growth, birth. The birth metaphor would not have been so useful to the *Gitlow* majority since the metaphor does not carry with it the imminence and danger of a "sweeping and destructive conflagration." Holmes and Brandeis were rejecting the majority's "revolutionary spark" as applicable to Gitlow's "redundant discourse."

In *Abrams v. United States*, decided the same year the Supreme Court upheld Schenck's conviction, the Court decided against five anarchists and Socialists who had been charged with conspiring to publish and distribute circulars that contained language "intended to bring the form of Government of the United States into contempt, scorn, contumely and disrespect" and "disloyal scurrilous and abusive language about the form of the Government of the United States."[26] Quoting from material appearing in Abrams's circulars, the majority noted that President Wilson had been denounced as a hypocrite and a coward, and that "growing more inflammatory as it proceeds, the circular culminates in: 'The Russian Revolution cries: Workers of the World! Awake! Rise! Put down your enemy and mine! Yes! Friends, there is only one enemy of the workers of the world and that is CAPITALISM.'"[27] The majority saw in Abrams's "inflammatory" circulars "threats of armed rebellion." The contents of the circulars were identified with "riots," "sedition," and "revolution."[28]

Where the majority saw the circulars as "inflammatory," leading to destruction and rebellion, Justices Holmes and Brandeis, dissenting, saw the "surreptitious printing of a silly leaflet by an unknown man."[29] It was in his dissenting opinion that Holmes introduced into judicial discourse the concept of the "free trade of ideas" and "the power of the thought to get itself accepted in the competition of the market."[30] As Holmes and Brandeis saw it, the American public "market" was an appropriate place for Abrams to present his ideas through "a silly leaflet by an unknown man," the publication of which presented no clear and present danger.

There was no place for the market metaphor in the majority's argument, for there was nothing in the majority's opinion to indicate that the justices viewed Abrams and his coconspirators as buyers and sellers of anything that belonged in the market. In fact, as the majority would see it, the "inflammatory" words were used with the intent of burning down the market. Holmes, on the other hand, contended not only that "nobody can suppose that the surreptitious publishing of a silly leaflet by an unknown man, without more, would present any immediate danger that its opinions would hinder the success of the government arms or have any appreciable tendency to do so" but further minimized the "inflammatory" nature of the leaflets when he wrote: "Even if I am technically wrong, and enough can be squeezed from these poor and puny anonymities to turn the color of legal litmus paper . . . , the most nominal punishment seems to me all that possibly could be inflicted, unless the defendants are to be made to suffer not for what the indictment alleges, but for the creed that they avow."[31]

Different courts used different tropes in their arguments to justify their decisions against the "radicals" criticizing compulsory conscription, advocating "criminal anarchy," and "attempting to cause insubordination in the armed forces." While in *Gitlow* the Supreme Court concluded that the state could suppress Gitlow's speech because a "revolutionary spark" could "kindle a fire," the Third Circuit Court of Appeals, deciding against a critic of war, argued in *United States v. Krafft* (1918) that the purpose of the Espionage Act of 1917 "was not to wait and see if the seed of insubordination—in this case, sown in August in Newark; at a later date, in some camp— sprang into life and brought forth fruit, but it was to prevent the seed from being sown initially. Moreover, it is clear that this new statute was to enable the civil courts to prevent the sowing of the seeds of disloyalty, for with the fruits of disloyalty, to which a misguided soldier might be led by the disloyal advice, the military court-martial already provided was sufficient. The statute was not addressed to the misguided man who was in the service, but was manifestly to include any one—for 'whoever' is a broad inclusive word—

who in any way willfully created or attempted to cause insubordination."[32]

While "seeds of insubordination" and "sowing the seeds of disloyalty" sound ominous and dangerous enough, they do not have the implications of the death, destruction, and devastation found in the "fire" metaphors. This was especially true at the turn of the century when the fear of fire was widespread in the nation. Prior to and during the prosecutions of Schenck, Gitlow, Abrams, and other "radicals," the nation had experienced the Chicago fire of 1871, the Seattle fire of 1889, the San Francisco fires of 1849 and 1851, and the fires that came with the San Francisco earthquake of 1906. In 1900, fire devastated the Hoboken, New Jersey, docks, killing 326 people; in 1903, the Iroquois Theater fire in Chicago killed 602; Chelsea, Massachusetts, was destroyed by fire in 1908; in 1918, the Cloquet, Minnesota, fire killed 400. These and other fires demonstrated the power and destructiveness that came from uncontrollable fires destroying the wooden structures of the time.

There was also the rural fear of fires, for once a home, barn, or haystack was aflame, there was little one could do to put out the fire. The burning haystacks entered into the brief presented by the state of California to the Supreme Court in *Whitney v. California*.[33] In 1920, Anita Whitney had been tried and convicted of violating California's Criminal Syndicalism Act as a result of her organizational ties with the Communist Labor Party. When her case reached the Supreme Court, California argued in its brief: "It is true that the record does not show that this defendant threw bombs, fired hay stacks, or preached on street corners inciting men to assassinate the President, governors and other officials of the nation and this commonwealth, but this was not necessary. The charge was that she assisted in organizing and became a member of a society or group of persons organized to advocate, teach and aid criminal syndicalism."[34] Placing "fired hay stacks" alongside "threw bombs" and "inciting men to assassinate the President" indicates the impact of the fires purposely set, whether for personal or political reasons.

When in 1925 the majority of the Supreme Court compared Gitlow's speech to a "spark" that "may burst into a sweeping and destructive conflagration" and argued that the state was justified in silencing such speech, as "it seeks to extinguish the spark without waiting until it has enkindled the flame or blazed into the conflagration, it drew on a term then widely used in reports on fires across the nation.

In his 1871 work *History of the Great Fires in Chicago and the West* (with the subtitle *A Proud Career Arrested by Sudden and Awful Calamity; Towns and Counties Laid Waste by the Devastating Element*), E. J. Goodspeed, after reviewing the burning of ancient Rome, the burning of Moscow in 1812, and the burning of London in 1666, briefly reviewed some of the fires in American cities: "Pittsburg, Pa., was visited by a most destructive conflagration the 10th of April, 1845."[35] "A conflagration, by which an immense amount of property was destroyed, took place in Philadelphia, on the 9th of July, 1850."[36] "The most terrible conflagration in which Philadelphia was the theatre, after that of July, 1850, occurred there on the morning of 1865. Like its predecessor, it brought death to many, and in the most horrible and painful manner."[37] "The city of San Francisco was retarded in its progress toward its present proud position by many causes, but by nothing more than fire. The most destructive of the many conflagrations which have occurred in that city began on the 3rd of May, 1851."[38]

Once the courts identified the "radical" circulars, pamphlets, and speeches with the dreaded conflagrations the nation was witnessing and the dreaded fires in the "crowded theatres," it was clear that the "radical" speech and publications were not going to receive constitutional protection.

Conclusion

B*reathing, chilling, color-blind, constellation, fire,* *marketplace, penumbra, progeny, maze, shed, shortcut, stagnate,* *standing, wall* — this is the world of the animate and physical; this is the world of seeing, feeling, experiencing. Yet these terms, and many others of the animate world, have become an important part of judicial vocabulary when judges and justices have integrated them into their reasoning leading to decisions dealing with abstract constitutional concepts. As Burr Henly has argued, "Language in law is rife with metaphors. Judges and commentators have created a legal landscape inhabited with, among other things, slippery slopes, bright and blurred lines, constitutional foothills, scales of justice, level playing fields, and a wall of separation between church and state. Metaphors are not just illustrations offering graphic images or concrete versions of legal concepts. They are models — shorthand versions of reality that emphasize or exclude in order to make a point."[1]

Like religious, scientific, fictional, philosophical, and historical discourse, legal discourse has relied heavily on the tropes. This reliance on figurative language was recognized, and yet not investigated, early in the twentieth century. Wesley Hohfeld wrote in the November 1913 issue of the *Yale Law Review*: "Much of the difficulty, as regards legal terminology arises from the fact that many of our words were originally applicable only to physical things; so that their use in connection with legal relations is, strictly speaking, figurative or fictional."[2] It was not till the end of the twentieth century that legal scholars began to show an interest in the metaphors

199

of the law.[3] In his 1988 *Stanford Law Review* article, "The Metaphor of Standing and the Problem of Self-Governance," Steven Winter observed that "there is a developing body of work on human cognition which suggests that human thought is grounded in physical experience and extended by means of idealized cognitive models and metaphoric projections."[4] "To the reader unfamiliar with this new scholarship," continued Winter, "this may seem either strange or far afield for an article about the law of standing. But by bringing to the surface the models and metaphors that animate standard legal thinking, we will be able to see and talk about both the history of standing and troublesome aspects of the doctrine in a new and enlightening way."[5]

Some metaphors relied on by the courts are "troublesome." There is a serious question whether the nostalgic, metaphoric "marketplace of ideas" is applicable in today's society. There is a serious question whether "lines" and "entanglements" between church and state are preferable to the "wall of separation" of which Jefferson spoke. There is a serious question whether the "captive audience" can be defined accurately enough to act as a principle in judicial decision making. The metaphoric "penumbral"-rights doctrine has been questioned.[6] The "chilling-effect" doctrine has been criticized by Justice Harlan as "ubiquitous," "slippery," and "amorphous."[7]

In his examination of the metaphoric "standing," Winter warned: "Metaphor can . . . have as great a potential to mislead as to enlighten."[8] If ever there was one institution to which this should be evident, it is our judicial system, which has so much power over us all. Seemingly objective principles of law are expressed in nonliteral language; but since the principles are expressed in tropes, what appears on the surface to be objective becomes rather subjective since a metaphor can be replaced with a different metaphor. By choosing one metaphor over another, like the poet, novelist, or politician, the jurist makes a subjective choice. Since there is no literal marketplace of ideas in the world, a jurist might just as well rely on a metaphoric "quest," "war," "forest," "galaxy," or "rainbow" of ideas. Had Justice Holmes not been so much a part of a laissez-faire society, his "free trade in ideas" in the "competition of the market" might never have entered our judicial parlance. By relying on the Holmes metaphor, we have chosen to highlight competitiveness in the buying and selling of ideas; had a "quest" metaphor prevailed, we would be highlighting searching, a journey, inquiry, as in the word *quest-ion*.

After expressing his misgivings about the metaphoric "penumbra" surrounding the guarantees in the Bill of Rights, Burr Henly warns: "Metaphors like 'penumbra' are useful and are even, at some level, inescapable. In the long run, though, they are not a substitute for theory."[9] Indeed, a metaphor in a judicial opinion should not be a "substitute for theory," but the metaphor may *embody* a theory. Further, while we can escape being misled by misleading metaphors, they are, along with other tropes, hardly inescapable. The same judges and justices who have warned about the misuses of metaphor in legal reasoning have themselves relied heavily on the tropes.[10]

What cannot be ignored is that judicial passages expressed through tropes, especially in landmark decisions, have so often been cited as support in the reasoning of subsequent decisions. For example, in the landmark *West Virginia State Bd. of Education v. Barnette*, Justice Jackson, delivering the opinion of the Court, often developed his arguments in nonliteral, figurative terms, some of which were subsequently cited again and again by courts at all levels. Judge Griffin Bell's observation that style may "govern the frequency with which the opinion will be cited in other cases and thus determine the influence the opinion will ultimately have" is illustrated especially well by Jackson's *Barnette* opinion. Further, Jackson's opinion illustrates Richard Weisberg's observation of what Justice Cardozo realized, that "the *form of an opinion actively contributes to its correctness*; style thus conceived is an element to be evaluated as part of the correctness of a decision, not as ancillary or merely ornamental element."[11]

The most memorable and influential tropological passage from Justice Jackson's *Barnette* opinion is "If there is any fixed star in our constitutional constellation, it is that no official, high or petty, can prescribe what shall be orthodox in politics, nationalism, religion, or other matters of opinion or force citizens to confess by word or act their faith therein."[12]

Jackson's enthymeme put into a syllogism would read as follows: First premise: All officials who prescribe what shall be orthodox in politics and religion and who force citizens to confess by word or act their faith therein are acting unconstitutionally. Second premise: The West Virginia State Board of Education prescribed orthodoxy and forced the students to confess their faith therein. Conclusion: The West Virginia State Board of Education acted unconstitutionally. Once the premises are accepted by the reader, the conclusion must follow.

As part of the reasoning, the metaphoric "fixed star in our constitutional constellation" adds to the persuasiveness of the argument. When in 1972 the Second Circuit Court of Appeals decided for a high school art teacher who had been dismissed because of her refusal to salute the flag during the school's homeroom hour, Judge Kaufman incorporated the metaphoric "fixed star in our constitutional constellation" into the court's reasoning. Just before citing the passage from *Barnette*, Judge Kaufman wrote: "To compel a person to speak what is not in his mind offends the very principles of tolerance and understanding which for so long have been the foundation of our great land."[13] Then, having cited the "fixed star" passage, Kaufman referred to it in the following terms: "We believe that to be an accurate and thoughtful statement of the underlying spirit of the First Amendment and we abide by it here."[14]

Other figurative passages from *Barnette* have had a prominent place in judicial decision making. Justice Jackson argued that free minds must not be "strangled": "That they [Boards of Education] are educating the young for citizenship is reason for scrupulous protection of Constitutional freedoms of the individual, if we are not to strangle the free mind at its source and teach youth to discount important principles of our government as mere platitudes."[15] Certain political subjects, said Jackson, are "beyond the reach of majorities": "The very purpose of the Bill of Rights was to withdraw certain subjects from the vicissitudes of political controversy, to place them beyond the reach of majorities and officials and to establish them as legal principles to be applied by the courts. One's right to life, liberty, and property, to free speech, a free press, freedom of worship and assembly and other fundamental rights may not be submitted to vote; they depend on the outcome of no elections."[16] Jackson asserted that allowing differences of opinion only on matters that are not important is a "mere shadow of freedom": "Freedom to differ is not limited to things that do not matter much. That would be a mere shadow of freedom. The test of its substance is the right to differ as to things that touch the heart of the existing order."[17] Having given freedom a shadow, Jackson proceeded to provide the existing order with a heart.

Still other tropes, though not as widely cited, were incorporated into the Court's reasoning in *Barnette*. Justice Jackson argued that the Fourteenth Amendment protects us against the state and "all of its creatures — Boards of Education not excepted."[18] Coercion to achieve national unity leads to the "unanimity of the graveyard": "Those who begin coercive elimination of dissent soon find themselves eliminating dissenters. Compulsory unification of opinion achieves only the unanimity of the graveyard."[19] Transforming the inanimate to the animate, Jackson declared: "These principles [in the Bill of Rights] grew in soil which also produced a philosophy that the individual was the center of society, that his liberty was attainable through mere absence of governmental restraints, and that government should be entrusted with few controls and only the mildest supervision over men's affairs. We must transplant these rights to a soil in which the *laissez-faire* concept or principle of non-interference has withered at least as to economic affairs."[20]

Jackson's *Barnette* opinion, with its reliance on such non-literal, figurative language as "fixed star in our constitutional constellation," "strangle the free mind," "mere shadow of freedom," "unanimity of the graveyard," "principles grew in soil," and "transplant these rights to a soil" exemplifies the "conflation of the concepts of poetry and prose" referred to by Hayden White in his discussion of the rhetoric of historical

discourse. After asserting that "every discourse is a media-
tion between the metaphorical and the metonymic poles of
language behavior through the instrumentality of those 'figures of speech' originally studied by classical rhetoricians,"
White draws on the work of Roman Jakobson:

> In Jakobson's view, stylistics must seek to analyze the po-
> etic dimension of every merely putatively *prose* discourse,
> just as it must seek to uncover the prosaic kernel of "mes-
> sage" contained in every manifestly *poetic* utterance. This
> conflation of the prosaic and the poetic within a general
> theory of discourse has important implications for our un-
> derstanding of what is involved in those fields of study
> which, like historiography, seek to be objective and realis-
> tic in their representations of the world but which, by vir-
> tue of the unacknowledged *poetic* element in their
> discourse, hide their own objectivity and culture-bound-
> edness from themselves.[21]

Judicial opinions like Jackson's *Barnette* opinion that appear on the surface "to be objective and realistic in their
representations of the world" by virtue of their "unacknowl-
edged poetic element" hide their "own subjectivity and cul-
ture-boundedness." Reading judicial opinions from this perspective raises serious questions about the accuracy of Justice
Holmes's assertion that "the law is not the place for the artist
or the poet."[22]

Piero Calamandrei has explained that "ever since justice
descended from heaven to earth and the idea gained ground
that the judge is a human being and not a supernatural and
infallible oracle to be adored, whose authority is beyond
question, man has felt the need of a rational explanation to
give validity to the word of the judge."[23] It is through the
published judicial opinion that we get that "rational explanation."

What has become clear is the extent to which that rational
explanation has been expressed in influential nonliteral language. To examine the reasoning of a judicial opinion without
acknowledging its tropes is to do an incomplete examination
of the discourse. To some, this may appear an anomaly —

rational explanation through nonliteral language. But it is not an anomaly when we listen to Kenneth Burke as he explains the metaphor:

> It is customary to think that objective reality is dissolved by such relativity of terms as we get through the shifting of perspectives (the perception of one character in terms of many diverse characters). But on the contrary, it is by the approach through a variety of perspectives that we establish a character's reality. If we are in doubt as to what an object is, for instance, we deliberately try to consider it in as many different terms as its nature permits: lifting, smelling, tasting, tapping, holding in different lights, subjecting to different pressures, dividing, matching, contrasting, etc.[24]

The tropes can help us comprehend what may have been incomprehensible, can help us find new "truths," clarify and create new realities; however, there always remains the danger that through the tropes we can also mislead, conceal, create misunderstandings, and come to rely on clichéd thinking. It is not a question of whether the courts do and will rely on figurative language in the reasoning of their opinions. Our task is to recognize and be a bit wary of the tropology of the law, for while tropes can help us comprehend the abstract legal concepts and appreciate new perspectives, tropes can also cramp out thinking and result in outmoded and dangerous legal language and precedents. All this being so, it is especially incumbent that judicial tropes be identified and examined, for the acceptance or rejection of specific metaphors, metonymies, and personifications of the law will determine the legal principles and doctrines by which we will be guided and ruled.

Notes

Index

Notes

Introduction

1. Margaret Hall, ed., *Selected Writings of Benjamin Cardozo* (Albany, N.Y., 1947), 51.

2. *Abington School Dist. v. Schempp*, 374 U.S. 203, 343–44 (1963).

3. *Goodson v. Northside Bible Church*, 261 F. Supp. 99, 103 (1966).

4. *Jeannette Rankin Brigade v. Chief of Capital Police*, 342 F. Supp. 575, 585 (1972).

5. *University of California Regents v. Bakke*, 438 U.S. 265, 401 (1977).

6. *Bantam Books, Inc. v. Sullivan*, 357 U.S. 58, 66 (1963).

7. *Meese v. Keene*, 481 U.S. 465, 485 (1986).

8. *Airport Commr's v. Jews for Jesus, Inc.*, 482 U.S. 569, 574 (1987).

9. *National Student Association v. Hershey*, 412 F.2d 1103, 1114 (1969).

10. *F.C.C. v. Pacifica Foundation*, 438 U.S. 726, 745 (1978).

11. *United States v. Associated Press*, 52 F. Supp. 362, 372 (1943).

12. *Keyishian v. Board of Regents*, 385 U.S. 589, 604 (1967).

13. *NAACP v. Button*, 371 U.S. 415, 466 (1963).

14. Anthony Amsterdam, "The Void-for-Vagueness Doctrine in the Supreme Court," *University of Pennsylvania Law Review* 109 (1960), 75.

15. *Cohen v. California*, 403 U.S. 15, 21–22 (1971).

16. See below; pp. 95–117.

17. *Roe v. Wade*, 410 U.S. 113, 129 (1973).

18. *Wallace v. Jaffree*, 472 U.S. 38, 92 (1985).

19. *Gormley v. Director, Conn. State Dept. of Prob.*, 632 F.2d 938, 942, 944 (1980).

20. Lawrence Tribe, "The Idea of the Constitution: A Metaphor-morphosis," *Journal of Legal Education* 37 (1987), 170–71.

21. *Plessy v. Ferguson*, 163 U.S. 537, 559 (1869).

22. *Hazelwood School Dist. v. Kuhlmeier*, 484 U.S. 260, 290 (1988).

23. *Abrams v. United States*, 250 U.S. 616, 630 (1919).

24. *Webster v. Reproductive Health Services*, 109 S. Ct. 3040, 3071 (1989).

25. *Shanley v. Northeast Ind. Sch. Dist.*, 462 F.2d 960, 968 (1972).

26. *Gertz v. Robert Welch, Inc.*, 418 U.S. 323, 354 (1974).

27. *Trachtman v. Anker*, 563 F.2d 512, 517 (1977).

28. *University of California Regents v. Bakke*, 438 U.S. 265, 327 (1977).

29. Richard Posner, *Law and Literature* (Cambridge, Mass., 1988), 296.

30. Robert Prentice, "Supreme Court Rhetoric," *Arizona Law Review* 25 (1983), 86.

31. David Cole, "Agon at Agora: Creative Misreadings in the First Amendment Tradition," *Yale Law Review* (April 1986), 894.

32. Burr Henly, "'Penumbra': The Roots of a Legal Metaphor," *Hastings Constitutional Law Quarterly* (Autumn 1987), 100.

33. Steven Winter, "The Metaphor of Standing and the Problem of Self-Governance," *Stanford Law Review* (July 1988), 1382.

34. *Ibid.*, 1387.

35. Steven Winter, "Transcendental Nonsense: Metaphoric Reasoning and the Cognitive Stakes for Law," *University of Pennsylvania Law Review* (April 1989), 1190.

36. Thomas Ross, "Metaphor and Paradox," *Georgia Law Review* (Summer 1989), 1053.

37. *Ibid.*, 1076.

38. See, for example, R. Dreistadt, "An Analysis of the Use of Analogies and Metaphors in Sciences," *Journal of Psychology* 68 (1968), 97–116; R. M. Young, "Darwin's Metaphor: Does Nature Select?" *The Monist* 55 (1971), 442–503; A. L. MacKay, "A Metaphor for Molecular Evolution," *Journal of Theoretical Biology* 54 (1975), 399–401; J. C. Marshall, "Minds, Machines and Metaphors," *Social Studies of Science* 7 (1977), 475–88; R. R. Hoffman, "Some Implications of Metaphor for Philosophy and Psychology of Science," in R. Dirven and W. Paprotte (eds.), *The Ubiquity of Metaphor: Problems and Perspectives* (Brighton, 1982), 89–105; W. H. Leatherdale, *The Role of Analogy, Model and Metaphor in Science* (Amsterdam, 1974).

39. Hugh Petrie, "Metaphor and Learning," in Andrew Ortony, ed., *Metaphor and Thought* (London, 1979), 445.

40. K. N. Llewellyn, *The Bramble Bush* (New York, 1960), 43.

41. Cited in William Fryer and H. Orentlichen, *Legal Method and Legal System* (St. Paul, 1967), 89.

42. Frank Coffin, *The Ways of a Judge* (Boston, 1980), 12–13.

43. Susan Tiefendrum, "Legal Semiotics," *Cardozo Arts and Entertainment Journal* 5 (1986), 118–19.

44. *Berky v. Third Ave. Ry. Co.*, 155 N.E. 58, 61 (1926).

45. *McCollum v. Board of Education*, 333 U.S. 203, 247 (1948).

46. *Engel v. Vitale*, 370 U.S. 421, 445 (1962).

47. *Wallace v. Jaffree*, 472 U.S. 38, 92 (1985).

48. *Ibid.*, 107.

49. Posner, 298.

50. Griffin Bell, "Style in Judicial Writing," *Journal of Public Law* 15 (1966), 214.

51. *Abrams v. United States*, 250 U.S. 616, 630 (1919).

52. *Adler v. Board of Education*, 342 U.S. 485, 510 (1952).

53. *Keyishian v. Board of Regents*, 385 U.S. 589, 603 (1967).

54. *Tinker v. Des Moines Sch. Dist.*, 393 U.S. 503, 506 (1969).

55. *Griswold v. Connecticut*, 381 U.S. 479, 483 (1965).

56. *Roe v. Wade*, 410 U.S. 113, 129 (1973).

57. *James v. Board of Education*, 461 F.2d 566, 571–75 (1972).

58. *Hustler Magazine v. Falwell*, 108 S. Ct. 876, 879–82 (1988).

59. Piero Calamandrei, *Procedure and Democracy*, trans. John C. Adams and Helen Adams (New York, 1956), 21.

60. *Ibid.*, 53.

61. Bell, 214.

62. Benjamin Cardozo, *Law and Literature* (New York, 1931), 9.

63. Richard Weisberg, "Law, Literature and Cardozo's Judicial Poetics," *Cardozo Law Review* (Spring 1979), 309–10.

64. Murray Edelman, *Politics as Symbolic Action* (Chicago, 1971), 67.

65. George Lakoff and Mark Johnson, *Metaphors We Live By* (Chicago, 1980), 158.

66. *Ibid.*, 157.

67. Haig Bosmajian, *The Language of Oppression* (Lanham, 1983), 6.

68. *Ibid.*, 5–6.

69. *Hyde v. United States*, 225 U.S. 347, 391 (1912).

70. James Bradley Thayer, cited in Wesley Hohfeld, "Some Fundamental Legal Conceptions as Applied in Judicial Reasoning," *Yale Law Journal* 23 (1913), 29.

1. The Functions of the Judicial Opinion

1. Richard Kluger, *Simple Justice* (New York, 1971), 706.

2. *Jacobellis v. Ohio*, 378 U.S. 184, 200 (1964).

3. Karl Llewellyn, *The Common Law Tradition* (Boston, 1960), 26.

4. Piero Calamandrei, *Procedure and Democracy*, trans. John C. Adams and Helen Adams (New York, 1956), 21–22.

5. *Encyclopaedia Britannica* (Chicago, 1970), 16:1044.

6. G. Gordon Post, *An Introduction to the Law* (Englewood Cliffs, N.J., 1963), 18.

7. *Ibid.*, 24.

8. E. J. White, *Legal Antiquities* (St. Louis, 1913), 143.

9. Ronald Walker and M. G. Walker, *The English Legal System* (London, 1967), 49.

10. See White, chap. 5.

11. Lois G. Forer, *A Chilling Effect* (New York, 1987), 51–52.

12. Arthur Hogue, *Origins of the Common Law* (Bloomington, Ind., 1966), 171.

13. W. S. Holdsworth, *A History of English Law* (London, 1909), 2:444.

14. *Yearbooks of Edward II*, 17:122.

15. Holdsworth, 457.

16. Carleton K. Allen, *Law in the Making* (Oxford, 1930), 131.

17. Emlin McClain, "The Evolution of the Judicial Opinion," *The American Law Review* (November–December 1902), 809.

18. William Bolland, *A Manual of Yearbook Studies* (Cambridge, 1925), 29.

19. *Ibid.*, 51–52.

20. Frederick Pollock and Frederic Maitland, *History of English Law* (Cambridge, 1905), 1:84.

21. *Ibid.*, 81.

22. Walker and Walker, 134.

23. *Ibid.*,136.

24. Cited in Francis Aumann, *The Changing American Legal System* (New York, 1969), 3.

25. *Ibid.*, 75.

26. "The American Jurist," *North American Review* (October 1829), 418.

27. Grant Gilmore, *The Ages of American Law* (New Haven, 1977), 8.

28. *Ibid.*, 9.

29. *Ibid.*, 23.

30. Aumann, 77.

31. David O'Brien, *Storm Center: The Supreme Court in American Politics* (New York, 1986), 138.

32. Gilmore, 72.

33. Elijah Paine, "Necessity of Common Law," *North American Review* (July 1928), 179–80.

34. Jerome Frank, *Law and the Modern Mind* (Gloucester, Mass., 1970), 136.

35. D. W. Stevenson, "Writing Effective Opinions," *Judicature* (October 1975), 135.

36. Marc Franklin, *The Dynamics of American Law* (Mineola, N.Y., 1968), 266.

37. Calamandrei, 54.

38. *Ibid.*, 59.

39. Frank Coffin, *The Ways of a Judge* (Boston, 1980), 57.

40. Robert Leflar, "Some Observations Concerning Judicial Opinions," *Columbia Law Review* 61 (1961), 810–13.

41. Roger Traynor, "Some Questions on the Work of State Appellate Courts," *University of Chicago Law Review* (Winter 1957), 218.

42. Emlin McClain, "The Evolution of the Judicial Opinion," *American Law Review* (November–December 1902), 820.

43. Glendon Schubert, *The Judicial Mind* (Evanston, Ill., 1965), 14.

44. John Reid, "Doe Did Not Sit — The Creation of Opinions by an Artist," *Columbia Law Review* (January 1963), 59–60.

45. Leflar, 811.

46. Stevenson, 135.

47. James Hopkins, "Notes on Style in Judicial Opinions," *Trial Judges Journal* (1969), 49.

48. George Rose Smith, "A Primer of Opinion Writing for Four New Judges," *Arkansas Law Review* (Summer 1967), 201.

49. *Ibid.*

50. *Ibid.*, 200–201.

51. Thomas Marvell, *Appellate Courts and Lawyers* (Westport, Conn., 1978), 110.

52. *Ibid.*, 111.

53. Joseph Weintraub, "Writing, Consideration and Adoption of Opinions," *New Jersey Law Journal*, September 22, 1960, p. 2.

54. Leflar, 813–14.

55. *Ibid.*, 812.

56. *Ibid.*

57. *Ibid.*, 811.

2. Style and Tropes

1. Benjamin Cardozo, *Law and Literature* (New York, 1931), 5.

2. *Ibid.*, 6.

3. Stendhal, quoted in Stephen Ullman, *Language and Style* (Oxford, 1964), 101.

4. Louis Halle, "The Language of Statemen," in G. Goshgarian, ed., *Exploring Language* (Boston, 1977), 101.

5. Carl Becker, *The Declaration of Independence* (New York, 1942), 203.

6. *Ibid.*, 196.

7. Richard Posner, *Law and Literature* (Cambridge, Mass., 1988), 272.

8. *Ibid.*, 248.

9. M. I. Sastri, "Legaleze Revisited," *Law Library Journal* (Spring 1989), 214.

10. Thomas Hobbes, *Leviathan* (Oxford, 1909), 54.

11. John Locke, *An Essay Concerning Human Understanding* (Philadelphia, n.d.), 327.

12. George Lakoff and Mark Johnson, *Metaphors We Live By* (Chicago, 1980), 3, 6.

13. Kenneth Burke, *A Grammar of Motives and A Rhetoric of Motives* (Cleveland, 1962), 503.

14. Lakoff and Johnson, 157.

15. Monroe Beardsley, *Thinking Straight*, 2d ed. (Englewood Cliffs, N.J., 1950), 245.

16. *Ibid.*

17. Warreb Shibbles, "The Metaphorical Method," *Journal of Aesthetic Education* 8 (1984), 27.

18. George Eliot, *Middlemarch* (Boston, 1956), 63.

19. Stephen Ullman, *Language and Style* (Oxford, 1964), 237–38.

20. Lakoff and Johnson, 236.

21. Milner Ball, *Lying Down Together: Law, Metaphor and Theology* (Madison, Wis., 1985), 22.

22. Sustan Sontag, *Illness as Metaphor* (New York, 1977), 83.

23. Haig Bosmajian, *The Language of Oppression* (Lanham, Md., 1983), 19–29.

24. Sontag, 84.

25. *Seattle Times*, May 12, 1984.

26. *New York Times*, April 9, 1982.

27. *New York Times*, March 9, 1983.

28. Leo Lowenthal and Nobert Guterman, *Prophets of Deceit* (Palo Alto, Calif., 1970), 55.

29. Thomas Friedman, "Heard Any Good Jews Lately?" in G. Goshgarian, *Exploring Language*, 5th ed. (Glenview, Ill., 1989), 254–55.

30. *Tinker v. Des Moines School Dist.*, 393 U.S. 503, 506 (1969).

31. *West Virginia State Bd. of Ed. v. Barnette*, 319 U.S. 624, 642 (1943).

32. Thomas Ross, "Metaphor and Paradox," *Georgia Law Review* (Summer 1989), 1053.

33. *Ibid.*

34. Allan Paivio, "Psychological Processes in the Comprehension of Metaphor," in Andrew Ortony, ed., *Metaphor and Thought* (Cambridge, 1979), 151–52.

35. Max Black, 34.

36. Monroe Beardsley, *Thinking Straight*, 4th ed. (Englewood Cliffs, N.J., 1975), 164.

37. Howard Pollio et al., *Psychology and the Poetics of Growth* (New York, 1977), 11–12.

38. Roland Bartel, *Metaphors and Symbols* (Urbana, Ill., 1983), 15–16.

39. Judith A. Best, "Teaching Political Theory: Meaning Through Metaphor," *Improving College and University Teaching* (Fall 1984), 166.

40. David Rumelhart, "Some Problems with the Notion of Literal Meanings," in Andrew Ortony, ed., *Metaphor and Thought* (Cambridge, 1979), 69.

41. Murray Edelman, *Politics as Symbolic Action* (Chicago, 1971), 67.

42. I. A. Richards, *The Philosophy of Rhetoric* (London, 1936), 92.

43. Lon Fuller, *Legal Fictions* (Stanford, Calif., 1967), 54.

44. *Johnson v. Texas*, 109 S. Ct. 2533, 2548 (1989).

45. *Ibid.*, 2555.

46. Cardozo, 5.

3. The Metaphoric "Marketplace of Ideas"

1. *Lamont v. Postmaster General*, 381 U.S. 301, 308 (1965).

2. *Keyishian v. Board of Regents*, 385 U.S. 589, 603 (1967).

3. *Red Lion Broadcasting Co. v. F.C.C.*, 395 U.S. 367.

4. *Healy v. James*, 408 U.S. 169, 180–81 (1972).

5. *Right to Read Defense Committee v. School Committee*, 454 F. Supp. 703, 715 (1978).

6. *Sheck v. Baileyville School Committee*, 530 F. Supp. 679, 687 (1982).

7. *Hustler Magazine v. Falwell*, 108 S. Ct. 876, 882 (1988).

8. *Texas v. Johnson*, 109 S. Ct. 2533, 2546 (1989).

9. *United States v. Eichman*, 110 S. Ct. 2404, 2412 (1990).

10. Jerome, Barron, "Access to the Press—A New First Amendment Right," *Harvard Law Review* 80 (1967), 1641.

11. *Abrams v. United States*, 250 U.S. 616, 630 (1919).

12. C. Edwin Baker, "Scope of the First Amendment Freedom of Speech," *UCLA Law Review* 25 (1978), 964.

13. C. Edwin Baker, *Human Liberty and Freedom of Speech* (New York, 1989), 6.

14. *Ibid.*, 286.

15. Stanley Ingber, "The Marketplace of Ideas: A Legitimizing Myth," *Duke Law Journal* (1984), 2–3.

16. David Kretzmer, "Freedom of Speech and Racism," *Cardozo Law Review* 8 (1987), 468–69.

17. Marc Franklin and Robert Trager, *The First Amendment and the Fourth Estate* (Mineola, N.Y., 1981), 20.

18. *Central Hudson Gas and Electric v. Public Serv. Comm'n*, 447 U.S. 557, 592 (1980).

19. *Ibid.*, 596–97.

20. John Milton, *Areopagitica and Of Education* (New York, 1951), 6.

21. *Ibid.*

22. *Ibid.*, 50.

23. *Ibid.*, 51.

24. *Ibid.*, 32.

25. David Cole, "Agon at Agora: Creative Misreadings in the First Amendment Tradition," *Yale Law Journal* 95 (1986), 886.

26. John S. Mill, *On Liberty* (New York, 1947), 23.

27. *Ibid.*, 28.

28. *Ibid.*, 45.

29. *Ibid.*, 47.

30. Thomas Jefferson, *Writings of Thomas Jefferson* (Washington, D.C., 1903), 3:318–19.

31. *Ibid.*, 2:302.

32. *Lamont v. Postmaster General*, 381 U.S. 301, 308 (1965).

33. Cole, 894.

34. Ingber, 85–86.

35. Baker, 974.

36. *Ibid.*, 976.

37. *Ibid.*, 979.

38. *Miami Herald Publishing Co. v. Tornillo*, 418 U.S. 241, 248–51 (1974).

39. *Ibid.*, 254.

40. *Oxford English Dictionary* (Oxford, 1970), 6:172.

41. *Webster's Third New International Dictionary*, 3d ed. (Springfield, Mass., 1981), 1383.

42. *In re Kay*, 83 Cal. Rptr. 686, 692 (1970). The California Court was quoting from *Landry v. Daley*, 280 F. Supp. 968, 970 (1968).

43. Petition for Rehearing, at 6–7. *Kaplan v. California*, 413 U.S. 115 (1973).

44. Motion of the American Library Association to file an *Amicus curiae* Brief in Support for Rehearing, at 17–18. *Kaplan v. California*, 413 U.S. 115 (1973).

45. *Associated Press v. United States*, 326 U.S. 1, 28 (1945).

46. Milton, 32.

47. *Chaplinsky v. New Hampshire*, 315 U.S. 568, 571–72 (1942).

48. *Feiner v. New York*, 340 U.S. 315, 330 (1951).

49. *Ibid.*, 326–27.

50. *Solmitz v. Maine Sch. Admin. Dist.*, 495 A.2d 812, 815 (1985).

51. *Ibid.*, 815–16.

52. *Ibid.*, 816–17.

53. Barron, 1648.

54. *Ibid.*, 1647.

55. Monroe Beardsley, *Thinking Straight*, 2d ed. (Englewood Cliffs, N.J., 1950), 245.

56. George Lakoff and Mark Johnson, *Metaphors We Live By* (Chicago, 1980), 236.

57. Zechariah Chafee, Jr., *Blessings of Liberty* (Philadelphia, 1956), 107.

58. *Ibid.*, 109.

59. *Ibid.*, 111.

60. *Board of Education v. Pico*, 457 U.S. 853, 892 (1982).

61. *Ibid.*, 915.

62. *Minarcini v. Strongsville City School Dist.*, 541 F.2d 577, 582 (1977); *Salvail v. Nashua Bd. of Ed.*, 469 F. Supp. 1269, 1275 (1979).

63. Baker, 968.

64. *Texas v. Johnson*, 109 S. Ct. 2533, 2552 (1989).

65. *Ibid.*, 2556.

66. *Shapero v. Kentucky Bar Association*, 486 U.S. 466, 483 (1988).

67. Benno Schmidt, *Freedom of the Press vs. Public Access* (New York, 1976), 39.

68. *Ibid.*, 40.

69. *Ibid.*, 45.

70. *Miami Herald Publishing Co. v. Tornillo*, 418 U.S. 241, 249 (1974).

71. *Ibid.*, n. 13.

72. Cited in Roland Bartel, *Metaphors and Symbols* (Urbana, Ill., 1983), 16.

4. The Metaphoric "Wall of Separation" between Church and State

1. *McCollum v. Board of Education*, 333 U.S. 203, 211 (1948).

2. *Ibid.*, 212.

3. *Ibid.*, 213.

4. *Ibid.*, 231.

5. *Ibid.*, 232.

6. *Board of Education v. Allen*, 392 U.S. 236, 254 (1968).

7. *Wolman v. Walter*, 433 U.S. 229, 266 (1976).

8. *Committee for Public Education and Religious Liberty v. Regan*, 444 U.S. 646, 671 (1980).

9. *McCollum v. Board of Education*, 333 U.S. 203, 247 (1948).

10. *Engel v. Vitale*, 370 U.S. 421, 445–46 (1962).

11. *Abington School Dist. v. Schempp*, 374 U.S. 203, 309 (1963).

12. *Wallace v. Jaffree*, 472 U.S. 38, 107 (1985).

13. *Ibid.*, 92.

14. Robert Hutchins, "The Future of the Wall," in Dallen Oaks, ed., *The Wall Between Church and State* (Chicago, 1963), 19.

15. Harold Fey, "Problems of Church and State in the United States: A Protestant View," in Dallen Oaks, ed., *The Wall Between Church and State* (Chicago, 1963), 37.

16. *Reynolds v. United States*, 98 U.S. 145, 164 (1879).

17. *Everson v. Board of Education*, 330 U.S. 1, 18 (1947).

18. *Ibid.*, 15–16.

19. *Ibid.*, 29.

20. Roger Williams, *The Bloudy Tenent of Persecution* (London, 1848), 435.

21. Mark Dewolfe Howe, *The Garden and the Wilderness* (Chicago, 1965), 6–7.

22. *Ibid.*, 10–11.

23. Williams, 315.

24. *Ibid.*, 171.

25. *Reynolds v. United States*, 98 U.S. 145, 164 (1879).

26. *United States v. Ballard*, 322 U.S. 78, 79–80 (1944).

27. *Ibid.*, 86.

28. *McCollum v. Board of Education*, 333 U.S. 203, 255–56 (1948).

29. *Johansen v. United States*, 343 U.S. 427, 439 (1951).

30. *Zorach v. Clauson*, 343 U.S. 306, 325 (1952).

31. *Ibid.*, 317.

32. *Walz v. Tax Commission*, 397 U.S. 664, 669 (1969).

33. *Ibid.*, 669–70.

34. *Ibid.*, 670.

35. *Ibid.*, 672.

36. *Lemon v. Kurtzman*, 403 U.S. 602, 612 (1971).

37. *Ibid.*, 614.

38. *Ibid.*, 625.

39. *The American Heritage Dictionary* (Boston, 1978, 1314.

40. *Oxford English Dictionary* (Oxford, 1961), 11:72.

41. *Wolman v. Walter*, 433 U.S. 229, 235 (1977).

42. *Ibid.*, 236.

43. *Ibid.*

44. *Larkin v. Grendel's Den, Inc.*, 459 U.S. 116, 123 (1982).

45. *Wallace v. Jaffree*, 472 U.S. 38, 40 (1985).

46. *Ibid.*, 106–7.

47. *Ibid.*, 108.

48. *Ibid.*, 112.

49. Griffin Bell, "Style in Judicial Writing," *Journal of Public Law* 15 (1966), 214.

50. *Berky v. Third Ave. Ry. Co.*, 155 N.E. 58, 61 (1926).

51. *Wallace v. Jaffree*, 472 U.S. 38, 113–14 (1985).

52. *Edwards v. Aguillard*, 107 S. Ct. 2573, 2577 (1987).

53. *Ibid.*, 2587, 2583.

54. *Duffy v. Las Cruces Public Schools*, 557 F. Supp. 1013, 1015 (1983).

55. *Ibid.*, 1018.

56. *Kaplan v. City of Burlington*, 700 F. Supp. 1315, 1319 (1988).

57. *Ibid.*

58. *Ibid.*, 1320.

59. *Ibid.*, 1322.

60. *Oxford English Dictionary* (Oxford, 1961), 8:1460.

61. *Ibid.*, 11:351.

62. *Sherbert v. Verner*, 374 U.S. 398, 400 (1963).

63. *PEARL v. Regan*, 444 U.S. 646, 663 (1980).

64. *Catholic H.S. Ass'n of Archdiocese of NY v. Culbert*, 753 F.2d 1161, 1162 (1985).

65. *Ibid.*, 1166.

66. *Everson v. Board of Education*, 330 U.S. 1, 63 (1947).

67. *Abington School Dist. v. Schempp*, 374 U.S. 203, 225 (1963).

68. *McCollum v. Board of Education*, 333 U.S. 203, 232 (1948).

69. *PEARL v. Regan*, 444 U.S. 646, 671 (1980).

5. The Metaphoric "Chilling Effect" and Related Tropes

1. *Zwickler v. Koota*, 389 U.S. 241, 252 (1967).

2. *Ibid.*, 256.

3. *Citizens Committee to Save WEFM v. F.C.C.*, 506 F.2d 246, 281 (1974).

4. *Abrams v. United States*, 250 U.S. 616, 630 (1919).

5. *Lamont v. Postmaster General*, 381 U.S. 301, 308 (1965).

6. Thomas Jefferson, *Writings of Thomas Jefferson* (Washington, D.C., 1903), 16:381–82.

7. Roger Williams, *The Bloudy Tenent of Persecution* (London, 1848), 435.

8. *Reynolds v. United States*, 98 U.S. 145, 164 (1879).

9. *Everson v. Board of Education*, 330 U.S. 1, 16, 18 (1947).

10. *Wieman v. Updegraff*, 344 U.S. 183, 195 (1952).

11. *Gibson v. Florida Legis. Investigating Comm.*, 372 U.S. 539, 555–57 (1963).

12. Frederick Schauer, "Fear, Risk and the First Amendment: Unraveling the Chilling Effect," *Boston University Law Review* 58 (1978), 685.

13. *Dombrowski v. Pfister*, 380 U.S. 479 (1965).

14. *Ibid.*, 494.

15. *Oxford English Dictionary* (Oxford, 1961), 2:345.

16. *Ibid.*

17. *Meese v. Keene*, 481 U.S. 465, 473 (1986).

18. *Herbert v. Lando*, 568 F.2d 974, 984 (1977).

19. Schauer, 690.

20. *Ibid.*

21. *Ibid.*

22. *Ibid.*, 693.

23. See, for example, *Near v. Minnesota*, 283 U.S. 697 (1931); *Freedman v. Maryland*, 380 U.S. 51 (1965); *Organization for a Better Austin v. Keefe*, 402 U.S. 415 (1971); *New York Times Co. v. United States*, 403 U.S. 713 (1971).

24. *New York Times v. Sullivan*, 376 U.S. 254, 271–79 (1964).

25. *Ibid.*, 300–301.

26. *Walker v. City of Birmingham*, 388 U.S. 307, 344–45 (1967).

27. *W. E. B. Dubois Clubs of America v. Clark*, 389 U.S. 309, 317–18 (1967).

28. *Ibid.*, 318.

29. *Zwickler v. Koota*, 389 U.S. 241, 252 (1967).

30. *Peter Wolff and Richard Short v. Selective Service Local Bd. No. 66, etc.*, 372 F.2d 817, 823–24 (1967).

31. *Duvernay v. United States*, 394 F.2d 979, 982 (1968).

32. *Ibid.*

33. *National Student Association v. Hershey*, 412 F.2d 1103, 1105 (1969).

34. *Ibid.*, 1119.

35. *Laird v. Tatum*, 408 U.S. 1, 6 (1972).

36. *Ibid.*

37. *Ibid.*, 24–25.

38. *Ibid.*, 13–14.

39. *Ibid.*, 28.

40. James Simon, *Independent Journey* (New York, 1980), 425.

41. Gene Lanier, "Libraries Invaded by FBI," *Free Speech Yearbook* (Carbondale, Ill., 1989), 70.

42. *School Library Journal* 35 (December 1989), 10.

43. *Keefe v. Geanakos*, 418 F.2d 359, 362 (1969).

44. *Parducci v. Rutland*, 316 F. Supp. 352, 355 (1970).

45. *Ibid.*, 357.

46. *Webb v. Lake Mills Community Sch. Dist.*, 344 F. Supp. 791, 804 (1972).

47. *Pratt v. Ind. Sch. Dist. No. 831, Forest Lake*, 670 F.2d 771, 774 (1982).

48. *Ibid.*, 778.

49. *Ibid.*, 779.

50. *Pico v. Board of Education*, 638 F.2d 404, 434 (1980).

51. *Island Trees Union Free School Dist. v. Pico*, 457 U.S. 853, 868, 877 (1982).

52. *Gibson v. Florida Legis. Investigating Committee*, 372 U.S. 539, 544 (1963).

53. *NAACP v. Button*, 371 U.S. 415, 432–33 (1963).

54. *Gibson v. Florida Legis. Investigating Committee*, 372 U.S. 539, 556–57 (1963).

55. *Arnett v. Kennedy*, 416 U.S. 134, 229 (1974).

56. *Ibid.*, 230–31.

57. *Gasparinetti v. Kerr* 568 F.2d 311, 314–15 (1977).

58. *Ibid.*, 316–17.

59. *Philadelphia Newspapers, Inc. v. Hepps*, 475 U.S. 767, 772 (1986).

60. *Ibid.*, 777.

61. *Hustler Magazine v. Falwell*, 485 U.S. 46, 52 (1988).

62. *Ibid.*, 56.

63. *Oxford English Dictionary* (Oxford, 1961), 1:1070.

64. *Broadrick v. Oklahoma*, 413 U.S. 601, 611 (1973).

65. *Ibid.*, 613.

66. *Oxford English Dictionary* (Oxford, 1961), 6:122.

67. *Ibid.*

68. *Webster's New World Dictionary* (Cleveland, 1962), 892.

69. *Osborne v. Ohio*, 110 S. Ct. 1691, 1703 (1990).

70. *Airport Comm'rs v. Jews for Jesus*, 482 U.S. 569, 574 (1987).

71. Richard Posner, *The Problems of Jurisprudence* (Cambridge, Mass., 1990), 395.

6. The Metaphoric "Captive Audience"

1. *Oxford English Dictionary* (Oxford, 1961), 2:102.

2. *U.S. S.W. Africa/Namibia Trade & Cult. Count. v. United States*, 708 F.2d 760, 767 (1983).

3. *Lehman v. City of Shaker Heights*, 418 U.S. 298 (1974).

4. *Ibid.*, 307.

5. *Ibid.*, 317.

6. *Ibid.*, 318–19.

7. *Ibid.*, 320.

8. *Rosen v. Port of Portland*, 641 F.2d 1243 (1981).

9. *Ibid.*, 1252.

10. *Ibid.*

11. *Fernandes v. Limmer*, 465 F. Supp. 493, 501 (1979).

12. *Ibid.*

13. *Intern. Soc. for Krishna Consciousness v. Lee*, 721 F. Supp. 572, 579 (1989).

14. *Ibid.*, 578.

15. *Ibid.*

16. *Pollak v. Public Utilities Commission of the Dist. of Col.*, 191 F.2d 450, 454 (1951).

17. *Ibid.*, 456.

18. *Public Utilities Commission of Dist. of Col. v. Pollak*, 343 U.S. 451 (1952).

19. *Ibid.*, 463.

20. *Ibid.*, 464.

21. *Ibid.*, 466.

22. *Ibid.*, 468.

23. *Planned Parenthood Assoc./Chicago Area v. Chicago Transit Authority*, 592 F. Supp. 544, 555 (1984).

24. *Ibid.*, 555.

25. *Rowen v. Post Office Dept.*, 397 U.S. 728, 736 (1970).

26. *Ibid.*, 738.

27. *Consolidated Edison Co. v. Public Service Comm'n.*, 447 U.S. 530, 532 (1980).

28. *Ibid.*, 542.

29. *Bolger v. Youngs Drug Products Corp.*, 463 U.S. 60, 72 (1983).

30. *Pacifica Foundation v. F.C.C.*, 556 F.2d 9, 17 (1977).

31. *F.C.C. v. Pacifica Foundation*, 438 U.S. 726, 748 (1978).

32. *Ibid.*, 758.

33. *Ibid.*, 765.

34. *Ibid.*, 766.

35. *Oxford English Dictionary* (Oxford, 1961), 1:500.

36. *Cohen v. California*, 403 U.S. 15, 21–22 (1971).

37. *Collin v. Smith*, 578 F.2d 1197, 1207 (1978).

38. *Spence v. Washington*, 418 U.S. 405, 412 (1974).

39. *Erznoznik v. City of Jacksonville*, 422 U.S. 205, 209 (1974).

40. *Ibid.*, 210–11.

41. *Keyishian v. Board of Regents*, 385 U.S. 589, 603 (1967).

42. *Eisner v. Stamford Bd. of Education*, 440 F.2d 803, 807 (1971).

43. *Sheck v. Baileyville Sch. Committee*, 550 F. Supp. 679, 687 (1982).

44. *Martin v. Parrish*, 805 F.2d 583, 584 (1986).

45. *Ibid.*

46. *Ibid.*, 586.

47. *Healy v. James*, 408 U.S. 169, 180 (1971).

48. *Close v. Lederle*, 424 F.2d 988, 990 (1970).

49. *Moore v. School Bd. of Gulf County*, 364 F. Supp. 355, 359 (1973).

50. *Ibid.*, 360.

51. *Ibid.*

52. *Ibid.*, 361.

53. *Bethel Sch. Dist. No. 403 v. Fraser*, 478 U.S. 675, 684 (1986).

54. *Fraser v. Bethel Sch. Dist. No. 403.* No. C83-306 (D. Wash. June 3, 1983).

55. *Bethel Sch. Dist. No. 403 v. Fraser*, 755 F.2d 1356 (1985).

56. *Bethel Sch. Dist. No. 403 v. Fraser*, 478 U.S. 675, 684 (1986).

57. *Salvail v. Nashua Board of Education*, 469 F. Supp. 1269, 1275 (1979).

58. *Gambino v. Fairfax City Sch. Dist.*, 429 F. Supp. 731, 736 (1977).

59. *Gambino v. Fairfax City Sch. Dist.*, 564 F.2d 157, 158 (1977).

60. *Thomas v. Board of Education, Granville Cent. Sch. Dist.*, 607 F.2d 1043, 1057 (1979).

61. *Quarterman v. Byrd*, 453 F.2d 54 (1971); *Fujishima v. Bd. of Education*, 460 F.2d 1355 (1972); *Jacobs v. Bd. of Sch. Commissioners*, 490 F.2d 601 (1973).

62. *Papish v. Board of Curators of Univ. of Missouri*, 410 U.S. 667 (1973).

63. *Tinker v. Des Moines Ind. Sch. Dist.*, 393 U.S. 503, 511 (1969).

64. *Bethel Sch. Dist. No. 403 v. Fraser*, 478 U.S. 675, 681 (1986).

65. *Board of Ed., Island Trees Union Free Sch. Dist. v. Pico*, 457 U.S. 853, 914 (1982).

66. *Ibid.*, 915.

67. *Bethel Sch. Dist. No. 403 v. Fraser*, 478 U.S. 675, 681 (1986).

68. *Oxford English Dictionary* (Oxford, 1961), 5:186.

69. *Intern. Soc. for Krishna Consciousness v. N.J. Sports*, 532 F. Supp. 1088 (1981).

70. *F.C.C. v. Pacifica Foundation*, 438 U.S. 726, 748–49 (1978).

71. *Packer Corporation v. Utah*, 285 U.S. 105, 110 (1932).

7. "Shedding" Rights at the "Schoolhouse Gate" and Other Judicial Metonymies

1. Murray Edelman, *Political Language* (Orlando, 1977), 16.

2. Kenneth Burke, *A Grammar of Motives and a Rhetoric of Motives* (Cleveland, 1962), 506.

3. George Lakoff and Mark Johnson, *Metaphors We Live By* (Chicago, 1980), 36.

4. J. David Sapir, ed., *The Social Use of Metaphor* (Philadelphia, 1977), 4.

5. Lakoff and Johnson, 39.

6. Joseph Priestly, *A Course of Lectures on Oratory and Criticism* (Carbondale, Ill., 1965), 231–32.

7. *Ibid.*, 233.

8. *Tinker v. Des Moines School Dist.*, 393 U.S. 503, 506 (1969).

9. *Smith v. Univ. of Tennessee*, 300 F. Supp. 777, 779 (1969).

10. *Ibid.*, 781.

11. *Vought v. Van Buren Public Schools*, 306 F. Supp. 1388 (1969).

12. *Ibid.*, 1391.

13. *Esteban v. Central Missouri State College*, 415 F.2d 1077, 1085–87 (1969).

14. *Westley v. Rossi*, 305 F. Supp. 706, 713 (1969).

15. *Solmitz v. Maine Sch. Admin. Dist.*, 495 A.2d 812, 816 (1985).

16. *Tinker v. Des Moines School Dist.*, 258 F. Supp. 971 (1966).

17. *Tinker v. Des Moines School Dist.*, 383 F.2d 988 (1967).

18. *Webster's New World Dictionary* (Cleveland, 1961), 1341.

19. *Tinker v. Des Moines School Dist.*, 393 U.S. 503, 511 (1969).

20. *Ibid.*, 512.

21. *United States v. Associated Press*, 52 F. 362, 372 (1943).

22. *Associated Press v. United States*, 326 U.S. 1, 28 (1945).

23. *Keyishian v. Board of Regents*, 385 U.S. 589, 603 (1967).

24. *Times-Picayune v. United States*, 345 U.S. 594, 692–03 (1953).

25. *New York Times Co. v. Sullivan*, 376 U.S. 254, 270 (1964).

26. *Ibid.*

27. *Red Lion Broadcasting Co. v. F.C.C.*, 381 F.2d 908, 928 (1967).

28. *Ibid.*, 929.

29. *Starsky v. Williams*, 353 F. Supp. 900, 907, 915 (1972).

30. *Ibid.*, 920.

31. *Right to Read Defense Committee v. School Committee*, 454 F. Supp. 703, 710 (1978).

32. *Seyfried v. Walton*, 668 F.2d 214, 217 (1981).

33. *Ibid.*, 218.

34. *American Arab Anti-Defamation Com. v. Meese*, 714 F. Supp. 1060, 1063 (1989).

35. *Ibid.*, 1078–79.

36. *Oxford English Dictionary* (Oxford, 1961), 11:128.

37. *Ibid.*

38. *As You Like It*, II, i, 16.

39. *Taming of the Shrew*, I, i, 24.

40. *Macbeth*, II, iii, 125.

41. *The Merchant of Venice*, II, iv, 27.

42. *Julius Caesar*, III, ii, 228–34.

43. *Texas v. Johnson*, 109 S. Ct. 2533, 2548 (1989).

44. *New York Trust Co. v. Eisner*, 256 U.S. 345, 349 (1921).

45. *Texas v. Johnson*, 109 S. Ct. 2533, 2555 (1989).

46. *Oxford English Dictionary* (Oxford, 1961), 6:169.

47. *Texas v. Johnson*, 109 S. Ct. 2533, 2555 (1989).

48. *West Virginia State Bd. of Ed. v. Barnette*, 319 U.S. 624, 642 (1943).

49. *Ibid.*, 638.

50. C. P. Hill, *Who's Who in History* (New York, 1966), 3:100–101.

51. *Oxford English Dictionary* (Oxford, 1961), 2:637.

52. J. E. S. Simon, "English Idioms from the Law," *Law Quarterly Review* 76 (1960), 440.

53. *Cohen v. California*, 403 U.S. 12, 25 (1971).

54. *Ginzburg v. United States*, 383 U.S. 463, 489 (1966).

55. *Miller v. California*, 413 U.S. 15, 40–41 (1973).

56. *Thomas v. Bd. of Ed., Granville Cent. Sch. Dist.*, 607 F.2d 1043, 1057 (1979).

57. *Bethel School Dist. No. 403 v. Fraser*, 478 U.S. 675, 682 (1986).

58. *Lehman v. City of Shaker Heights*, 418 U.S. 298, 299 (1974).

59. *Ibid.*, 304.

60. *Poe v. Ullman*, 367 U.S. 497, 519–20 (1961).

61. *Ibid.*, 520, n. 10.

62. *Ibid.*, 521.

63. *Ibid.*

64. *County of Allegheny v. American Civil Liberties U.*, 109 S. Ct. 3086, 3115–16 (1989).

65. *Ibid.*, 3146.

66. *Ibid.*, 3110.

67. *Ibid.*

68. *Ibid.*

69. *Ibid.*

70. George Orwell, *1984* (New York, 1961), 35.

71. *Ibid.*, 36.

72. *Lochner v. New York*, 198 U.S. 45 (1905).

73. *Ibid.*, 75.

74. Richard Posner, *Law and Literature* (Cambridge, Mass., 1988), 284.

75. *Ibid.*, 285–86.

76. Lakoff and Johnson, 39.

8. Personifying Justice, the Constitution, and Judicial Opinions

1. Hugh Blair, *Lectures on Rhetoric and Belles Lettres* (Carbondale, Ill., 1965), 1:327.

2. *Ibid.*, 327–28.

3. Richard Whately, *Elements of Rhetoric* (Carbondale, Ill., 1963), 275.

4. *Ibid.*, 283.

5. *Ibid.*, 284–85.

6. Bertrand Bronson, "Personification Reconsidered," *Journal of English Literary History* 14 (September 1947), 173.

7. George Lakoff and Mark Johnson, *Metaphors We Live By* (Chicago, 1980), 33.

8. *Avery v. Georgia*, 345 U.S. 559, 564 (1953).

9. *State v. Altrui*, 448 A.2d 837, 844 (1982).

10. "Questions and Answers," *Law Library Journal* 73 (1980), 745–46.

11. Susan Carbon, "Women in the Judiciary: An Introduction," *Judicature* 65 (December–January 1982), 285.

12. Joan Dempsey Klein, "Women Judges Join Together," *Women Lawyers Journal* 67 (1981), 11.

13. *Human Rights* 11 (Winter 1983), 3–4.

14. *Plessy v. Ferguson*, 163 U.S. 537, 554 (1996).

15. *University of California Regents v. Bakke*, 438 U.S. 265, 336 (1977).

16. *Ibid.*, 355.

17. *Ibid.*, 401.

18. *R.I. Chapter, Assoc. Gen. Contractors v. Kreps*, 450 F. Supp. 338, 360–67.

19. *Ibid.*, 362.

20. *Garner v. Louisiana*, 368 U.S. 157, 185 (1961).

21. *Taylor v. Board of Education of City School Dist.*, 191 F. Supp. 181, 196 (1961).

22. *Ibid.*

23. *United States v. Jefferson County Bd. of Education*, 372 F.2d 836, 876 (1966).

24. *Ibid.*, 877.

25. *Lumpkin v. Smith*, 309 F. Supp. 1325, 1328 (1970).

26. *Oxford English Dictionary* (Oxford, 1961), 2:639.

27. *Missouri v. Holland*, 252 U.S. 416, 433 (1920).

28. *Hazelwood School Dist. v. Kuhlmeier*, 484 U.S. 260, 290 (1988).

29. Peter Roget, *Roget's International Thesaurus* (New York, 1977), 149–50.

30. *Shanley v. Northeast Ind. School Dist.*, 462 F.2d 960, 972 (1972).

31. *Watson v. Jones*, 13 Wall 679, 728 (1872).

32. *Ibid.*

33. *United States v. Ballard*, 322 U.S. 78, 86 (1944).

34. *Epperson v. Arkansas*, 393 U.S. 97, 103 (1968).

35. *Ibid.*, 104.

36. *Presbyterian Church v. Hull Church*, 393 U.S. 440, 441 (1969).

37. *Ibid.*, 445–46.

38. *Serbian Orthodox Diocese v. Millivojevich*, 426 U.S. 696, 710 (1976).

39. *Reverendo Arcadis Natal v. The Christian and Missionary Alliance*, 1988 U.S. Dist. LEXIS 16447.

40. *United Christian Scientists v. First Church of Christ*, 829 F.2d 1152, 1167 (1987).

41. *Shanley v. Northeast Ind. School Dist.*, 462 F.2d 960, 967–68 (1972).

42. *The American Heritage Dictionary* (Boston, 1978), 1067.

43. *Shanley v. Northeast Ind. School Dist.*, 462 F.2d 960, 968 (1972).

44. *Ibid.*, 978.

45. Arthur Quinn, *Figures of Speech* (Salt Lake City, 1982), 74.

46. *University of California Regents v. Bakke*, 438 U.S. 265, 327 (1977).

47. *Webster v. Reproductive Health Services*, 109 S. Ct. 3040, 3078 (1989).

48. *Ibid.*, 3079.

49. *Trachtman v. Anker*, 563 F.2d 512, 517 (1977).

50. *Thomas v. Board of Education*, 607 F.2d 1043, 1050 (1979).

51. *Reineke v. Cobb County School Dist.*, 484 F. Supp. 1252, 1257 (1980).

52. *Gertz v. Robert Welch, Inc.*, 418 U.S. 323, 354 (1974).

53. *Aguilar v. Felton*, 473 U.S. 402, 422 (1985).

54. *Hobbs v. Thompson*, 448 F.2d 456, 458 (1971).

55. *Gordon v. Christenson*, 317 F. Supp. 146, 149 (1970).

56. *Brandenburg v. Ohio*, 395 U.S. 444, 453 (1968).

57. *Texas v. Johnson*, 109 S. Ct. 2533, 2540 (1989).

58. *Whitney v. California*, 274 U.S. 357, 375 (1927).

9. Metaphorizing Speech into "Fire" Leading to a "Conflagration"

1. Zechariah Chafee, Jr., *Free Speech In the United States* (New York, 1969), 3.

2. *Debs v. United States*, 249 U.S. 211 (1919); *Frohwerk v. United States*, 249 U.S. 204 (1919); *Abrams v. United States*, 250 U.S. 616 (1919).

3. *Gitlow v. New York*, 268 U.S. 652 (1925); *Whitney v. California*, 274 U.S. 357 (1927).

4. *Schenck v. United States*, 249 U.S. 47, 51 (1919).

5. *Ibid.*, 52.

6. Thomas Emerson, David Haber, Norman Dorsen, *Political and Civil Rights in the United States* (Boston, 1967), 37.

7. James Smith, *Freedom's Fetters* (Ithaca, N.Y., 1956), 421.

8. *Ibid.*, 422.

9. *Frohwerk v. United States*, 249 U.S. 204, 207 (1919).

10. *Ibid.*, 209.

11. *Gitlow v. New York*, 268 U.S. 652 (1925).

12. *Ibid.*, 665.

13. *Ibid.*, 656.

14. *Ibid.*, 669.

15. *Ibid.*

16. *Webster's New World Dictionary* (Cleveland, 1962), 307.

17. *Ibid.*, 1378.

18. Brief for Defendant-in-Error, at 26. *Gitlow v. New York*, 268 U.S. 652 (1925).

19. *Gitlow v. United States*, 268 U.S. 652, 669 (1925).

20. Brief for Defendant-in-Error, 20.

21. Chafee, 318.

22. Ibid., 319.

23. Memorandum of Attorney General of the State of New York in Opposition to Application for Writ of Error, at 4. *Gitlow v. New York*, 268 U.S. 652 (1925).

24. *Gitlow v. New York*, 268 U.S. 652, 673 (1925).

25. *Ibid.*

26. *Abrams v. United States*, 250 U.S. 616, 617 (1919).

27. *Ibid.*, 620.

28. *Ibid.*, 623.

29. *Ibid.*, 628.

30. *Ibid.*, 630.

31. *Ibid.*, 629.

32. *United States v. Krafft*, 249 F. 919, 924–25 (1918).

33. Brief of Defendant-in-Error on Rehearing, at 34. *Whitney v. California*, 274 U.S. 357 (1927).

34. *Ibid.*, 34.

35. E. G. Goodspeed, *History of the Great Fires in Chicago and the West* (New York, 1871), 658.

36. *Ibid.*, 659.

37. *Ibid.*, 659–60.

38. *Ibid.*, 660–61.

Conclusion

1. Burr Henley, " 'Penumbra': The Roots of a Legal Metaphor," *Hastings Constitutional Law Quarterly* 15 (Fall 1975), 81.

2. Wesley Hohfeld, "Some Fundamental Legal Conceptions as Applies in Judicial Reasoning," *Yale Law Journal* 23 (November 1913), 24.

3. See above, pp. 7–9.

4. Steven Winter, "The Metaphor of Standing and the Problem of Self-Governance," *Stanford Law Review* 40 (July 1988), 1384.

5. *Ibid.*, 1386.

6. See Henley; also, Henry Greely, "A Footnote to 'Penumbra' in *Griswold v. Connecticut*," *Constitutional Commentary* 6 (Summer 1989), 251–265.

7. *Zwickler v. Koota*, 389 U.S. 241, 256 (1967).

8. Winter, 1387.

9. Henley, 100.

10. See above, pp. 000–000.

11. Richard Weisberg, "Law, Literature and Cardozo's Judicial Poetics," *Cardozo Law Review* 1 (Spring, 1979), 309–10.

12. *West Virginia State Bd. of Education v. Barnette*, 319 U.S. 624, 642 (1943).

13. *Russo v. Central School Dist. No. 1*, 469 F.2d 623, 634 (1972).

14. *Ibid.*

15. *West Virginia State Bd. of Education v. Barnette*, 319 U.S. 624, 637 (1943).

16. *Ibid.*, 638.

17. *Ibid.*, 642.

18. *Ibid.*, 637.

19. *Ibid.*, 641.

20. *Ibid.*, 639–40.

21. Hayden White, *Tropics of Discourse* (Baltimore, 1978), 104.

22. Oliver Wendell Holmes, *Collected Legal Papers* (New York, 1920), 29.

23. Piero Calamandrei, *Procedure and Democracy*, trans. John C. Adams and Helen Adams (New York, 1965), 53.

24. Kenneth Burke, *A Grammar of Motives and a Rhetoric of Motives* (Cleveland, 1962), 504.

Index

HAIG BOSMAJIAN is a professor in the Department of Speech Communication, University of Washington. He received the George Orwell Award from the National Council of Teachers of English in 1983 for his book *The Language of Oppression* and the Bicentennial of the Bill of Rights Award for "scholarship in defense of freedom of speech and other human rights" at the Western Speech Communication Association convention in 1991.